STEWART SCOTT CAIRNS, Ph.D., Harvard University, is Professor of Mathematics at the University of Illinois. He previously taught at Syracuse University, Lehigh University, Queens College of The City University of New York, Yale University, and Harvard University. Professor Cairns has also spent three years at the Institute for Advanced Study in Princeton.

INTRODUCTORY
TOPOLOGY

STEWART SCOTT CAIRNS

UNIVERSITY OF ILLINOIS

REVISED PRINTING

THE RONALD PRESS COMPANY · NEW YORK

Library of Congress Catalog Card Number: 68–8995
PRINTED IN THE UNITED STATES OF AMERICA

To

My Wife

Kathleen

Preface

This book is the culmination of repeatedly revised sets of class notes used by the author in teaching introductory topology courses. Its purpose is to progress as far as practicable into the fundamental concepts and the principal results of homology theory, both in their combinatorial development and in their application to topological spaces.

First, some of the properties of linear graphs and of surfaces are presented in such a way as to give an intuitive geometric impression of the nature of topology. Then enough set-theoretic topology is given to motivate the subsequent combinatorial theory and to provide a background for its geometric interpretation. Cohomology groups are defined and are used in connection with the duality theorems of Poincaré and Lefschetz. Certain aspects of homotopy theory are treated, and there is a chapter on the fundamental group and covering complexes. The essential facts from group theory are collected in an Appendix.

The book can be used as text for a first course in topology either with or without set-theoretic and group-theoretic prerequisites. It is, however, advisable to give such a course at the advanced under-graduate and graduate levels in order to ensure a certain mathematical maturity and a familiarity with the role of continuity in the calculus. A class with a background in set theory and group theory might complete the book in a single semester, using Chapter 3 and the Appendix for review and reference. For a class without such a back-ground, portions of the last three chapters could be omitted, or else an entire academic year could be devoted to the book, perhaps supple-mented with additional topics from set-theoretic topology and group theory.

The author is deeply indebted to Professor Arthur B. Brown of Queens College of the City of New York. He read and reread the manuscript in detail, making numerous valuable suggestions for its correction and improvement. In several instances, he suggested alternative arguments or supplied entirely new proofs, leading to a more efficient and illuminating exposition. In addition, he contributed a strengthening of Sperner's lemma (Chapter 6, Theorem 4), which permits a substantial simplification of earlier proofs of the topological invariance of homology properties.

The drawings were executed by Dr. Ali R. Amir-Moez of Purdue University.

STEWART SCOTT CAIRNS

Urbana, Illinois
March, 1961

Many of the corrections and improvements incorporated in this Revised Printing were suggested by students and colleagues. The author gratefully acknowledges their assistance.

S. S. C.

Urbana, Illinois
July, 1968

Contents

5 Homology and Cohomology Groups

6 Topological Invariance of Homology Properties

7 Manifolds

8 The Fundamental Group; Covering Surfaces

INTRODUCTORY
TOPOLOGY

1

Illustrative Geometric Examples

The purpose of this chapter is to present a few examples which appeal to the intuition and suggest the general nature of topology.

1-1. The Seven-Bridges Problem

In its original form, the problem of the seven Koenigsberg bridges relates to a situation of the sort shown in Fig. 1-1. The problem is to

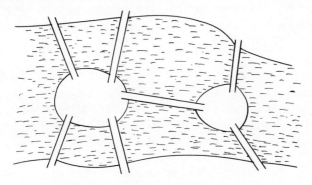

Fig. 1-1. The Koenigsberg bridges.

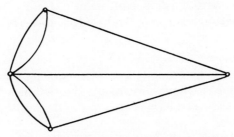

Fig. 1-2. An equivalent linear graph.

devise, if possible, a promenade which crosses each bridge once and only once. A characteristic of this problem, which makes it topological in nature, is that it depends in no way on the size or shape of the river, bridges, and islands, but only on the general manner in which they are put together. That is, the problem is the same, essentially, as that of tracing all of Fig. 1-2 without lifting the pencil and without tracing any arc more than once. One can convince himself experimentally of the impossibility of doing so in this particular case; not so, however, with the general problem of unicursal graphs, next to be discussed, which Leonhard Euler (1707–1783), stimulated by the seven-bridges problem, invented and solved in 1736.

1-2. Unicursal Graphs

A **linear graph** G will mean a finite set of points, called the **vertices** of G, together with a finite set of arcs, called the **edges** of G, such that (a) each edge has two distinct vertices for end points, (b) each vertex is an end point of at least one edge, (c) any two edges are distinct except that they may have one or two common vertices. The graph may be thought of as being in 3-dimensional space, where any set of points can be joined in pairs by non-intersecting arcs. In the plane, it is impossible, for example, to join five points each to each by non-intersecting arcs.

By a **path** on G will be meant a sequence

(1.1) $\pi = (p_1, E_1, p_2, E_2, \ldots, E_{n-1}, p_n)$

where (1) the p's are vertices, (2) the E's are edges, and (3) E_i has p_i and p_{i+1} for end points ($i = 1, \ldots, n - 1$). If $p_1 = p_n$, the path π will be referred to as **closed**; otherwise π will be called a path **from** p_1 **to** p_n. The graph G is **connected** if there exists at least one path from each vertex of G to each other vertex thereof.

The path π will be described as **simple** if no two of its vertices or its edges are coincident, save perhaps p_1 and p_n.

LEMMA 1. **If there exists a path π on G from a to b, then there exists a simple path from a to b, whose edges and vertices are a subset of those of π.**

Proof of Lemma. If p_i and p_j ($j > i$) coincide in (1.1), then $p_i, E_i, \ldots, E_{j-1}$ can be dropped from the sequence and the remaining terms renumbered, without destroying the defining properties of a path. This procedure can be repeated until all repetitions are removed from the sequence.

The graph G will be called **unicursal** if there exists a sequence (1.1) where E_i has p_i, p_{i+1} for end points ($i = 1, \ldots, n - 1$), and where each edge of G appears exactly once in the sequence. Intuitively, this means that it is possible to trace all of G continuously from p_1 to p_n without traversing any edge more than once. It will then be said that G is **unicursal from** p_1 **to** p_n or can be **unicursally traced from** p_1 **to** p_n.

The following notation will be useful in certain inductive arguments. Let G be a linear graph with at least two edges, and let G_E denote the graph obtained from G by deleting an edge E; it being understood that if a vertex p of E belongs to no other edge, then p is also to be deleted.

A vertex of a linear graph will be called **even** or **odd** according as it belongs to (or is **incident** with) an even or an odd number of edges.

LEMMA 2. **A linear graph G has an even number of odd vertices.**

Proof of Lemma. If G has one edge, this result is obvious. Assume it true for all graphs with j edges for some $j \geq 1$, and let G be a graph with $j + 1$ edges. Then, for each edge E of G, G_E differs from G in the number of its odd vertices by 0 or 2. By hypothesis, the lemma holds for G_E. Hence it holds for G.

LEMMA 3. **If G is connected, then G_E either is connected or falls into two connected linear graphs.**

Proof of Lemma. Let a and b denote the end points of E. Let $G(a)$ and $G(b)$ denote the subgraphs of G_E consisting of all vertices, plus incident edges, which can be joined to a and b respectively by sequences of the form (1.1), hence (see Lemma 1) by simple paths. Let p be an arbitrary vertex of G. Since G is connected, p can be joined by simple paths on G to a and to b. If each simple path joining p to b includes the edge E, necessarily as its last edge, then p is joined to a by a path not involving E, and similarly with a and b interchanged. Hence each vertex can be joined to either a or b on G by a path not involving E. But this means that $G(a)$ and $G(b)$ exhaust G_E, and Lemma 3 follows.

THEOREM 1. **The linear graph G is unicursal if and only if it is connected and either (1) there are no odd vertices, in which case the initial and terminal points of a unicursal tracing must coincide but can otherwise be arbitrarily selected; or (2) there are exactly two odd vertices, in which case the unicursal tracing must start at one odd vertex (either will do) and terminate at the other.**

Proof. The proof of this theorem will be largely left to the reader. The following suggestions, however, are offered as a guide to one particular proof, which is inductive with respect to the number of edges of G. For the initial case, where G has only one edge, the theorem is obvious. The inductive hypothesis assumes the theorem for all graphs with $j \geq 1$ edges. The general step then consists in deducing it for an arbitrary graph G with $j + 1$ edges. Note that the inductive hypothesis applies to G_E, as defined above, or to its connected subgraphs, where E is an edge of G, and that Lemma 3 is useful in the argument. It may prove convenient to divide the general step into the three cases: where G has no odd vertices, where it has two such, and where it has more than two.

EXERCISES

1. Prove the following, for a connected graph G: (a) If G has fewer than four vertices, it is unicursal. (b) If G has exactly four vertices and is not unicursal, then the graph obtained by adjoining a new edge to G, joining two of its vertices, is unicursal. (c) If G has exactly five vertices and is not unicursal, it is possible to obtain a unicursal graph from it by adjoining an edge connecting two suitably chosen vertices.

2. (a) Show that the removal of any one of the Koenigsberg bridges would make the unicursal promenade possible, but that no such promenade would end where it started. (b) Give an example of a connected graph with four vertices and with an edge whose removal does not lead to a unicursal graph.

1–3. The Cyclomatic Number

Consider a linear graph G. Let us think of the edges as wires. Then, from the electrical viewpoint, one might be interested in knowing whether G is connected and whether or not G contains circuits, where a **circuit** means a simple closed path, that is, a sequence of the form (1.1) in which all the vertices (hence all the edges) are distinct, except that $p_1 = p_n$. A graph G which is connected and on which no circuit exists is called a **tree**.

A **terminal vertex** of a graph G will mean a vertex incident with only one edge thereof, and an edge incident with a terminal vertex will be called a **terminal edge**. The other edges of G will be called **inner edges**.

LEMMA 4. **A tree G is characterized, among connected graphs, by either of the following properties:**

   (1) **For two arbitrary vertices, a and b, of G there exists only one simple path from a to b.**

   (2) **If E is any inner edge of G, then G_E is not connected.**

Proof of Lemma. To establish (1) as a necessary property, note that the existence of at least one simple path from a to b follows from the connectedness of the graph. If more than one should exist, then the reader can prove that a circuit could be put together from any two of them, or from selected portions thereof. As for the sufficiency, the existence of a circuit would imply a violation of condition (1), where a and b are two vertices on such a circuit. The proof of Lemma 3 above can be readily adapted to establish condition (2) as a characteristic property and also to establish the following corollary.

(A)* If E is any inner edge of a tree G, then G_E consists of two separate trees.

(B) A tree has at least two terminal vertices. The proof of (B) is left to the reader.

Given a linear graph G, let α_0 denote the number of its vertices and α_1 the number of its edges. If G is connected, then the number

$$(1.2) \qquad \mu = \alpha_1 - \alpha_0 + 1$$

is called the **cyclomatic number**, also the **first Betti number**, of G.

THEOREM 2. **A connected graph G is a tree if and only if $\mu = 0$. If $\mu > 0$, then it is possible to reduce G to a tree by the removal of μ suitably selected inner edges. This cannot be done by the removal of fewer than μ edges, and G is necessarily disconnected by the removal of $\mu + 1$ inner edges.**

Proof. Note first that the theorem implies that μ is the number of wires which must be cut, under the above electrical interpretation, in order to break every circuit without separating G into distinct components.†

As in the case of Theorem 1, the proof will be left to the reader, with the comment that an argument inductive in α_1 is practicable (Exercise 3). The initial case, $\alpha_1 = 1$, is trivial, and the passage from $\alpha_1 = j$ to $\alpha_1 = j + 1$ offers no substantial difficulties. The following auxiliary result, which is readily established, is stated for its intrinsic interest.

(C) Any connected graph for which $\alpha_1 > 1$ can be built up from a single edge by the successive adjunction of other edges, the graph being connected at all times.

Like various other aspects of pure mathematics, the study of linear graphs was partly stimulated by practical problems. In fact, as just noted, the first important contribution to the theory of such graphs was made by Kirchhoff in the course of investigating currents in a connected electrical network. There are two types of equations, all of the first degree, entering into the determination of the currents, given an arbitrary distribution of electromotive forces on the wires of the network, namely:

(1) Equations for circuits made up of subsets of the wires, such as the wires numbered (1, 2, 6), (1, 2, 4, 5), and (4, 5, 6) in Fig. 1–3.

* Letters (A), (B), (C), ... , with parentheses, are given for convenience in later reference.

† See the article by G. Kirchhoff in Poggendorf's *Annalen der Physik* 72 (1847), p. 497. This article contains "the first important contribution to the theory of linear graphs" [V, p. 26]. (Here, and throughout this text, such bracketed symbols as [V] refer to books and articles listed in the bibliography.) The number μ, discovered by Kirchhoff, was named the **cyclomatic number** by another physicist, James Clerk Maxwell, *A Treatise on Electricity and Magnetism* (Oxford: Clarendon Press, 1873).

(2) Equations expressing the fact that the sum of all the currents flowing into each vertex is zero, provided those flowing out are taken negatively.

The reader sufficiently familiar with electrical theory should write the equations and follow through the remainder of this article in detail.

In the notation of linear graphs, there are α_1 wires and α_0 vertices in the network. The unknowns of the equations are the currents i_h

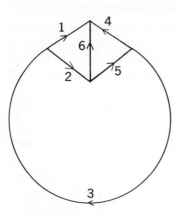

Fig. I–3. A network.

$(h = 1, \ldots, \alpha_1)$ in the wires. To determine them, there must be α_1 independent equations in the sets (1) and (2) just described; that is, it should be possible to pick out exactly α_1 equations from these two sets, no one of the selected equations being a consequence of the others, and to assert that all other equations of the two sets are consequences of those selected. It turns out, for example, that the equations for the three circuits mentioned under (1) are not independent. Let the wires be oriented by the arrows in Fig. 1–3, a current being positive if in the direction of the arrow and negative if in the opposite direction. As a consequence of the connectedness of the network, one can show that there are just $\alpha_0 - 1$ independent equations in set (2). All the equations in set (1) are independent of those in set (2). Since a total of α_1 independent equations is needed to determine the currents in the wires, there must be $\alpha_1 - \alpha_0 + 1$ independent equations in (1). This is the cyclomatic number μ of Eq. (1.2) and is the least number of wires whose cutting will break every circuit. Kirchhoff selected a complete set of independent equations as follows. Let the wires be so numbered that the cutting of wires $(1, 2, \ldots, \mu)$ breaks every circuit. Then, in the network left when all but one of these μ wires is removed, there is just one circuit. If all the wires save wire i are removed, call the circuit in the remaining network C_i $(i = 1, \ldots, \mu)$. The equations for the μ circuits C_i are independent, since each contains a current not in any of the others. Every equation for a circuit depends on these μ, since every circuit can be expressed as a combination of the C_i. The reader should, like Kirchhoff, demonstrate this by an argument recurrent in μ. Thus Kirchhoff was led to discover the cyclomatic number.

EXERCISE

3. Carry out the suggested inductive proof of Theorem 2.

I-4.   Restrictions on Polyhedra*

For the next elementary geometric results, consider the polyhedral shapes into which one might deform a spherical piece of modeling clay. It is understood that there is to be no pulling apart or sticking together of the clay; for example, it is not permissible to punch a hole, like a tunnel, all the way through it. The surface of the clay is called a **polyhedron** π when it is made up of a finite number of plane polygonal regions, with their edges and vertices. These plane regions will be called the **faces** of π.

(A) The following properties of π offer no difficulties: (1) Each face has at least three edges. (2) Each vertex belongs to at least three edges. (3) The vertices on each face can be cyclically ordered so that each is joined to its successor by an edge. (4) The faces having a given vertex in common can be cyclically ordered so that each has an edge in common with its successor.

The results of this section are topological in that they apply even if the surface of the clay is not polyhedral but is divided into regions such that (1) each region has a simple closed boundary with at least three points, called vertices, on it, (2) each vertex belongs to at least three regions, (3) if two regions have in common a boundary point other than a vertex, then they have in common the entire edge† through that point.

Let

$$\alpha_0 = \text{the number of vertices of the polyhedral surface } \pi,$$

(1.3) $$\alpha_1 = \text{the number of edges of } \pi,$$

$$\alpha_2 = \text{the number of faces of } \pi.$$

Let

$$V_i = \text{the number of vertices each belonging to}$$
$$\text{exactly } i \text{ edges } (i = 3, 4, \ldots),$$

(1.4)

$$F_i = \text{the number of faces possessing exactly } i \text{ edges}$$
$$(i = 3, 4, \ldots).$$

The following theorems, presently to be proved, state some of the possibly surprising restrictions on the structure of π.

THEOREM 3. **It is impossible that π have exactly seven edges, though it may have six or any number higher than seven. That is, $\alpha_1 \neq 7$, but $\alpha_1 = 6, 8, 9, \ldots$ are all possible.**

---

* The material of this article is adapted from the writer's expository paper, "Peculiarities of polyhedra," *American Mathematical Monthly* 58 (1951), pp. 684–689, where references to sources can be found.

† An edge is here the arc of a boundary between two consecutive vertices.

THEOREM 4. There must be at least (1) four faces of π with fewer than six edges and (2) four vertices of π belonging to fewer than six edges. This can be formulated thus:

(1.5)   (a) $F_3 + F_4 + F_5 \geq 4,$ (b) $V_3 + V_4 + V_5 \geq 4.$

THEOREM 5. It is impossible that, simultaneously, every face have more than three vertices and every vertex belong to more than three faces. In fact, the number of triangular faces plus the number of vertices each belonging to exactly three faces is at least 8; or, formulated:

$$(1.6) \qquad\qquad F_3 + V_3 \geq 8.$$

THEOREM 6. It is impossible that π have either (1) an odd number of odd-sided faces or (2) an odd number of vertices each belonging to an odd number of edges. That is, both $(F_3 + F_5 + F_7 + \cdots)$ and $(V_3 + V_5 + V_7 + \cdots)$ must be even.

THEOREM 7. (1) If each vertex belongs to just three faces and each face is pentagonal or hexagonal, then exactly twelve faces are pentagonal. (2) If each face is triangular and each vertex belongs to either five or six faces, then exactly twelve vertices belong to five faces each. The first part of this theorem is expressible thus:

(1.7)
$$\left.\begin{array}{l} \alpha_0 = V_3 \\[6pt] \alpha_2 = F_5 + F_6 \end{array}\right\} \text{ imply } F_5 = 12.$$

The second can be formulated as follows:

(1.8)
$$\left.\begin{array}{l} \alpha_2 = F_3 \\[6pt] \alpha_0 = V_5 + V_6 \end{array}\right\} \text{ imply } V_5 = 12.$$

THEOREM 8. If all faces have the same number i of edges and all vertices belong to the same number j of edges, then there are only five possible topologically* different polyhedral structures, typified by the tetrahedron, cube, octahedron, dodecahedron, and icosahedron.

In other words, the theorem, known from Grecian antiquity, that only five regular solids exist is a topological theorem, and the hypothesis that the faces be congruent in the euclidean sense is superfluous, since the conclusion of Theorem 8 is a consequence of

(1.9)
$$\begin{array}{ll} \alpha_0 = V_i & \text{for some } i \quad \text{ and} \\[6pt] \alpha_2 = F_j & \text{for some } j. \end{array}$$

* The significance of this term is clarified later.

The above six theorems all follow from certain equations and inequalities among the V's, F's, and α's. In the first place

(1.10)
$$\alpha_0 = V_3 + V_4 + \cdots + V_{\alpha_2-1},$$
$$\alpha_2 = F_3 + F_4 + \cdots + F_{\alpha_0-1}$$

since (1) each vertex belongs to at least three and at most $\alpha_2 - 1$ edges and (2) each face has at least three and at most $\alpha_0 - 1$ edges.

(*B*) The above theorems illustrate a so-called **duality principle**; two statements being **dual** to one another if each is carried into the other by the simultaneous interchange of α_0 and the V's with α_2 and the respective F's. The property of two faces having a common edge is described as **dual** to the property of two vertices being joined by an edge.

Thus, the two numbered parts of Theorem 4 are dual to one another, and similarly for Theorems 6 and 7. Theorem 5 is self-dual and so, in a trivial way, is Theorem 3. Equations (1.10) are a dual pair. As for Theorem 8, the reader should verify (1) that the tetrahedron is self-dual, (2) that the cube and octahedron are dual structures, and (3) that the dodecahedron and icosahedron are dual. The concept of dual maps, explained below, will be helpful.

As the present discussion continues, let it be observed that all the equations on which the proofs of Theorems 3 to 8 depend either are self-dual or fall into dual pairs. Hence it will suffice to prove only one of each pair of dual results in the theorems, since interchanging α_0 and the V's with α_2 and the F's will yield a proof of the other.

A geometric insight into the reason for duality can be obtained as follows. Regard the faces of π as maps of countries on a polyhedral earth; or, what amounts to the same thing, let the faces, edges, and vertices be mapped, preserving their incidence relations, onto a spherical surface S. The edges need not be arcs of circles, but can be any simple non-intersecting arcs joining pairs of vertices in accordance with the structure of the original polyhedron. Interior to each face, select a vertex. The vertices thus selected will belong to a so-called **dual map** and will be called **dual vertices**. If two faces φ_1 and φ_2 have in common an edge ε, let the dual vertices v_1' and v_2' on them be joined by a new edge ε', crossing ε at a single point and otherwise meeting no edge or vertex of either the given map or the new dual map (see (*B*) above and Fig. 1–4). The possibility of this requires a proof which would take us too far afield. Accordingly, let it be assumed possible, or let the edges be restricted to curves on the sphere for which it is clearly possible. The new edges, which are the edges of the dual map, subdivide S into new faces, each containing exactly one vertex of the original map. It is easy to verify that if v is a vertex of π on a given face Φ' of the dual map, then v belongs to as many faces of π as Φ' has vertices in the dual map. Since the relations between the maps are symmetric, the duality principle follows.

The same mathematician who solved the problem of unicursal graphs also established the following identity, known as **Euler's theorem in two dimensions:**

$$(1.11) \qquad \alpha_0 - \alpha_1 + \alpha_2 = 2.$$

It holds for a more general subdivision of a spherical surface than described above, in which there may be as few as two vertices on the

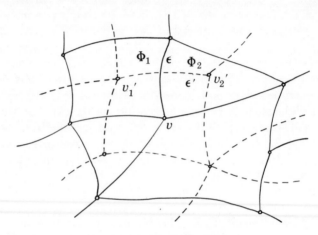

Fig. 1–4. Dual maps.

boundary of a region and, dually, as few as two regions with a given vertex in common. The simplest such subdivision consists of two regions, two edges, and two vertices, which obviously satisfies (1.11). Any subdivision can be obtained* from this simplest one by a sequence of steps, each consisting of either (1) the separation of an edge into two edges by the introduction of a new vertex or (2) the separation of a region into two regions by the introduction of a new edge joining two vertices. The first type of step increases α_0 and α_1 by one each, leaving α_2 unchanged; the second leaves α_0 unchanged and increases α_2 and α_1 by one each. Since (1.11) is therefore preserved by each step, it holds for all subdivisions of the sphere.

Since each edge of a polyhedron belongs to exactly two faces,

$$(1.12) \qquad 2\alpha_1 = 3F_3 + 4F_4 + \cdots + (\alpha_0 - 1)F_{\alpha_0-1};$$

---

* This statement requires proof. The reader might consider how he would go about to develop an inductive demonstration of it. However, certain fine points in the argument depend on material in later chapters.

and, dually, since each edge has exactly two vertices,

(1.13) $$2\alpha_1 = 3V_3 + 4V_4 + \cdots + (\alpha_2 - 1)V_{\alpha_2-1}.$$

Theorem 6 follows from the fact that the right sides of (1.12) and (1.13) are equal to even numbers.

From (1.10), (1.12), and (1.13),

(1.14) $$\text{(a) } 3\alpha_2 \le 2\alpha_1, \qquad \text{(b) } 3\alpha_0 \le 2\alpha_1,$$

where the equality sign prevails in (1.14a) if and only if all faces are triangular, and in (1.14b) if and only if each vertex belongs to exactly three edges.

Substituting from (1.11) into (1.14), one finds

(1.15)
$$\text{(a) } 3\alpha_1 - 3\alpha_0 + 6 \le 2\alpha_1,$$
$$\text{(b) } 3\alpha_1 - 3\alpha_2 + 6 \le 2\alpha_1$$

or

(1.16)
$$\text{(a) } \alpha_1 + 6 \le 3\alpha_0,$$
$$\text{(b) } \alpha_1 + 6 \le 3\alpha_2.$$

The equality sign in (1.16a) holds if and only if all faces are triangular; that in (1.16b), if and only if each vertex belongs to exactly three edges.

From (1.16a) and (1.14b),

(1.17) $$\tfrac{1}{3}\alpha_1 + 2 \le \alpha_0 \le \tfrac{2}{3}\alpha_1.$$

If $\alpha_1 = 7$, this would imply the absurdity

(1.18) $$4\tfrac{1}{3} \le \alpha_0 \le 4\tfrac{2}{3}.$$

To complete the proof of Theorem 3, one would have to establish that $\alpha_1 = 6, 8, 9, \ldots$ are all possible, for which see *Vorlesungen über die Theorie der Polyeder* by Ernst Steinitz (Springer, 1934), edited by Hans Rademacher.

Next, let Eqs. (1.10) be multiplied on both sides by 6 and, from the result, let the respective Eqs. (1.13) and (1.12) be subtracted. The resulting equations imply

(1.19)
$$\text{(a) } 6\alpha_0 - 2\alpha_1 \le 3V_3 + 2V_4 + V_5,$$
$$\text{(b) } 6\alpha_2 - 2\alpha_1 \le 3F_3 + 2F_4 + F_5.$$

From (1.16a), $6\alpha_0 - 2\alpha_1 \ge 12$. Hence, from (1.19a),

(1.20) $$12 \le 3V_3 + 2V_4 + V_5 \le 3(V_3 + V_4 + V_5),$$

and (1.5b) follows. The other part of Theorem 4 similarly follows with the aid of (1.16b) and (1.19b).

In relations (1.19), both equality signs prevail if and only if $V_j = F_j = 0 \ (j > 6)$. This condition is implied by the hypotheses of the first part of Theorem 7. Since the only non-zero terms on the right side of (1.19) are then V_3 and F_5, it follows that $6\alpha_2 - 2\alpha_1 = F_5$. Since $\alpha_0 = V_3$ has been seen to imply the equality sign in (1.16b), the latter becomes $\alpha_1 + 6 = 3\alpha_2$. Accordingly, (1.7) follows and, by a dual argument, so does (1.8).

Next, let the quantity $4(\alpha_0 + \alpha_2 - \alpha_1)$ be figured by (1) multiplying Eqs. (1.10) each by 4 and adding the results, so as to get an expression for $4(\alpha_0 + \alpha_2)$, (2) adding Eqs. (1.12) and (1.13) so as to obtain an expression for $4\alpha_1$, and (3) subtracting the latter expression from the former. This gives

$$(1.21) \quad 4(\alpha_0 + \alpha_2 - \alpha_1) = (F_3 + V_3) - (F_5 + V_5) - 2(F_6 + V_6) - \cdots,$$

which, with Euler's theorem, implies Theorem 5.

It remains only to establish Theorem 8. From (1.9), (1.12), and (1.13), $2\alpha_1 = iV_i = jF_j$. Hence, again using (1.9),

$$\alpha_0 = V_i = \frac{jF_j}{i},$$

(1.22)

$$\alpha_2 = F_j = \frac{iV_i}{j},$$

and Euler's relation (1.11) becomes, in terms of V_i,

$$(1.23) \qquad \left(1 + \frac{i}{j} - \frac{i}{2}\right)V_i = 2.$$

Relations (1.5) and (1.9) yield $i = 3$, 4, or 5 and $j = 3$, 4, or 5. By (1.6), either $i = 3$ or $j = 3$. If $i = j = 3$, then, by (1.23), $V_3 = 4$ and, dually, $F_3 = 4$, so that the tetrahedral type is implied. If $i = 3$ and $j = 4$, then, by (1.23), $V_3 = 8$ and hence, by (1.22), $F_4 = 6$. Dually, if $i = 4$ and $j = 3$, then $F_3 = 8$ and $V_4 = 6$. It is readily verified that these possibilities correspond to the cubic and octahedral types. If $i = 3$ and $j = 5$, then (1.23) and (1.22) yield $V_3 = 20$, $F_5 = 12$. Dually, if $i = 5$ and $j = 3$, then $F_3 = 20$, $V_5 = 12$. The reader should verify that these possibilities imply the dodecahedral and icosahedral types.

The proofs of Theorems 3 to 8 are now complete. Most of these results date back to Euler, but the present proofs have been adapted from more recent sources.

EXERCISES

4. Show that a pyramid with a polygonal base is self-dual.

5. Draw a figure showing (a) a truncated pyramid with a triangular base and (b) a solid having a dual boundary structure.

2

Topological Classification
of Surfaces

We continue in the intuitive spirit of Chapter 1, reserving precise definitions and proofs for later chapters.

2-1. Polygonal Regions with Matched Edges

A surface is an idealization of such an object as a sheet of rubber. Topology includes the study of properties preserved when a surface is deformed in various ways, without being torn. A surface may have edges, like a rubber disk or a disk with a hole in it, in which case the edges constitute its **boundary**. If, like a sphere or the surface of a doughnut, it has no edges, we refer to it as **closed**.

From the viewpoint of combinatorial topology, surfaces are investigated by imagining them cut into little patches, "curvilinear triangles" for example, and considering how these patches are fitted together.

(*A*) Accordingly, let us regard a **surface** M as a collection of triangular regions $(\tau_1, \ldots, \tau_n)$, with some edges matched (or **identified**) in pairs. If an edge A of τ_i is identified with an edge of τ_j, we refer to τ_i and τ_j as **adjacent across** A. A surface is required to be **connected**, in the sense that it is possible to pass from any triangle σ of M to any other triangle τ by a sequence of triangles $(\sigma_1 = \sigma, \sigma_2, \ldots, \sigma_m = \tau)$, each belonging to M, where σ_i and σ_{i+1} are adjacent $(i = 1, \ldots, m - 1)$. If there are **free edges**, that is, edges not matched with other edges, they constitute the **boundary** of M. If there are none, M is **closed**.

Given $(\tau_1, \ldots, \tau_n)$ and a specification of the identifications of paired edges, we are led to the problem of deforming the regions τ_i so as to bring the matched edges into coincidence, thus piecing $(\tau_1, \ldots, \tau_n)$ together into a continuous surface M, as though we had a topological jigsaw puzzle with deformable pieces. See, for example, Fig. 2–1, where identified edges are denoted by identical letters and are supplied with arrows to specify their matching.

When two directed edges are matched, their initial vertices, also their terminal vertices, are necessarily identified. Thus the twelve vertices in Fig. 2–1a reduce to the four vertices of the tetrahedron in Fig. 2–1b. Figure 2–2 illustrates a surface with boundary.

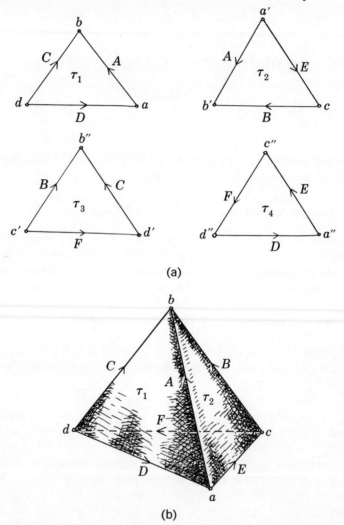

(a)

(b)

Fig. 2–1. A closed surface as a set of matched triangles. (a) The triangles; (b) the surface assembled into a tetrahedron.

Topologically, the surfaces of a tetrahedron and a sphere are equivalent. Figure 2–3 shows a dissection of the spherical surface, topologically equivalent to Fig. 2–1b. Figure 2–4 shows two other representations of a spherical surface.

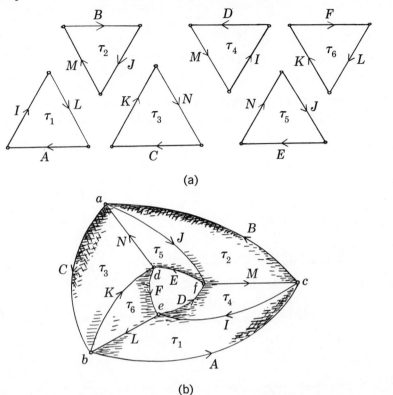

(a)

(b)

Fig. 2–2. A surface with boundary. (a) The triangles; (b) the assembled surface.

An edge and its end points are said to be **incident** with one another. So are a triangle and its edges or vertices.

Up to a certain point, the piecing together of $(\tau_1, \tau_2, \ldots, \tau_n)$ can be carried out in the plane as follows. Let τ_i be a triangle having an edge in common with τ_1. Then τ_1 and τ_i can be brought together and amalgamated into a quadrilateral region τ_{1i} along edge A. See Fig. 2–5, where τ_1 and τ_2 of Fig. 2–1 are thus amalgamated, τ_2 being first "turned over" and perhaps changed in size and shape. Next let τ_j be a triangle having an edge B in common with τ_{1i}. Then τ_j and τ_{1i} can be amalgamated across B to obtain a pentagonal region τ_{1ij}.

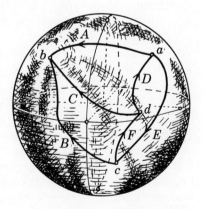

Fig. 2–3. A representation equivalent to Fig. 2–1b.

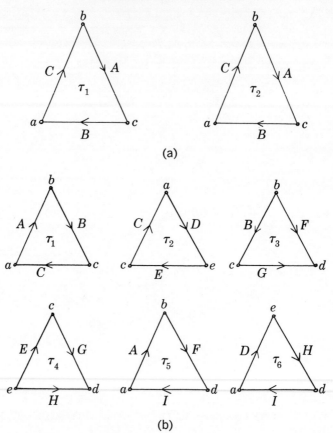

(a)

(b)

Fig. 2–4. Two other representations of the sphere.

Continuing thus, step by step, one can fuse all the regions (τ_1, $\tau_2, \ldots, \tau_n$) into a single $(n + 2)$-edged polygonal region, some of whose outer edges would, in general, have to be fitted together in pairs to obtain a model of the surface. In the case of Fig. 2–5, where $n = 4$, a hexagonal region is obtained. This suggests the following definition, equivalent to (A).

(B) A **surface** or **2-manifold** M is a plane region bounded by a single polygon, some of whose edges are identified in pairs according to prescribed relative directions.

To illustrate (B), it suffices to draw a polygonal region, assign directions to all its edges, then assign a symbol to each edge, no symbol being used more than twice. It is easily seen that the same surface admits many different polygonal representations. For example, note that the octagonal representation in Fig. 2–6 is equivalent to the hexagonal representation in Fig. 2–7b, since the paired edges E can be eliminated as suggested by the intermediate Fig. 2–7a.

(C) A convenient symbol for a polygonal representation of a closed surface is obtained as follows: (1) Select a positive sense for the polygon (clockwise or counterclockwise). (2) Select any edge as "first edge" of the symbol. (3) Write the edges in cyclic order, starting with the first edge and proceeding in the positive sense around the polygon,

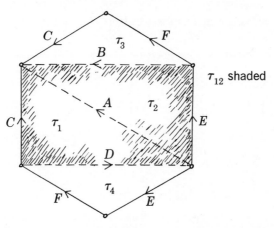

Fig. 2–5. Amalgamation of the triangles of Fig. 2–1a into a polygonal region.

supplying each edge with the superscript $+1$ if its sense agrees with the positive sense of the polygon and -1 otherwise. The superscript $+1$ will generally be omitted in writing symbols. Figures 2–5 to 2–7 can be thus symbolized as follows:

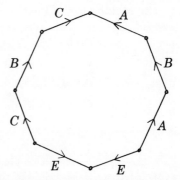

(2.1)

    (a) $CC^{-1}F^{-1}E^{-1}EF$
        (Fig. 2–5),

    (b) $ABAC^{-1}B^{-1}C^{-1}EE^{-1}$
        (Figs. 2–6 and 2–7a),

    (c) $ABAC^{-1}B^{-1}C^{-1}$
        (Fig. 2–7b).

(D) Any string of letters in which no letter appears more than twice and in which the superscripts 1 and -1 are arbitrarily distributed represents a surface and will be called a **polygonal**

Fig. 2–6. An octagonal polygonal representation.

symbol for it. Each letter in a symbol will be called an **edge** and will be described as **free** or **paired** according as it appears just once or twice. Every surface has infinitely many polygonal representations.

(E) Some obvious ways of changing a symbol without changing the surface represented are as follows:

(1) On a free edge, changing the superscript from 1 to -1 or from -1 to 1. On a paired edge, simultaneously changing the superscript on both appearances of the edge. These changes clearly do not affect the matching of the edges of the polygon.

(2) Writing a symbol in reverse order, changing all or none of the superscripts.

(3) Moving a block of letters from the end of a symbol to the beginning.

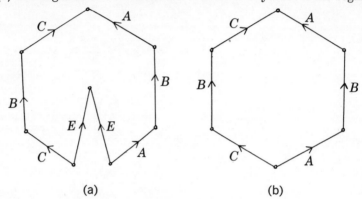

(a)   (b)

Fig. 2–7. Two equivalent representations.

We will admit two-edged regions, as suggested by AA and AA^{-1} in Figs. 2–8a and 2–8b, and even one-edged regions, as symbolized by A and shown in Fig. 2–8c.

(F) Making use of Part (1) of (E), we will generally write a polygonal symbol so that the suppressed superscript 1 appears on the first occurrence of each edge. Thus the symbols (2.1) are altered as follows.

(2.2)
$$\text{(a)} \quad CC^{-1}F^{-1}E^{-1}EF \to CC^{-1}FEE^{-1}F^{-1},$$
$$\text{(b)} \quad ABAC^{-1}B^{-1}C^{-1}EE^{-1} \to ABACB^{-1}CEE^{-1},$$
$$\text{(c)} \quad ABAC^{-1}B^{-1}C^{-1} \to ABACB^{-1}C.$$

EXERCISE

1. Draw eight triangles and indicate, after the fashion of Fig. 2–1, a matching of their edges corresponding to the surface of an octahedron.

2-2. Some Elementary Surfaces

Some examples of familiar surfaces are now given.

(A) *The Disk A :* The only one-edged symbol A represents the disk, which is also represented by any symbol made up entirely of free edges.

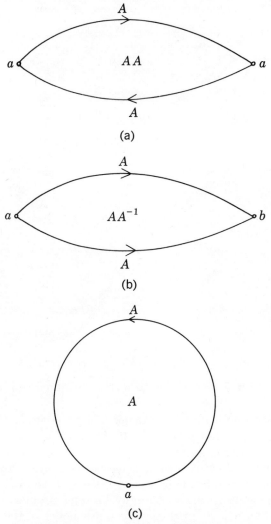

Fig. 2–8. Two-edged and one-edged polygons.

(B) *The Sphere AA^{-1}:* Given the 2-edged symbol AA^{-1}, one can imagine a zipper along the matched edges, whereby the surface can be closed and then deformed into a spherical shape (Fig. 2–9).

(C) *The Projective Plane or Sphere with Crosscap CC:* Let the disk-like surface CC be modified into the form of a sphere with a slit in it. Then let a part of the sphere containing the slit be blown up into a sort of blister (Fig. 2–10a). In Fig. 2–10b, the blister is "pinched in" to bring the matched end points c of the slit close together and to bring the entire slit close to a vertical line. Finally (Fig. 2–10c) the

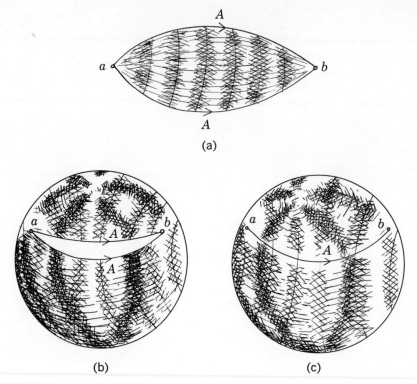

Fig. 2–9. Equivalence of AA^{-1} to a sphere.

edges cpm are brought into coincidence along the vertical line, and so are the edges cqm. This creates a self-penetration, not regarded as a self-intersection of the surface. As a horizontal plane moves down from m, its intersections with the surface, called **contour lines**, resemble a figure 8 until c is reached (Fig. 2–10d). Below c, the self-intersection is lost and the contour lines gradually become circular. The part of the sphere above K is a **crosscap**. The equivalence of the sphere with crosscap to a projective plane is discussed later.

(D) *The Moebius Strip K_1BK_2B or Crosscap KCC:* If the crosscap of Fig. 2–10c is cut off around the circle K, slit open along the segment C, and flattened out in the plane, the representation suggested by Fig. 2–11a is obtained. In this figure, K is divided by two points, b and a, into the arcs K_1 and K_2. Let cuts be made along the dotted lines B_1 and B_2, separating the surface into two parts, I and II. In Fig. 2–11b, the separate parts are shown deformed into rectangles. In Fig. 2–11c, rectangle I is turned over to permit a matching with II along C. After this matching, B_1 and B_2 are amalgamated into a single edge B, which leads to the symbol $K_1^{-1}BK_2B$, or, by a change in notation,

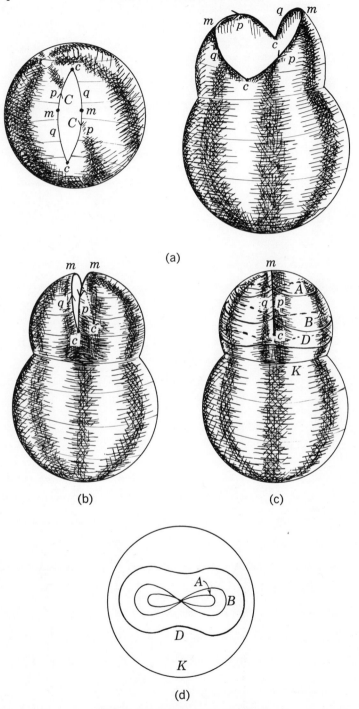

(a)

(b)

(c)

(d)

Fig. 2–10. Representation of CC.

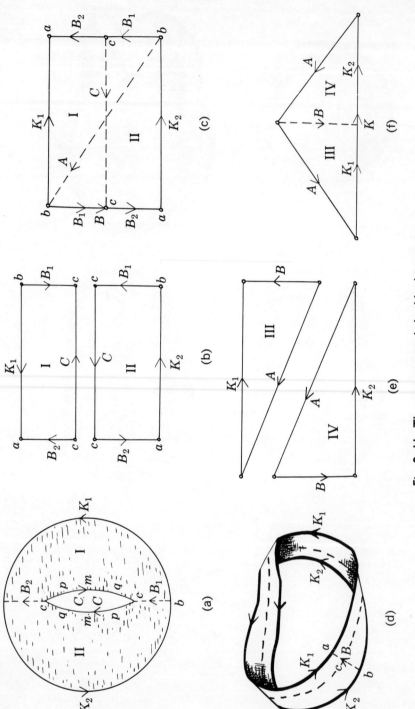

Fig. 2–11. The crosscap and the Moebius strip.

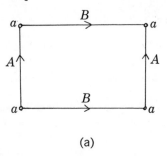

(a)

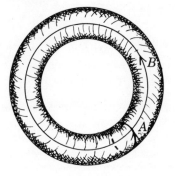

(b)

Fig. 2–12. The torus.

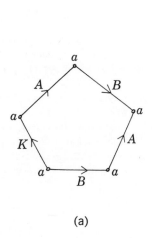

(a)

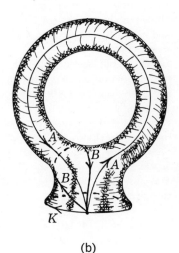

(b)

Fig. 2–13. The handle.

K_1BK_2B. In Fig. 2–11d, the rectangle of Fig. 2–11c has its edges B matched, to produce the **Moebius strip**, named for the German mathematician G. F. Moebius (1858). To obtain another representation, let the diagonal cut A (Fig. 2–11c) separate the rectangle into triangular pieces III and IV (Fig. 2–11e). Then let III be turned over, so as to permit a matching with IV along B, which leads to the representation KAA (Fig. 2–11f). A change of notation yields KCC.

(E) *The Torus* $ABA^{-1}B^{-1}$: This, the simplest to visualize of the closed surfaces requiring a four-edged symbol, is shown in Fig. 2–12a and, assembled, in 2–12b.

(F) *The Handle* $KABA^{-1}B^{-1}$: This surface (Fig. 2–13) is equivalent to a torus with a hole in it.

EXERCISES

2. Give a matching of edges of two triangles such that they fit together to cover the plane band bounded by two concentric circles.

3. Let $(\tau_1, \ldots, \tau_n)$ be a set of triangles, some of whose edges are matched in pairs, and whose vertices are identified only as implied by the matching of edges. Suppose no edge has its two vertices identified. (a) Show that all the triangles incident with a given vertex v can be arranged in a cyclic order or a linear order (with a first and a last element) so that consecutive triangles are adjacent. (b) Show that the linear order results if and only if v is incident with some *free edge*; that is, an edge not matched with any other.

• 4. State and prove the dual of Exercise 3, insofar as it holds.

5. Under the hypotheses of Exercise 3, with the connectedness condition of Art. 2–1(A), show that the edges and vertices of $(\tau_1, \ldots, \tau_n)$, as identified, constitute a connected linear graph.

6. Under the hypotheses of Exercise 3, show that the boundary of a surface, as defined in Art. 2–1(A), consists of a number of circuits, no two of which have a vertex in common.

7. Let the hypotheses of Exercise 3 be modified by making one identification $p = q$ of vertices not joined by an edge, in addition to the induced identifications. What statements can be made analogous to (a) and (b) in Exercise 3 with respect to the resulting vertex?

8. Show (a) that a 2-letter symbol represents a disk or a sphere or a sphere with crosscap; (b) that a 3-letter symbol represents a Moebius strip or a disk.

9. Show that a 4-letter symbol is equivalent to one of the following seven possibilities: (a) the disk, (b) the Moebius strip, (c) the plane band between two concentric circles, (d) the sphere, (e) the torus, (f) the form $CCDD$, (g) the sphere with crosscap. The surface $CCDD$ is considered in more detail in Exercise 18 below.

10. Show that $ABA^{-1}B^{-1}KDK^{-1}$ is equivalent to the handle $KABA^{-1}B^{-1}$.

2–3. Orientability and Non-Orientability

A model of the Moebius strip is made by pasting together the ends of a narrow strip of paper after putting one twist in it (Figs. 2–11cd and 2–14). Let a small circle with an assigned positive sense (called an **oriented circle**) be slid once around the strip. When it returns to its original position, its orientation is reversed (see positions 4 and 1 in Fig. 2–14). The Moebius strip is accordingly described as **non-orientable.**

Now imagine a normal vector N from the center of the moving circle, so directed that the orientation is clockwise as viewed from the tip of N. When the moving circle returns to its initial position, the sense of N is reversed. The Moebius strip is accordingly said to be **one-sided** in euclidean three-dimensional space.

(A) In general, a surface M is **non-orientable** or **orientable** according as there does or does not exist on it a closed curve C such that a small oriented circle slid once around C returns to its original position with orientation reversed.

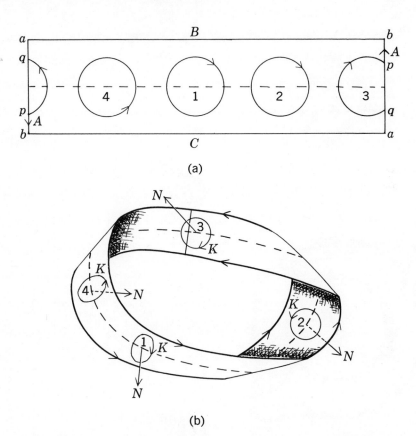

(a)

(b)

Fig. 2–14. Non-orientability and one-sidedness of the Moebius strip.

THEOREM 1. **A polygonal symbol represents a non-orientable surface if it contains two paired edges with equal superscripts.**

Proof. A symbol with two paired edges having equal superscripts can be put in the form

$$(2.3) \qquad\qquad \pi = \ldots A \ldots A \ldots .$$

Just as in the case of the Moebius strip, a path cutting across the polygonal region from the midpoint of one copy of A to that of the other has the non-orientability property of Definition (A).

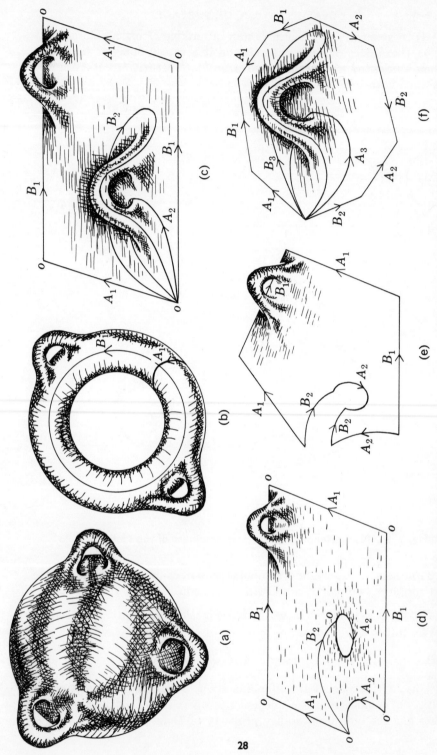

Fig. 2–15. Reduction of $H(3)$ to standard form. (a) $H(3)$; (b) $H(3)$ as a torus with two handles; (c) $H(3)$ as a torus with two handles; (d) separation along A_2 with handle shrunk back; (e) separation along B_2; (f) preparation to eliminate

28

2–4.   Standard Form for Spheres with Contours and Handles or Crosscaps

The discussion in Arts. 2–4 and 2–5 is based on some results due to H. R. Brahana.* His work has been reproduced, with modifications, several times in the literature ([K_2], Ch. II, §§6–7; [S–T], §§37–39, for example).

From a sphere S, let a number $h > 0$ of pieces be removed by circular cuts, and let each of the resulting holes be capped with a handle (Fig. 2–13b) to obtain a sphere with h handles, which we will denote with $H(h)$.

LEMMA 1. **The surface $H(h)$ can be represented by the symbol**

$$(2.4) \qquad \mathbf{H}_h = A_1 B_1 A_1^{-1} B_1^{-1} A_2 B_2 A_2^{-1} B_2^{-1} \ldots A_h B_h A_h^{-1} B_h^{-1}.$$

To establish this result, intuitively, we first interpret $H(h)$ as a torus with $h - 1$ handles. Figures 2–15a, b illustrates the case $h = 3$. Cuts A_1 and B_1, analogous to the cuts A and B of Fig. 2–12b, serve to reduce $H(h)$ to a rectangular region $A_1 B_1 A_1^{-1} B_1^{-1}$ with $h - 1$ handles (Fig. 2–15bc).

The $h - 1$ handles on the region $A_1 B_1 A_1^{-1} B_1^{-1}$ can now be eliminated one at a time, each by a pair of cuts. Figure 2–15cde shows the elimination of one of these handles, leading to a representation of $H(h)$ as an octagonal region $A_1 B_1 A_1^{-1} B_1^{-1} A_2 B_2 A_2^{-1} B_2^{-1}$ with $h - 2$ handles. A repetition of such steps leads eventually to (2.4).

Now let $q > 0$ pieces be removed from the sphere S and let each of the resulting holes be capped with a crosscap to obtain a sphere with q crosscaps, $C(q)$ (Figs. 2–16, 2–17).

LEMMA 2. **The surface $C(q)$ can be represented by the symbol**

$$(2.5) \qquad \mathbf{C}_q = C_1 C_1 C_2 C_2 \ldots C_q C_q.$$

As in the case of the previous lemma, we outline an intuitive argument. We commence by showing that the cut C_1 indicated in Fig. 2–16 permits a representation of $C(1)$ as $C_1 C_1$. First make a cut C through both sheets along the self-penetration cm of the surface; then, without making the cut C_1, proceed in reverse order through the stages illustrated in Fig. 2–10abc. This permits a flattening of the surface into the disk of Fig. 2–16b, where C_1 appears as a diameter, divided by the points o and c into two segments C_1', C_1''. In Fig. 2–16c, the cut C_1 has been made, separating the disk into parts I and II. In Fig. 2–16d, part I has been turned over and the two parts stuck together along C.

* "Systems of circuits on two-dimensional manifolds," *Annals of Mathematics* 23 (1921), pp. 144–168.

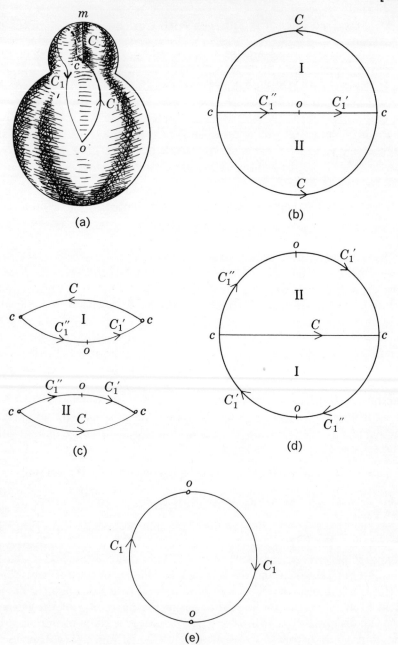

(a)

(b)

(c)

(d)

(e)

Fig. 2–16. Another reduction of the sphere with a crosscap.

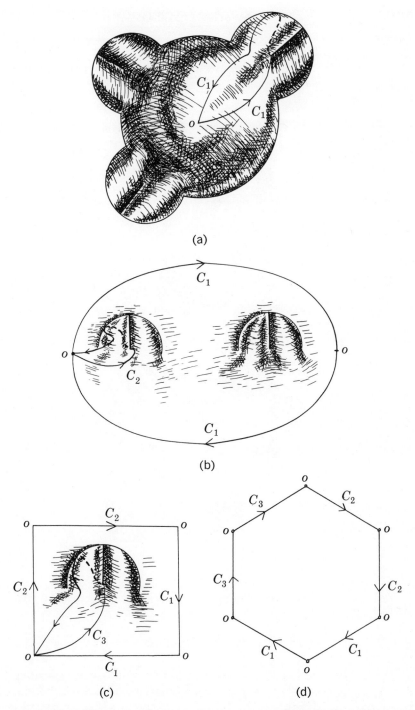

(a)

(b)

(c)   (d)

Fig. 2–17. Reduction of $C(3)$ to standard form. (a) $C(3)$; (b) $C(3)$ as C_1C_1 with two crosscaps; (c) $C(3)$ as $C_1C_1C_2C_2$ with one crosscap; (d) $C(3) = C_1C_1C_2C_2C_3C_3$.

In Fig. 2–16e, the point c and the line C have been eliminated, and the arcs C_1', C_1'' combined into C_1.

In the case $q > 1$, a procedure like the foregoing reduces $C(q)$ to a disk C_1C_1 with $q - 1$ crosscaps. Analogous steps, partly illustrated in

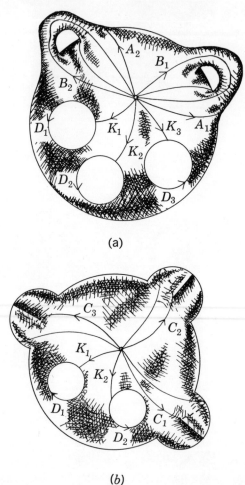

(a)

(b)

Fig. 2–18. Surfaces with contours and handles or crosscaps. (a) $H(2, 3)$; (b) $C(3, 2)$.

Fig. 2–17, eliminate the remaining crosscaps one at a time and lead to (2.5).

Let $H(h)$ be modified by the removal of r disk-like pieces, leading to $H(h, r)$, a **sphere with h handles and r contours** (Fig. 2–18). Let $C(q)$ be similarly modified, leading to $C(q, r)$, a **sphere with q crosscaps and r contours** (Fig. 2–18).

LEMMA 3. **The surfaces** $H(h, r)$ **and** $C(q, r)$ **can be represented by**

(2.6)	(a) $\mathbf{H}(h, r) = \mathbf{H}_h \mathbf{K}_r$,	(b) $\mathbf{C}(q, r) = \mathbf{C}_q \mathbf{K}_r$,

where

(2.7)	$$\mathbf{K}_r = K_1 D_1 K_1^{-1} K_2 D_2 K_2^{-1} \ldots K_r D_r K_r^{-1}.$$

To verify Lemma 3 for $H(h, r)$, let the procedure of Lemma 1 be carried through so that the cuts avoid the holes. Thus $H(h, r)$ can be reduced to the polygonal region symbolized by $\mathbf{H}_h$ with r circular pieces removed. Figure 2–18 suggests a method of making cuts which lead to (2.6).

(*A*) The methods used in establishing Lemmas 1, 2, and 3 can be summarized as follows: (1) After $2h + r$ cuts, two for each handle and one for each contour (Fig. 2–18a), it is possible to deform $H(h, r)$ into a polygonal region with matched edges symbolized by $\mathbf{H}_h \mathbf{K}_r$. (2) After $q + r$ cuts, one for each crosscap and one for each contour (Fig. 2–18b), it is possible to deform $C(q, r)$ into a polygonal region with matched edges symbolized by $\mathbf{C}_q \mathbf{K}_r$. The cuts just described afford **canonical dissections** of $H(h, r)$ and $C(q, r)$.

EXERCISES

11. Make a paper model of a Moebius strip. Cut it in two along the center of the strip and describe the results in terms of connectedness and orientability of the resulting model.

12. Proceed as in Exercise 11, but make the cut along a line one-third the way across the strip.

2–5. A Classification Theorem

The converse of Theorem 1 is also true; namely, that a polygonal symbol represents an orientable surface if it contains no paired edges with equal superscripts. We omit the proof.

THEOREM 2. (a) **An orientable surface can be represented as a sphere with** h **handles and** r **contours for some** $h \geq 0$, $r \geq 0$. (b) **A non-orientable surface can be represented as a sphere with** q **crosscaps and** r **contours for some** $q > 0$, $r \geq 0$.

Proof. (*A*) By Lemma 3, the theorem can be proved by showing that a polygonal symbol π for a surface M can be reduced to the form $\mathbf{H}_h \mathbf{K}_r$ ($h \geq 0$, $r \geq 0$) if M is orientable and to the form $\mathbf{C}_q \mathbf{K}_r$ ($q > 0$, $r \geq 0$) if M is non-orientable. The reductions will be by a sequence of steps, each of which converts a symbol into an equivalent symbol.

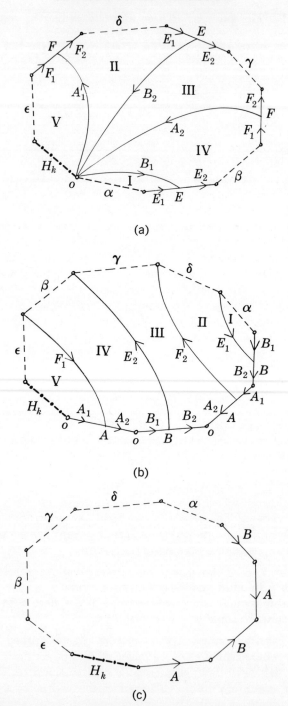

Fig. 2–19. Bringing together the elements of a handle.

(B) An **elementary reduction** of π means any one of the following changes: (1) the replacement of a sequence of free edges by a single free edge; (2) if two edges E_1 and E_2 appear only in the forms E_1E_2 and $E_2^{-1}E_1^{-1}$, the simultaneous replacement of E_1E_2 by a single edge E and $E_2^{-1}E_1^{-1}$ by E^{-1}; (3) the elimination of a pair of successive edges EE^{-1}, provided this does not eliminate the entire symbol. An elementary reduction does not change the surface represented by a symbol.

(C) If π contains no paired edges, it represents a disk, which is equivalent to $H(0, 1)$, the sphere with no handles and one contour. Hereafter, we assume that π has at least one pair of identified edges.

By Theorem 1, the orientable case is characterized by the property that each paired edge in π appears once with superscript 1 and once with superscript -1. We follow the convention of Art. 2–1(F).

(D) The symbol π will be said to **contain a handle** if it is of the form

$$(2.8) \qquad \pi = \alpha E \beta F \gamma E^{-1} \delta F^{-1} \varepsilon$$

where the small Greek letters represent sequences of edges. If β, γ, δ are all vacuous, then π contains the **handle block** $EFE^{-1}F^{-1}$. Thus $\mathbf{H}_h$ in (2.4) is a sequence of h handle blocks. The identifications of edges in $\mathbf{H}_h$ induce an identification of the end points of A_i and B_i $(i = 1, \ldots, h)$ into a single vertex o, to be called the **vertex of $\mathbf{H}_h$**.

LEMMA 4. **In the orientable case, there exists a symbol π_h, equivalent to π, of the form**

$$(2.9) \qquad \pi_h = \mathbf{H}_h \pi_h' \qquad (h \geq 0)$$

where the vertex o of $\mathbf{H}_h$ is not on a free edge and where π_h' contains no handles.

Proof of Lemma. In the case $h = 0$, $\mathbf{H}_0$ is to be interpreted as vacuous, but a vertex o of π_0 will be assigned to it.

Inductive Hypothesis. For some $k \geq 0$, there exists a symbol $\pi_k = \mathbf{H}_k \pi_k'$ equivalent to π, where the vertex of $\mathbf{H}_k$ is not on a free edge. If π has a vertex belonging to paired edges only, let such a vertex be regarded as the vertex of the vacuous set of edges $\mathbf{H}_0$. If not, let a paired edge be divided into two edges by the introduction of its midpoint o as a new vertex, and let π_0 be the modified symbol, with o as vertex of $\mathbf{H}_0$. This verifies the hypothesis for $k = 0$.

If π_k' contains no handle, let $k = h$ and the lemma is proved. If π_k' contains a handle, then π_k is of the form

$$(2.10) \qquad \pi_k = \mathbf{H}_k \alpha E \beta F \gamma E^{-1} \delta F^{-1} \varepsilon.$$

Figure 2–19 shows how to cut and reassemble the polygonal region bounded by π_h into a region with the symbol

$$(2.11) \qquad \pi_{k+1} = \mathbf{H}_k ABA^{-1}B^{-1}\alpha\delta\gamma\beta\varepsilon = H_{k+1}\pi_{k+1}'$$

where $\pi'_{k+1} = \alpha\delta\gamma\beta\varepsilon$. Note that $A = A_1A_2$ and $B = B_1B_2$, using the elementary reduction (2) of (B) above.

The symbol π_{k+1} fulfills the hypothesis with $k + 1$ in place of k, and π_{k+1} has four fewer edges than π_k. Repetitions of this procedure must therefore lead to a situation where all the handles are in the initial sequence of handle blocks, as required by the lemma.

We postpone the discussion of π'_h until after a partial treatment of the non-orientable case.

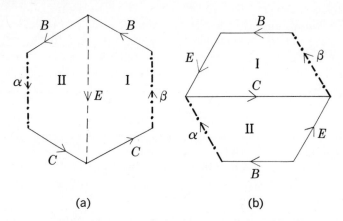

(a)   (b)

Fig. 2–20. Conversion of $BB\alpha CC\beta$ into $E\alpha^{-1}B^{-1}E\beta B$.

LEMMA 5. **The symbols $B\alpha B\beta$ and $BB\alpha^{-1}\beta$ are equivalent, where α^{-1} is the block of edges α in reverse order with all superscripts changed.**

A proof is suggested by Fig. 2–11ef, in which K_1 and K_2 are to be replaced by the sequences of edges α and β. The use of B in both symbols of the lemma amounts to a reassignment of notation.

LEMMA 6. **The symbols $BB\alpha CC\beta$ and $BBCC\alpha\beta$ are equivalent.**

To show this, first convert $BB\alpha CC\beta$ into $B\alpha^{-1}C^{-1}B\beta C$ as suggested by Fig. 2–20, with reassignment of notation after the procedure. Then apply Lemma 5, with $\alpha^{-1}C^{-1}$ replacing α and βC replacing β, to obtain $BBC\alpha\beta C$, equivalent to $CBBC\alpha\beta$ by Art. 2–1(E3). Again apply Lemma 5, with BB playing the role of α, to obtain $CCB^{-1}B^{-1}\alpha\beta$. Finally, reassign notation, replacing C by B and B^{-1} by C.

LEMMA 7. **In the non-orientable case, π is equivalent to a symbol of the form**

(2.12) $$\rho_q = \mathbf{C}_q\rho'_q \qquad \text{for some } q > 0$$

where (a) **the vertex of $\mathbf{C}_q$ is not on a free edge, (b) ρ'_q does not contain two identified edges with equal exponents, and (c) ρ'_q does not contain a handle.**

Proof of Lemma. The concept of the vertex of $\mathbf{C}_q$ is like that for $\mathbf{H}_q$.

Inductive Hypothesis. For some $k \geq 1$, there exists a symbol $\rho_k = \mathbf{C}_k \rho'_k$ equivalent to π, where the vertex of $\mathbf{C}_k$ is not on a free edge.

In the non-orientable case, π can be put in the form $B\alpha B\beta$, with the aid of Art. 2–1(E). To verify the hypothesis for $k = 1$, subdivide B to obtain the form $DC\alpha DC\beta$. Then apply Lemma 5, with αD in place of α, to obtain $DCCD^{-1}\alpha^{-1}\beta$. A cyclic permutation yields $CCD^{-1}\alpha^{-1}\beta D$, as required.

If ρ'_k contains paired edges with equal exponents, ρ_k is of the form

$$(2.13) \qquad \rho_k = \mathbf{C}_k \gamma B\alpha B\delta.$$

By Art. 2–1($E3$) and Lemma 5 with $\beta = \delta \mathbf{C}_k \gamma$, ρ_k is equivalent to $\mathbf{C}_k \gamma BB\alpha^{-1}\delta$. By Lemma 6, with γ playing the role of α, the latter is equivalent to

$$(2.14) \qquad \rho_{k+1} = \mathbf{C}_k BB\gamma\alpha^{-1}\delta = \mathbf{C}_{k+1}\rho'_{k+1}$$

where $\rho'_{k+1} = \gamma\alpha^{-1}\delta$, which contains two fewer edges than ρ_k, and the hypothesis is verified with $k + 1$ replacing k.

If ρ'_k contains a handle, let ρ_k be written in the form

$$(2.15) \qquad \rho_k = \mathbf{C}_{k-1}CC\alpha E\beta F\gamma E^{-1}\delta F^{-1}\varepsilon.$$

By Lemma 5, with $\alpha E\beta F$ playing the role of α, ρ_k is equivalent to

$$\mathbf{C}_{k-1}CF^{-1}\beta^{-1}E^{-1}\alpha^{-1}C\gamma E^{-1}\delta F^{-1}\varepsilon.$$

Three additional applications of Lemma 5 lead to the following sequence of equivalent symbols:

$$\mathbf{C}_{k-1}CF^{-1}\beta^{-1}E^{-1}E^{-1}\gamma^{-1}C^{-1}\alpha\delta F^{-1}\varepsilon \qquad \text{(letting } B = E^{-1}\text{),}$$

$$\mathbf{C}_{k-1}CF^{-1}F^{-1}\delta^{-1}\alpha^{-1}C\gamma EE\beta\varepsilon \qquad \text{(letting } B = F^{-1}\text{),}$$

$$\mathbf{C}_{k-1}CC\alpha\delta FF\gamma EE\beta\varepsilon \qquad \text{(letting } B = C\text{).}$$

Finally, two applications of Lemma 6 lead to

$$(2.16) \qquad \rho_{k+2} = \mathbf{C}_{k-1}CCFFEE\alpha\delta\gamma\beta\varepsilon$$
$$= \mathbf{C}_{k+2}\rho'_{k+2}$$

where ρ'_{k+2} has four fewer edges than ρ'_k.

The final part of the proof of Lemma 7 is like that of Lemma 4.

To complete a proof of Theorem 2, we reduce the π'_h or ρ'_q of Lemma 4 or 7 to the form $\mathbf{K}_r$ (see (2.7)). If π'_h or ρ'_q is vacuous, we have $r = 0$ and the proof is complete. We assume the case where π'_h is non-vacuous. The arguments for π'_h and ρ'_q differ only in notation.

LEMMA 8. **The symbols $\alpha\beta KDK^{-1}\gamma$ and $\alpha KDK^{-1}\beta\gamma$ are equivalent.**

A proof is suggested by Fig. 2–21, with reassignment of notation after the process.

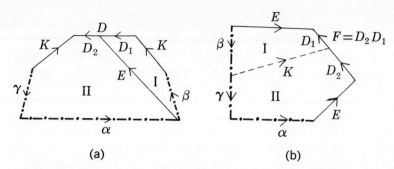

(a)   (b)

Fig. 2–21. Shifting the position of a contour in a symbol.

Let all possible elementary reductions be applied. If this eliminates π'_h entirely, then $r = 0$ and we are again through.

LEMMA 9. **If π'_h is non-vacuous and admits no elementary reductions, it contains a sequence of edges of the form KDK^{-1}.**

Proof of Lemma. Since π'_h is free from paired edges with equal exponents, and since the vertex of $\mathbf{H}_h$ is not on a free edge, π'_h is of the form $\alpha F \beta F^{-1} \gamma$. Since no elementary reductions are possible, β is non-vacuous. If β contains a copy G of a paired edge, β must also contain G^{-1}, since π'_h contains no handles. Hence β contains a sequence of edges of the form $G \beta_0 G^{-1}$, and β_0 consists of fewer edges than β.

Exercises 15 and 16 below will complete the proofs of Lemma 9 and Theorem 2.

(E) Later (Art. 5–5, Theorem 8) we show that two surfaces are topologically equivalent if and only if (1) they are both orientable or both non-orientable and (2) their representations as $H(h, r)$ or $C(q, r)$ agree in contour numbers and handle or crosscap numbers. *This means that a surface is characterized topologically by its orientability class, its contour number r, and its number of handles or crosscaps, h or q.*

EXERCISES

13. List the forms through which the symbol $CBB^{-1}ADA^{-1}C^{-1}D^{-1}$ would pass in carrying out the steps in the proof of Theorem 2.

14. Do the same for the symbol $ABCBDAC^{-1}$.

15. Complete the proof of Lemma 9.

16. With the aid of Lemmas 8 and 9, show that π'_h and ρ'_q can be reduced to the forms $\mathbf{K}_r$ without affecting $\mathbf{H}_h$ or $\mathbf{C}_q$, thus completing the proof of Theorem 2.

17. (a) Show that the polygonal symbol $FAECGBHDC^{-1}JDB^{-1}A^{-1}$ is equivalent to $C(3, 2)$. (b) Replace the second D by D^{-1} and find an equivalent symbol $H(h, r)$ or $C(q, r)$.

18. Figure 2–22 represents a Klein bottle, named after the German mathematician Felix Klein (1849–1925). Show that it can be represented by either

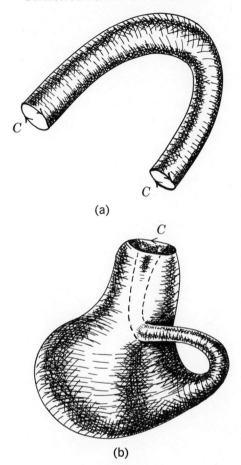

(a)

(b)

Fig. 2–22. The Klein bottle, or sphere with a twisted handle.

Fig. 2–23. A sphere with two twisted handles.

$ABA^{-1}B$ or $CCDD$. If, in Fig. 2–22a, one of the circles C were reversed, the resulting surface could be closed to a torus. As matters stand, we can close it to a Klein bottle if it is made of a topological material which, in addition to deformability, has the property of self-penetrability. One end of Fig. 2–22a is to be pushed through the wall of the tubular part, suitably blown up, and then brought along the "interior" to be sealed with its mate according to the specified orientations.

19. Give a polygonal symbol for the surface of Fig. 2–23. Note that a smart or lucky insect "trapped inside" a sphere with at least one *twisted handle* can escape through the latter. Hence the surface is one-sided. Show that it is also non-orientable, by considering what would happen to a watch (hence to "clockwise" orientations) if the insect, assumed strong as well as intelligent or fortunate, should slide it along from "inside" to "outside" the sphere, returning it to the point of departure.

20. Show that an inner tube with a hole in it can be "turned inside out," if made of a deformable but not self-penetrable substance.

21. Show that a Klein bottle is equivalent to two Moebius strips with identified edges.

3

Introduction to
Set-Theoretic Topology

We next develop general definitions of **space**, **continuity**, and other concepts fundamental to topology.

3–1. Sets and Mappings

We take as basic the idea of a **set** S of objects, called the **elements** of S. Sets are also referred to as **aggregates**, **classes**, and **collections**. The statement that s is an element of S is symbolized by $s \in S$. To illustrate a standard notation often used in defining a set, let P be the set of all living people, and let ρ be a certain room. Then the set of all people in room ρ is denoted by

(3.1) $$S = \{p \in P \mid p \text{ is in } \rho\}$$

or merely, if it has been made clear that p denotes a person, by

(3.2) $$S = \{p \mid p \text{ is in } \rho\}.$$

Such notation as $S = \{s\}$ is also used, if S has already been defined or if its defining condition is separately stated, instead of being written within the braces after a vertical bar.

If the room ρ is empty, then (3.2) defines the **vacuous** (or **empty**, **void**, or **null**) set, which means the set containing no elements, conventionally denoted by $\emptyset$.

A slanting line through a symbol for a relation negates that relation. Thus $p \notin S$ means "p does not belong to S."

(*A*) Any two sets, S and T, determine their

union: $S \cup T = \{s \mid s \in S \text{ or } s \in T, \text{ or } s \in S \text{ and } s \in T\}$,

intersection: $S \cap T = \{s \mid s \in S \text{ and } s \in T\}$,

difference: $S - T = \{s \mid s \in S \text{ and } s \notin T\}$.

The symbol $\Rightarrow$ stands for **implies**, $\Leftarrow$ for **is implied by** and $\Leftrightarrow$ for **implies and is implied by** or **if and only if**. We will sometimes use $\Leftrightarrow$ in giving definitions as well as in stating results.

(*B*) We thus define the following terms and symbols:

(1) S **equals** T, $S = T$: $s \in S \Leftrightarrow s \in T$;
(2) S is a **subset** of T, $S \subset T$ or $T \supset S$: $s \in S \Rightarrow s \in T$;
(3) S is a **proper subset** of T, $S \subsetneqq T$ or $T \supsetneqq S$: $S \subset T$ and $T - S \neq \emptyset$;
(4) S and T are **disjoint**: $S \cap T = \emptyset$;
(5) R and S are **complements** of each other in T: $R \cup S = T$ and $R \cap S = \emptyset$.

A set consisting of just one element s is called **singleton** s and is often denoted by (s). It differs logically from s, just as a person is different from a committee of one. A set with a finite number of elements, for example the numbers 1 and 2, will sometimes be denoted by the elements enclosed in parentheses, thus: $S = (1, 2)$.

The elements of a set may themselves be sets; for example, the set consisting of the 4060 possible committees of three from a class of thirty people, or the set $\{A\}$ of all subsets of a set S. In the latter case, if $S = (1, 2)$, then

(3.3) $\{A\} = (\emptyset, (1), (2), (1, 2))$.

(*C*) The definitions and notation for **union** and **intersection** in (*A*) above are generalized as follows. If $\{S\}$ is a collection of sets, then the **union** of the sets of $\{S\}$, denoted by $\cup\{S\}$, means the set of all objects, each belonging to at least one of the sets of $\{S\}$; and the **intersection** of the sets of $\{S\}$, denoted by $\cap\{S\}$, means the set of all objects each belonging to all of the sets of $\{S\}$.

Consider two sets, S and T, and a subset M of S. A **mapping** or **function** f **from** M **to** T (or **into** T), symbolized by $f : M \to T$, is a correspondence which associates one and only one element of T with each element of M. One writes $y = f(x)$ or $f : x \to y$ to mean that*
$y \in T$ is thus associated with $x \in M$, and one calls y the **image** or **map** of x or the **value** of f at x. The set M is the **domain** of f. Its **range** is the set N of all elements of T each of which is the image of an element of M. If $N = T$, f is said to map M **onto** T. The preposition **into** is consistent with $N = T$ and with $N \subsetneqq T$.

(*D*) A function f_1 with domain M_1 is an **extension** of f with domain M if (1) $M_1 \supset M$ and (2) $x \in M \Rightarrow f(x) = f_1(x)$. Under these conditions, f is the **restriction** of f_1 to M, symbolized by $f = f_1 \mid M$.

(*E*) Let A be a subset of the domain M of a mapping $f : M \to T$. It is conventional to denote with $f(A)$ the set of all image points of points of A. Symbolically,

(3.4) $f(A) = \{y \mid y = f(x) \text{ for some } x \in A\}$.

---

* Here ϵ means "which is an element of." Similar use will be made of other relationship symbols.

This notation can be interpreted as representing an extension of f to the domain $M \cup \{A\}$ where $\{A\}$ is the set of all subsets of M.

(F) Given a mapping f with domain A and a mapping g with domain $B = f(A)$, the **product** or the **composition** of f and g means the mapping h with domain A and range $g(B)$ defined by

(3.5) $h(a) = g(f(a))$ for each $a \in A$.

The formulations

(3.6)
$$h = gf,$$
$$h(a) = gf(a)$$

are also used. Though h represents f followed by g, it is conventional to write g before f, this being the natural order in (3.5).

(G) The mapping $f : A \to B$ is called a **one-to-one mapping** of A onto B if each element of B is the image of one and only one element of A. There then exists an **inverse mapping** $f^{-1} : B \to A$ defined by

(3.7) $f^{-1}(b) = a \Leftrightarrow b = f(a)$.

(H) A more general concept of an inverse function is defined as follows: Let f have domain $A \subset M$ and range $B \subset N$. If $X \subset M$, let

(3.8) $f(X) = \{y \in N \mid y = f(x) \text{ for some } x \in X\}$.

Note that this extends f even more than does (E), since X need not be a subset of A. If $X \subset M - A$, then $f(X) = \emptyset$. Then, for any $Y \subset N$, let

(3.9) $f^{-1}(Y) = \{x \in M \mid f(x) = y \text{ for some } y \in Y\}$.

This defines an inverse mapping f^{-1}. If $y \in f(A)$ and $y = f(x)$, then x is called an **inverse image** of y. The set of all inverse images of y is the image $f^{-1}((y))$ of singleton y under f^{-1}. It is frequently denoted by $f^{-1}(y)$. The mapping f^{-1} is from subsets of N to subsets of M.

(I) A **one-to-one correspondence** Γ between two sets M and N is a collection $\Gamma = \{(x, y)\}$ of pairs (x, y) of **associated elements**, where (1) $x \in M$ and $y \in N$ and (2) each element of M appears in exactly one pair and so does each element of N. Given Γ, let one-to-one mappings $f : M \to N$ and $g : N \to M$ be defined by

(3.10)
$$y = f(x) \Leftrightarrow (x, y) \in \Gamma,$$
$$x = g(y) \Leftrightarrow (x, y) \in \Gamma.$$

Obviously, f and g are inverse to one another. Conversely, any one-to-one mapping, or its inverse, defines a one-to-one correspondence.

(J) A set S is **finite** if it has exactly n elements for some natural number* $n \in (0, 1, 2, \ldots)$. Otherwise, it is **infinite**. It is **denumerable**

---

* We presuppose, throughout, a familiarity with certain basic properties of the real number system.

or **countable** if it either is finite or can be put in one-to-one correspondence with the natural numbers. Its elements can then be
denoted by $(s_1, \ldots, s_n)$ or $(s_1, s_2, \ldots, s_n, \ldots)$.

EXERCISES

1. Describe geometrically the following sets, given that (x, y) is a rectangular
cartesian coordinate system in the plane: (a) $\{(x, y) \mid x^2 + y^2 < 1\} \cap \{(x, y) \mid y > 0\}$, (b) $\{(x, y) \mid x > 0\} \cup \{(x, y) \mid y = 0\}$.

2. An equation $y = f(x)$ defines a mapping $f : A \to Y$, where A, on the
x-axis X, is the domain of definition of $f(x)$ and where Y is the y-axis. In each
of the following, give the domain and range, and tell whether f is a mapping onto
Y and whether f is one-to-one. Specify the set $f^{-1}(1)$: (a) $y = x^3$, (b) $y = \sqrt{1 + x}$,
(c) $y = \tan \pi x$.

3. Prove that (a) $S = T \Leftrightarrow S \subset T$ and $T \subset S$, (b) $S - T = S - S \cap T = (S \cup T) - T$.

4. Show that if S consists of n elements, then there are exactly 2^n elements in
the set of all subsets of S. List them for the case $S = (a, b, c, d)$.

5. With the domain of f extended as in (E) above, show that its range is
$N \cup \{B\}$, where $N = f(M)$ and $\{B\}$ is the set of all subsets of N. Show that
there is generally more than one subset of M with a given image $B' \subset N$.

6. Under what conditions are the product mappings gf and fg both defined?

7. Show that the extension of f in (E) is one-to-one between $M \cup \{A\}$ and
$N \cup \{B\}$, in the notation of Exercise 5, if and only if $f : M \to N$ is one-to-one.

8. (a) Show that $f(M) = N \Leftrightarrow f^{-1}$ in (H), is one-to-one between the set $\{B\}$ of
all subsets of N and $f^{-1}(\{B\})$. (b) Show that $f^{-1}(f(A))$ contains A, generally as
a proper subset. (c) What is $f^{-1}(\emptyset)$? (d) Show that $f^{-1}(\{N\})$ is the set of all
subsets of M if and only if f is a one-to-one mapping of M onto N.

3-2. Relations, Cartesian Products, Functions

We have used several symbols for so-called **relations** (1) between
two sets ($\supset, \subset, \ni, \in, =$), (2) between an element and a set, $x \in M$,
(3) between two properties ($\Rightarrow, \Leftarrow, \Leftrightarrow$).

A **relation** ρ is a set $\Gamma(\rho) = \{(a, b)\}$ of ordered pairs of objects. The
formulations $(a, b) \in \Gamma(\rho)$ and $a\rho b$ are equivalent. Thus ρ might stand
for $\subset$ between sets of elements, or for "is married to" among human
beings.

The **domain** of ρ is the set of all first elements of the pairs $\Gamma(\rho)$, and
its **range** is the set of all second elements.

A relation ρ is **symmetric** if $a\rho b \Rightarrow b\rho a$, **reflexive** if $a\rho a$ for each a in
the domain of ρ and **transitive** if $a\rho b$ and $b\rho c$ together imply $a\rho c$.

(A) An **equivalence** relation is one which is reflexive, symmetric,
and transitive. If A is the domain, hence also the range, of such a
relation ρ, then the **equivalence class** of an element $a \in A$ **with respect
to** ρ, or the ρ-**equivalence class** of a, means the set $[a] = \{b \in A \mid b\rho a\}$.

THEOREM 1. **Two ρ-equivalence classes are identical if they have an element in common; that is,**

$$(3.11) \qquad [a] \cap [b] \neq \emptyset \Rightarrow [a] = [b] \qquad \text{(Exercise 9)}.$$

(B) An equivalence relation ρ, by Theorem 1, defines an analysis of its domain A into a collection $\{\alpha\}$ of subsets, the ρ-equivalence classes, such that (1) A is the union of the subsets $\{\alpha\}$ and (2) no two of the subsets $\{\alpha\}$ intersect. A collection of subsets $\{\alpha\}$ of a set A with these two properties is called a **partition** or **decomposition** of A.

THEOREM 2. **A partition $\{\alpha\}$ of a set A determines an equivalence relation ρ defined by the condition that $a\rho b$ if and only if a and b belong to the same element of $\{\alpha\}$.**

Proof. By (B1), A is the domain of ρ. The relationship of belonging to the same class is obviously reflexive, symmetric, and transitive.

(C) *Theorems 1 and 2 mean that every equivalence relation defines a partition of its domain and every partition of a set is defined thus by some equivalence relation.*

(D) The **cartesian product** $S \times T$ of two sets S and T means the set of all ordered pairs (s, t) such that $s \in S$ and $t \in T$. In particular, $S \times S$ is the set of all ordered pairs of elements of a set S. The mappings $\pi_1 : S \times T \to S$ and $\pi_2 : S \times T \to T$ defined by

$$(3.12) \qquad \pi_1(s, t) = s \qquad \pi_2(s, t) = t$$

are, respectively, the S-**projection** and the T-**projection** of $S \times T$.

A relation ρ with domain $A \subset S$ and range $B \subset T$ can be represented by a unique subset $R \subset S \times T$, where $(s, t) \in R$ if and only if $s\rho t$. Conversely, every subset $R \subset S \times T$ represents the relation $s\rho t$ defined by the condition that $s\rho t$ if and only if $(s, t) \in R$. We express the fact that R represents ρ by writing $R = R(\rho)$, which can be interpreted as defining a mapping of the set of all relations with domain $A \subset S$ and range $B \subset T$ into the set of all subsets of $S \times T$. We call $R(\rho)$ the **graph** of the relation ρ.

(E) The properties of symmetry, reflexivity, and transitivity in a relation ρ are equivalent to the following properties of $R = R(\rho)$, where ρ has domain $A \subset S$ and range $B \subset T$:

(1) ρ is **reflexive**: $s \in A \Rightarrow (s, s) \in R\,[\Rightarrow B \supset A]$,

(2) ρ is **symmetric**: $(s, t) \in R \Rightarrow (t, s) \in R\,[\Rightarrow B = A]$,

(3) ρ is **transitive**: $\left.\begin{matrix} (s, t) \in R \\ (t, u) \in R \end{matrix}\right\} \Rightarrow (s, u) \in R.$

(F) A function or mapping f can be interpreted as a special type of relation, although we write $y = f(x)$ or $f : x \to y$ rather than xfy as in the case of relations. If, for the moment, we define xfy as equivalent to $y = f(x)$, we can say that *a relation ρ is a function if and only if the S-projection of its graph $R(\rho) \subset S \times T$ is one-to-one.* Furthermore, *a relation ρ is a one-to-one mapping (function) if and only if both the S-projection and the T-projection of $R(\rho)$ are one-to-one.*

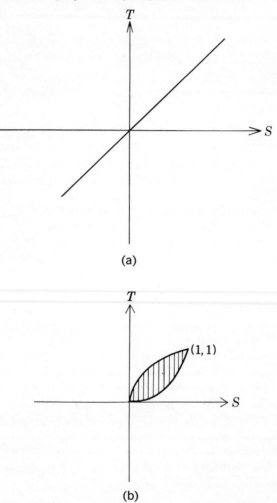

(a)

(b)

Fig. 3–1. The sets R for various relations. (a) $R(\rho_1) : t = s$;

To clarify the foregoing remarks, consider the special case where $S = T$ is the set of all real numbers. In diagrams, we will represent S and T as the usual rectangular coordinate axes for plane analytic geometry (Fig. 3–1). Then $S \times T$ is the set of all points (s, t) of the plane, and a relation ρ is represented by a subset $R(\rho)$ of the plane.

The following relations are illustrated in Fig. 3–1: (a) $s\rho_1 t$ if and only if $t = s$ (the **identity relation**), (b) $s\rho_2 t$ if and only if $s^2 \leq t \leq \sqrt{s}$, (c) $s\rho_3 t$ if and only if $t > s$, (d) $s\rho_4 t$ if and only if $st > 0$.

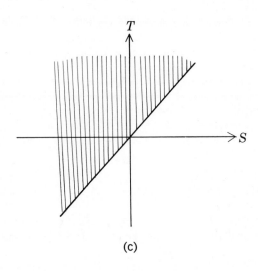

(c)

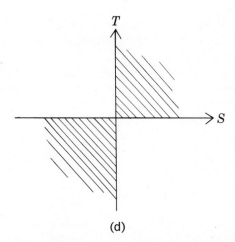

(d)

(b) $R(\rho_2) : s^2 \leq t \leq \sqrt{s}$; (c) $R(\rho_3) : t > s$; (d) $R(\rho_4) : st > 0$.

EXERCISES

9. Prove Theorem 1, first showing that $x \in [a] \Rightarrow [x] = [a]$.

10. Make diagrams analogous to Fig. 3–1 to illustrate the relations defined as follows: (a) $s^2 + t^2 < 1$, (b) $s^2 + s < t$, (c) $t < \sqrt{1 - s^2}$.

11. What are the domain and range of the relation "is a daughter of"?

12. (a) Give at least three examples each of symmetric and non-symmetric human relations. (b) The same with "reflexive" in place of "symmetric." (c) The same as (a) with "transitive" in place of "symmetric."

13. Discuss the relations between the domain and the range of a relation ρ implied by the statement that ρ is (a) symmetric, (b) reflexive, (c) transitive.

14. Make a table classifying the six relations ($\in$, $\supset$, $\subset$, $\ni$, $\subseteq$, $=$) with respect to symmetry, reflexivity, and transitivity.

15. Let $A \nu B$ if and only if a one-to-one mapping $A \to B$ can be defined. Show that ν is an equivalence relation.

16. Which of the relations ρ_1, ρ_2, ρ_3, ρ_4 shown in Fig. 3–1 are (a) functions, (b) symmetric, (c) reflexive, (d) transitive, (e) equivalence relations?

17. (a) Show that, in diagrams like Fig. 3–1, symmetric relations are represented by sets symmetric in the line $t = s$. (b) What geometric property characterizes sets representing reflexive relations? (c) The same for equivalence relations.

3–3.   Continuity for Real Functions of Real Variables

As a preparation for certain generalizations, we remind the reader of some of the limiting processes and continuity concepts involved in the theory of functions of real variables.

The real number system is intuitively interpreted as the set of points on an **axis**, in the sense of analytic geometry, and is sometimes called the **arithmetical continuum**. A **point** of the continuum, or axis, is merely a number. The **distance** between two points, x and y, is generally defined as* $|x - y|$.

(A) With distance thus defined, the arithmetical continuum becomes **euclidean 1-dimensional space**, denoted by E^1. The **euclidean plane**, or **2-space**, is the cartesian product $X \times Y = E^2$ of two real number systems, with the **distance** between two points (x_1, y_1) and (x_2, y_2) defined as†

$$(3.13) \qquad \rho((x_1, y_1), (x_2, y_2)) = \sqrt{(x_2 - x_1)^2 + (y_2 - y_1)^2}.$$

A **real function of a real variable** is a mapping

$$(3.14) \qquad\qquad f : A \to B \qquad A \subset X, B \subset Y.$$

An **open interval** on the x-axis X is a set of real numbers $\{x \mid a < x < b\}$ where a, b are any two numbers with $a < b$. Its closure, also called a **closed interval** or **segment**, is $\{x \mid a \le x \le b\}$.

---

* The vertical bars here are absolute value signs. Thus $|a| = a$ if $a \ge 0$ and $|a| = -a$ if $a < 0$.

† Strictly speaking, 2-dimensional number space is so defined, but it can be proved to satisfy the postulates of euclidean geometry.

The following notation and terminology is often used:

(a) closed interval $[a, b]$: $a \leq x \leq b$

(3.15)   (b) half-open intervals $\begin{cases} [a, b): & a \leq x < b \\ (a, b]: & a < x \leq b \end{cases}$

(c) (open*) interval (a, b): $a < x < b.$

However, (a, b) will mean a point of E^2 unless another meaning is explicitly specified.

In elementary calculus, it is said that a function $f : A \rightarrow B$, generally defined in the form $y = f(x)$, **approaches the limit** c **at** a (or **as** x **approaches** a) if (1) $f(x)$ is defined, for some $d > 0$, at all points x such that $0 < |x - a| < d$ and (2) for any $\varepsilon > 0$, however small, there exists a $\delta > 0$ so small that

(3.16) $|f(x) - c| < \varepsilon$ for all x such that $0 < |x - a| < \delta.$

Note that $f(x)$ may be defined or not when $x = a$ and, if defined, may have the value c or any other value.

A function f is said to be **continuous** at x_0 if (1) it is defined for every x in an interval containing x_0 and (2) for any $\varepsilon > 0$, there exists a $\delta > 0$ so small that

(3.17) $|f(x) - f(x_0)| < \varepsilon$ for every x such that $|x - x_0| < \delta.$

In other words, $f(x)$ approaches a limit as x approaches x_0 and that limit equals $f(x_0)$.

(*B*) An equivalent definition of f being continuous at x_0 is the following: (1) $f(x)$ is defined in an interval containing x_0 and (2) for every interval I_y on the y-axis containing $y_0 = f(x_0)$ there exists an interval I_x on the x-axis containing x_0 whose image points are all on I_y.

We next give a conventional calculus definition of continuity and associated concepts for a real function f of two real variables, defined by

(3.18) $z = f(x, y)$ $(x, y) \in S \subset E^2$

where (x, y) is interpreted as a point of a euclidean plane E^2 and z as a point on a z-axis Z.

A set S of points of E^2 is called **open** if, for each point $p : (x, y)$ belonging to S, there exists a $\delta > 0$ so small that all points within distance δ of p belong to S. The function $f : S \rightarrow T \subset Z$ or its value $f(x, y)$ is said to **approach the limit** c at (a, b) if f is defined on some

---

* The unmodified word **interval** means an open interval.

open set containing (a, b), save perhaps at (a, b) itself, and if, for each $\varepsilon > 0$, however small, there exists a $\delta > 0$ so small that

(3.19) $|f(x, y) - c| < \varepsilon$ provided $0 < \sqrt{(x - a)^2 + (y - b)^2} < \delta$.

(C) The function f is **continuous** at (x_0, y_0) if (1) it is defined on an open set S containing (x_0, y_0) and (2) for each open interval I_z on the z-axis containing $z_0 = f(x_0, y_0)$ there exists an open set N in E^2 containing (x_0, y_0) such that all the functional values at points of N lie on the interval I_z.

Euclidean 3-space, E^3, is defined by defining (1) a **point** as an ordered triple (x, y, z) of real numbers and (2) the **distance** between two points (x, y, z) and (x', y', z') as $\sqrt{(x - x')^2 + (y - y')^2 + (z - z')^2}$. **Euclidean n-space**, E^n, for each positive integer n, is defined as follows: (1) a **point** is an ordered set of n real numbers; (2) the **distance** between two points $p : (x_1, \ldots, x_n)$ and $q : (y_1, \ldots, y_n)$ is

(3.20) $$\rho(p, q) = \left[\sum_{i=1}^{n} (x_i - y_i)^2 \right]^{\frac{1}{2}}.$$

As in the case of E^2, a set $S \subset E^n$ is said to be **open** if, for each point $p \in S$, there exists a $d > 0$ so small that $\rho(p, q) < d \Rightarrow q \in S$.

A **real function of n real variables** with **domain** $A \subset E^n$ is a mapping $f : A \to Y$, where Y denotes the real numbers. The **range** of f is the set $B = f(A) \subset Y$. The image of a point $p : (x_1, \ldots, x_n)$ can be denoted by either $f(p)$ or $f(x_1, \ldots, x_n)$. It is said that f, or $f(p)$, **approaches the limit** c **at** $a : (a_1, \ldots, a_n)$, or as p **approaches** a, symbolized by

(3.21) $f(p) \to c$ as $p \to a$,   or $\lim_{p \to a} f(p) = c$,

if (1) for some $d > 0$, the domain A of f contains all points within distance d of a, with the possible exception of a itself, that is, $A \supset \{p \mid 0 < \rho(p, a) < d\}$, and (2) for each $\varepsilon > 0$, there exists a $\delta > 0$ such that

(3.22) $0 < \rho(p, a) < \delta \Rightarrow |f(p) - c| < \varepsilon$.

(D) The function f is **continuous** at a if (1) it is defined at a and (2) $f(p) \to f(a)$ as $p \to a$.

Consider two euclidean spaces, an m-space E^m and an n-space R^n. Let $p : (x_1, \ldots, x_m)$ and $q : (y_1, \ldots, y_n)$ denote points of E^m and R^n, respectively. The cartesian product $E^m \times R^n$ consists of all the ordered pairs $r = (p, q)$, hence of all the ordered sets $(x_1, \ldots, x_m, y_1, \ldots, y_n)$ of $m + n$ real numbers. The E^m-projection of $r : (x_1, \ldots, x_m, y_1, \ldots, y_n)$ is $p : (x_1, \ldots, x_m)$ and its R^n-projection is $q : (y_1, \ldots, y_n)$. Let the

distance between two points $r \in E^m \times R^n$ and $r' \in E^m \times R^n$, where $r = (p, q)$ and $r' = (p', q')$, be defined as

$$(3.23) \qquad \rho(r, r') = \sqrt{\rho_1^2(p, p') + \rho_2^2(q, q')},$$

where ρ_1 and ρ_2 are the distance functions in E^m and R^n, respectively.

(E) With distance thus defined, $E^m \times R^n$ becomes a euclidean space E^{m+n} (Exercise 22 below).

(F) Consider the euclidean space $E^{n+1} = E^n \times Y$, and let f, with domain $A \subset E^n$ and range $B \subset Y$, be interpreted as a relation (Art. 3–2(F)). Its representation $R(f) \subset E^{n+1}$ is called the **graph** or **locus** of f (see Exercise 23 below).

(G) The definitions of **limit** and **continuity** above can be extended to the case that condition (1) below (3.21) is replaced by the weaker condition: (1′) for every $d > 0$, the domain A of f contains at least one point p satisfying $0 < \rho(p, a) < d$. In this case the condition $p \in A$ is added to the hypotheses of (3.22). Furthermore, f is said to be **continuous** at each isolated point of A.

EXERCISES

18. (a) Let f be defined by $f(x) = x/|x|$ wherever the expression has meaning. Does f approach a limit as $x \to 0$? Is it continuous there? Justify your answers. (b) The same if $f(x) = x/x$. (c) Give an example of a function defined for all x which approaches a limit for each point, but is not continuous at $x = 0$.

19. Give a formal proof that the function f of two real variables defined by $f(x, y) = 2x + 3y$ is continuous at $(0, 0)$.

20. Demonstrate the equivalence of Definition (B) to the definition of *continuous* formulated in (3.17).

21. Prove that Definition (C), Part (2), is equivalent to saying that $f(x, y)$ approaches a limit at (x_0, y_0) and that the limit equals $f(x_0, y_0)$.

22. Prove Statement (E).

23. (a) As in Art. 3–2(F), interpret a function f of one real variable as a relation, and show that its representation $R(f)$ in the euclidean plane E^2 is the locus or graph $y = f(x)$ of the function, in the sense of analytic geometry. What geometric restriction on this graph is imposed by the condition that f be one-to-one? (b) The same for a function of two variables, represented in E^3.

3–4. Topological Spaces

In later chapters, various properties of euclidean n-space will be discussed and used. The definitions in the preceding article were presented primarily as a basis for defining the more general spaces which will concern us.

(A) A **topological space** $(S, \{\sigma\})$ is a set of objects S, to be called **points**, together with a collection $\{\sigma\}$ of subsets of S, called the **open sets** of S, such that

AXIOM 1. **The intersection of any finite collection of open sets is open.**

AXIOM 2. **The union of any collection of open sets is open.**

An example is E^n, with the open sets defined in Art. 3–3 (Exercise 24 below). A **neighborhood** of a point p of S is an open set containing p.

THEOREM 3. **The null subset $\emptyset$ of S and the entire set S are open sets.**

Proof. The union in S of the null collection Ω of open sets is the null set $\emptyset$ of S since the union consists of all points each of which belongs to at least one $\tau \in \Omega$, and there exists no $\tau \in \Omega$. Hence, by Axiom 2, $\emptyset$ is an open set. The intersection $\cap\Omega$, on the other hand, is S, since each point of S belongs to all the sets $\tau \in \Omega$, there being no such sets. Hence, by Axiom 1, S is open.

(*B*) The points of a topological space might be vectors, mappings, geometric loci, the states of a mechanical system, and so on. This fact permits a wide range of applications of topology.

A set S is **topologized** by the designation of a collection $\{\sigma\}$ of open sets satisfying the axioms, and $\{\sigma\}$ is then called a **topology** on S. There are generally many ways of topologizing a set. The **trivial topology** is the one in which only $\emptyset$ and S are open. The topology in which every set is open is called the **discrete topology**. For a number of interesting examples, see [K$_1$].

A **base** for a topology $\{\sigma\}$ on S is a subset $\mathfrak{B}$ of the open sets such that if $p \in \sigma \subset S$, there exists a $\beta \in \mathfrak{B}$ such that $p \in \beta \subset \sigma$. In other words, each open set containing a point $p \in S$ contains a set of the base which contains p.

(*C*) For example, (1) the set of open intervals is a base for the topology of E^1; (2) so is the set of open intervals with rational end points; (3) the set of open circular regions is a base for the topology of E^2; (4) so is the set of rectangular regions $(a < x < b, c < y < d)$ (Exercise 25).

If $\mathfrak{B}$ is a base for a topology $\{\sigma\}$ on S, we will use $(S, \mathfrak{B})$ as equivalent to $(S, \{\sigma\})$, a usage justified by Lemma 1 below. We will also write merely S for a topological space when it is not important to specify its topology or when the topology is implied by the context.

THEOREM 4. **Let S and T be topological spaces with bases $\mathfrak{B}$ and $\mathfrak{C}$. In the cartesian product $S \times T$, let $\mathfrak{B} \times \mathfrak{C}$ be the collection of all sets of the form $\beta \times \gamma$, where $\beta \in \mathfrak{B}$ and $\gamma \in \mathfrak{C}$. Then $\mathfrak{B} \times \mathfrak{C}$ is the base for a topology on $S \times T$.**

Proof. Let $\{\sigma\}$ be the open sets of $\{S, \mathfrak{B}\}$. By definition of **base**, each $\sigma \in \{\sigma\}$ is the union of the elements of $\mathfrak{B}$ which it contains. By Axiom 2 in (*A*), each union of elements of $\mathfrak{B}$ is an open set. This establishes the following result.

LEMMA 1. **Each open set of a topological space with a given base $\mathfrak{B}$ is the union of a collection of elements of $\mathfrak{B}$ and conversely.**

It remains to show that the collection $\{\varphi\}$ of all unions of subsets of $\mathfrak{B} \times \mathfrak{C}$ satisfies Axioms 1 and 2 of (A). If $p \in \varphi_1 \cap \varphi_2$, where $\varphi_i \in \{\varphi\}$ $(i = 1, 2)$, then, by definition of $\{\varphi\}$, there exist sets $\beta_i \in \mathfrak{B}$ and $\gamma_i \in \mathfrak{C}$ such that $p \in \beta_1 \times \gamma_1 \subset \varphi_1$ and $p \in \beta_2 \times \gamma_2 \subset \varphi_2$. But, writing p in the form (s, t) with $s \in S$ and $t \in T$, this implies that $s \in \beta_1 \cap \beta_2$, $t \in \gamma_1 \cap \gamma_2$. Since $\mathfrak{B}$ and $\mathfrak{C}$ are bases for S and T, this implies $s \in \beta \subset (\beta_1 \cap \beta_2)$, $t \in \gamma \subset (\gamma_1 \cap \gamma_2)$ for some $\beta \in \mathfrak{B}$, $\gamma \in \mathfrak{C}$. Hence $\varphi_1^\bullet \cap \varphi_2$ is the union of the subsets of $\mathfrak{B} \times \mathfrak{C}$ which it contains, and Axiom 1 is fulfilled for the case of two open sets. The remaining cases are covered in Exercise 26. Axiom 2 offers no difficulty (Exercise 27).

(D) The space $(S \times T, \mathfrak{B} \times \mathfrak{C})$ will be called the **topological product** of $(S, \mathfrak{B})$ and $(T, \mathfrak{C})$. Where confusion with the cartesian product is unlikely, the simpler notation $S \times T$ will be used for this topological product. Such products as $S_1 \times S_2 \times \cdots \times S_n$ are recursively defined by $(S_1 \times S_2 \times \cdots \times S_j) \times S_{j+1} = S_1 \times \cdots \times S_{j+1}$.

(E) Let A be a subset of S and let $\{\sigma\}$ be a topology on S. Let $\{\alpha\} = \{\alpha = A \cap \sigma \mid \sigma \in \{\sigma\}\}$. Then $\{\alpha\}$ is the topology (Exercise 28) **induced** on A by $(S, \{\sigma\})$, and A is a (**topological**) **subspace** of S.

(F) A point $p \in A \subset S$, where S is a topological space, is an **inner point** of A if there exists an open set σ such that $p \in \sigma \subset A$. Thus an open set either is vacuous or consists entirely of inner points. A set consisting entirely of inner points is open (Exercise 29). A **boundary point** of a set $A \subset S$ is a point p each neighborhood of which has a non-vacuous intersection with both A and its complement $S - A$. The **boundary** ∂A of A means the set of its boundary points.

(G) In a topological space S, a **closed** set means the complement of an open set. Thus $\emptyset$ and S, and possibly other sets, are both open and closed. The **closure** of a set $A \subset S$ means the set $\bar{A} = A \cup \partial A$. The set $\bar{A}$ is closed (Exercise 30).

A point p is a **limit point** (or **point of condensation**) of $A \subset S$ if, for each neighborhood σ of p, the intersection $A \cap (\sigma - p)$ is non-vacuous.

(H) Let $B_0 = S - \bar{A}$, the complement of the closure of an open set $A \subset S$. Then the open set $A_0 = S - \bar{B}_0$ is the union of A and the limit points of A which are not also limit points of B_0 (Exercise 32). The sets A_0 and B_0 are open sets such that

$$\text{(a)} \quad A_0 \cap \bar{B}_0 = \bar{A}_0 \cap B_0 = \emptyset,$$

(3.24) $$\text{(b)} \quad A_0 \cup \bar{B}_0 = \bar{A}_0 \cup B_0 = S,$$

$$\text{(c)} \quad \partial A_0 = \partial B_0 = \bar{A}_0 \cap \bar{B}_0.$$

(I) A set A is closed if and only if $\partial A \subset A$. Also $\bar{A}$ is the union of A and its limit points.

(J) In a topological space, an infinite sequence p_1, p_2, ... of not necessarily distinct points **converges** if there exists a point p, each neighborhood of which contains all but a finite subset of $(p_1, p_2, \ldots)$. In such case, p is a **limit** of the sequence.

EXERCISES

24. Show that E^n is a topological space in the sense of (A), using the definition of *open sets* in Art. 3–3. Define an infinite set of open sets whose intersection is not open.

25. Prove Statement (C).

26. Complete the proof in (C) for the case that the number of elements of $\{\varphi\}$ in the collection is (a) zero; (b) one; (c) $n > 2$, n an integer.

27. Verify Axiom 2 for $\{\varphi\}$, thus completing the proof of Theorem 4.

28. Prove that $\{\alpha\}$ is a topology in Statement (E).

29. Show that a set consisting entirely of inner points is open (see (F)).

30. Show that $\bar{A}$ is closed in Statement (G). (See (F).)

31. Show that regions of the form $a_i < x_i < b_i$ $(i = 1, \ldots, n)$ form a basis for the *open sets* of E^n, defined in Art. 3–3. Hence show that $E^n = E^m \times E^{n-m} = E^1 \times \cdots \times E^1$ (n factors).

32. Prove all parts of Statement (H).

33. The same for Statement (I).

3–5. Homeomorphisms; Definition of Topology

(A) A mapping $f : S \to T$, where $S = (S, \{\sigma\})$ and $T = (T, \{\tau\})$ are topological spaces, is **continuous at** $p \in S$ if, for each neighborhood τ of $f(p)$, there exists a neighborhood σ of p such that $f(\sigma) \subset \tau$. If f is continuous at each point of S, it is **continuous (on S)**.

If A is a subset of S, a mapping $f : A \to T$ is continuous at $p \in A$ if, for each neighborhood τ of $f(p)$ there exists a neighborhood σ of p such that $f(A \cap \sigma) \subset \tau$.

(B) A **homeomorphism** $f : S \to T$ is a mapping which (1) is one-to-one, (2) is continuous, and (3) has a continuous inverse $f^{-1} : T \to S$. **Topology** is the study of those properties of spaces which are preserved by homeomorphisms. A **topological property** of a space S is a property shared by each space homeomorphic to S, where two spaces are **homeomorphic** if it is possible to define a homeomorphism between them.

THEOREM 5. **If** $f : S \to T$ **is continuous and** $g : f(S) \to V$ **is continuous, then** $h = gf : S \to V$ **is continuous.**

Proof. For any neighborhood φ of $h(p)$ in V, there exists, by the continuity of g, a neighborhood τ of $f(p)$ in T, such that $g(\tau \cap f(S)) \subset \varphi$. By the continuity of f, there exists a neighborhood σ of p in S such that $f(\sigma) \subset \tau$ so that $f(\sigma) \subset (\tau \cap f(S))$. But $f(\sigma) \subset (\tau \cap f(S))$ and $g(\tau \cap f(S)) \subset \varphi$ imply $gf(\sigma) = h(\sigma) \subset \varphi$, and the theorem follows.

THEOREM 6. **Among topological spaces, the relationship of being homeomorphic is an equivalence relation.**

Proof. The relationship is reflexive, since the **identity mapping**, which maps each point onto itself, is a homeomorphism (Exercise 35). It is symmetric, since the inverse $f^{-1} : T \to S$ of a homeomorphism satisfies the definition of a homeomorphism. The property of being one-to-one is obviously transitive.

Theorem 5, applied to the product $h = gf$ of two homeomorphisms and its inverse $h^{-1} = f^{-1}g^{-1}$, completes the proof that the property of being a homeomorphism is transitive, thus establishing Theorem 6.

A mapping $f : S \to T$ is called **open** [**closed**] if it maps each open [closed] set of S onto an open [closed] set of T. This definition applies also to mappings from the subsets of S into those of T.

THEOREM 7. **A mapping $f : S \to T$ is continuous if and only if its inverse f^{-1} is open.**

Proof. See (3.9) for f^{-1}. Suppose f continuous. Consider $f^{-1}(\tau)$ where $\tau \subset T$ is open, and let $p \in f^{-1}(\tau)$. Then τ is a neighborhood of $f(p)$. Hence there exists a neighborhood σ of p such that $f(\sigma) \subset \tau$, which implies $\sigma \subset f^{-1}(\tau)$. Hence $f^{-1}(\tau)$ is open. The proof is completed by showing that if f^{-1} is open then f is continuous (Exercise 36).

COROLLARY. **A homeomorphism is both open and closed** (Exercise 36).

(*C*) In view of Theorem 7, a **homeomorphism** could be defined as a one-to-one open mapping with an open inverse.

The above definitions and results are applicable to a topological space subject only to Axioms 1 and 2 in Definition (*A*). In most of our work, other conditions will be satisfied, one of which is stated in the following definition.

(*D*) A **Hausdorff space** is a topological space S in which, for each pair of different points (p, q), there exist non-intersecting open sets σ and τ containing p and q respectively.

Exercise 37 gives an important property of Hausdorff spaces.

EXERCISES

34. Show that, for a real function of n real variables, Definition (*A*) of *continuity* is equivalent to Definition (*D*) in Art. 3–3.

35. Prove that the identity mapping is a homeomorphism. Show that a continuous one-to-one mapping need not have a continuous inverse.

36. Complete the proof of Theorem 7 and corollary.

37. Show that a convergent sequence (a) has only one limit in a Hausdorff space, (b) may have more than one limit in a non-Hausdorff space.

38. Show that $S \times T$ is homeomorphic to $T \times S$ for two topological spaces S and T.

3–6. Metric Spaces

Intuitively, a metric is a measure of distance from one point to another. Mathematically, for a set of points S, a metric is a function ρ of ordered pairs (s, t) of points of S, subject to appropriate axioms. Since the cartesian product $S \times S$ is the set of ordered pairs of points of S, it is convenient to define ρ as a function on $S \times S$.

(A) Let S be a set of points and R the real numbers. A **metric** ρ on S is a function or mapping $\rho : S \times S \to R$ such that

AXIOM* 1. $\rho(s, t) \geq 0$

AXIOM 2. $\rho(s, t) = 0 \Leftrightarrow s = t$

AXIOM 3. $\rho(s, t) = \rho(t, s)$

AXIOM 4 (THE TRIANGLE AXIOM). $\rho(s, t) + \rho(t, u) \geq \rho(s, u)$.

Given a set S, a metric ρ, and a number $\eta > 0$, the (**spherical**) η-**neighborhood** of a point $a \in S$ means the set $\{s \in S \mid \rho(a, s) < \eta\}$.

THEOREM 8. **The set $\mathfrak{B}$ of all spherical neighborhoods of points of a set S with a metric ρ is the base for a topology on S.**

Proof. Let $\{\sigma\}$ be the collection of all subsets of S each of which is a union of spherical neighborhoods. It is to be shown that $\{\sigma\}$ satisfies Axioms 1 and 2 of Art. 3–4(A). Axiom 2 is obviously satisfied. To prove Axiom 1, let p be a point on $\sigma_1 \cap \sigma_2$, where σ_1, σ_2 are members of $\{\sigma\}$ with a non-vacuous intersection. Then $p \in \sigma_\delta(s) \cap \sigma_\eta(t)$, where $\sigma_\delta(s)$ denotes the δ-neighborhood of a point s and $\sigma_\eta(t)$ is the η-neighborhood of a point t. Let

(3.25) $\zeta = \min \left(\delta - \rho(s, p), \eta - \rho(t, p) \right) > 0$

where $\min (x, y)$ means the smaller of two numbers x and y.

LEMMA 2. **The ζ-neighborhood of p, $\sigma_\zeta(p)$, is on $\sigma_\delta(s) \cap \sigma_\eta(t)$, hence on $\sigma_1 \cap \sigma_2$.**

Proof of Lemma. Note first that $u \in \sigma_\zeta(p) \Rightarrow \rho(p, u) < \zeta$. Hence, using the triangle axiom, $\rho(s, u) \leq \rho(s, p) + \rho(p, u) < \rho(s, p) + \zeta$, and $\rho(s, p) + \zeta \leq \rho(s, p) + \delta - \rho(s, p)$ by (3.25). Therefore, $\rho(s, u) < \delta$. Similarly, $\rho(t, u) < \eta$, and Lemma 2 follows. But Lemma 2 implies that $\sigma_1 \cap \sigma_2$ is the union of the spherical neighborhoods which it contains, verifying Axiom 1 for the case of two open sets. The proof for the case of zero, one, or $n > 2$ members of $\{\sigma\}$ presents no difficulty.

---

* Axiom 1 can be derived from Axioms 2, 3, and 4.

(*B*) The space $(S, \mathfrak{B})$ of Theorem 8 is the **metric space** (S, ρ) and its topology $\{\tau\}$ is **induced by** ρ. Euclidean n-space is an example.

(*C*) If $(S, \{\sigma\})$ is a topological space, then it may be possible to define a metric ρ on S so that ρ induces the topology $\{\sigma\}$. If so, $(S, \{\sigma\})$ is **metrizable** and any metric inducing the topology $\{\sigma\}$ is a **metric** on S.

(*D*) If $A \subset (S, \rho)$, then the restriction $\rho \mid A$, defined in Art. 3–1(*D*), is a metric on A. The same topology is induced on A by the metric $\rho \mid A$ and by the topology $\{\tau\}$ of (S, ρ) (Exercise 43).

(*E*) The property of being metrizable is a topological property. That is, if S_1 and S_2 are homeomorphic spaces and S_1 is metrizable, so is S_2. Indeed, if ρ_1 is a metric on S_1 and $h : S_1 \to S_2$ is a homeomorphism, then the function ρ_2 defined on $S_2 \times S_2$ by $\rho_2(h(s), h(t)) = \rho_1(s, t)$ is a metric on S_2 (Exercise 44). The metric ρ_2 is the metric **carried over** from (S_1, ρ_1) to S_2 by the homeomorphism h.

(*F*) If S is metrizable, it is a Hausdorff space (Exercise 45).

(*G*) Let $A \subset S$, $B \subset S$ be two non-vacuous subsets of a metric space $S = (S, \rho)$. The **distance** $\rho(A, B)$ between A and B is defined by

(3.26) $\rho(A, B) = \text{g.l.b. } \rho(a, b) \qquad a \in A, b \in B$

where g.l.b. means greatest lower bound.* Since $\rho(a, b) \geq 0$, $\rho(A, B)$ exists. It is either the smallest distance between a point of A and a point of B, or the largest number less than all such distances.

(*H*) The **diameter** of $A \subset (S, \rho)$ is

(3.27) $\text{diam } A = \text{l.u.b. } \rho(a, b) \qquad a \in A, b \in A$

provided the least upper bound exists. If it does not exist, A is **unbounded** or, symbolically, diam $A = \infty$. When it does exist, A is **bounded**.

THEOREM 9. **Let** $\{f\}$ **be the set of all continuous mappings of the unit segment** $[0, 1] : 0 \leq t \leq 1$ **into the real numbers, and let**

(3.28) $\rho(f, g) = \max |f(t) - g(t)| \qquad (0 \leq t \leq 1).$

Then the function defined by ρ **on** $\{f\}$ **is a metric.**

Proof. Since f and g are continuous functions on $[0, 1]$, the same is true (Exercise 48) of $|f(t) - g(t)|$, which therefore attains a maximum. Thus ρ is defined for each $(f, g) \in \{f\} \times \{f\}$. It obviously is non-negative, has the property $\rho(f, g) = 0 \Leftrightarrow f = g$, and is symmetric.

---

* Various properties of real numbers, and various standard concepts are assumed. The reader unfamiliar with them can readily find them in the literature; for example, in $[L_1]$ and $[T]$.

This leaves only the triangle axiom to be verified. Given three elements, $(f, g, h) \subset \{f\}$, let t_0, t_1, t_2 be points such that

(3.29)
$$|f(t_0) - g(t_0)| = \max |f(t) - g(t)| = \rho(f, g),$$
$$|g(t_1) - h(t_1)| = \max |g(t) - h(t)| = \rho(g, h),$$
$$|f(t_2) - h(t_2)| = \max |f(t) - h(t)| = \rho(f, h).$$

Then

(3.30)
$$|f(t_2) - g(t_2)| \leq |f(t_0) - g(t_0)|,$$
$$|g(t_2) - h(t_2)| \leq |g(t_1) - h(t_1)|.$$

Hence (Exercise 49)

(3.31)
$$\rho(f, h) \leq \rho(f, g) + \rho(g, h).$$

EXERCISES

39. Test the functions (a) $\rho_1(x, y) = (x - y)^2$ and (b) $\rho_2(x, y) = x^2 - y^2$ to see whether they are metrics on the set R of real numbers.

40. Find $\rho(A, B)$ and diam A where A and B are the following subsets of the euclidean (x, y)-plane.

$$A : 4x^2 + 9y^2 < 36 \quad \text{and} \quad B : 9x^2 + 4y^2 > 144.$$

41. Given a point set S, show that the equations $\rho(s, s) = 0$, $\rho(s, t) = 1$ for $s \neq t$ define a metric on S.

42. (a) Show that the metric of Exercise 41 induces the discrete topology on S. (b) Show that if S contains more than one point and has the trivial topology, it is not metrizable.

43. Prove Statement (D).

44. Prove Statement (E).

45. Prove (F) by showing that if ρ is a metric on S and (p, q) are two different points on S, then the δ-neighborhoods of p and q are disjoint if $2\delta < \rho(p, q)$.

46. In the (x, y)-plane, let

(3.32)
$$\rho_1((x_1, y_1), (x_2, y_2)) = \max (|x_2 - x_1|, |y_2 - y_1|).$$

Show that (3.32) defines a metric ρ_1 on the (x, y)-plane. Show that ρ_1 induces the same topology as the euclidean metric.

47. Show that, in a metric space,

(3.33)
(a) $\rho(A, B) = 0 \Leftrightarrow \bar{A} \cap \bar{B} \neq \emptyset$, if A or B is bounded,

(b) $\rho(A, B) = \rho(\bar{A}, B) = \rho(A, \bar{B}) = \rho(\bar{A}, \bar{B})$.

48. Show that $\rho(f, g)$ in (3.28), interpreted as a function of t, is continuous.

49. Deduce inequality (3.31) from (3.29) and (3.30), thus completing the proof of Theorem 9.

3-7. Compact Spaces

Let S be a topological space, and let $A \subset S$. A **covering** of A means a collection $\{\sigma\}$ of subsets of S, such that each point of A is in at least one set of $\{\sigma\}$. If all the sets of $\{\sigma\}$ are open, then $\{\sigma\}$ is an **open covering** of A. If they are all closed, it is a **closed covering**.

(A) The set $A \subset S$ is called **compact in S** if and only if each open covering of A contains a finite covering; that is, given an open covering $\{\sigma\}$ of A, there exists a finite subset $(\sigma_1, \ldots, \sigma_n)$ of $\{\sigma\}$ which is also a covering of A. In the case where $A = S$, this defines the concept of a space being **compact in itself** or, more briefly, **compact**. A compact metrizable space is called a **compactum**.

(B) If A is compact in S, then A, with the topology induced by S, is compact in itself. A compact subspace of a compactum is a compactum (Exercise 52).

THEOREM 10. **Let S and T be two topological spaces, and let A be compact in S. Then, if $f : A \to T$ is a continuous mapping, $f(A)$ is compact in T.**

Proof. Let $\{\tau\}$ be an open covering of $f(A)$ in T. Then, if $\tau \in \{\tau\}$, $f^{-1}(\tau)$ is an open set in S (Theorem 7). The set $\{f^{-1}(\tau) \mid \tau \in \{\tau\}\}$ is an open covering of A, and, because A is compact, it contains a finite covering $f^{-1}(\tau_i)$ $(i = 1, 2, \ldots, n)$. But $(\tau_1, \ldots, \tau_n) \subset \{\tau\}$ is then a finite covering of $f(A)$, and the proof is complete.

COROLLARY. **Compactness is a topological property** (Exercise 53).

THEOREM 11 (BOLZANO-WEIERSTRASS). **In a compact space S, a subset A containing an infinite collection of points possesses a limit point.**

Proof. Assume that A has no limit point. For each point p of S, take an open set containing p and containing at most one point of A. This yields an open covering. It contains a finite subcovering, since S is compact. Hence, A has only a finite number of points, contrary to hypothesis.

THEOREM 12. **If S is metrizable in Theorem 11, then A contains a convergent sequence of distinct points.**

Proof. Let p be a limit point of P. Let p_n be a point other than p in the spherical $(1/n)$-neighborhood of p for each $n = 1, 2, \ldots$, and let p_n be taken closer to p than p_{n-1}. Then $(p_1, p_2, \ldots)$ converges to p, since each neighborhood of p includes the $(1/n)$-neighborhood of p

for some n and hence includes all the points $(p_1, p_2, \ldots)$ except a subset of $(p_1, \ldots, p_n)$.

COROLLARY. **A compact subset A of a metrizable space S is closed.** If A is not closed, there is a limit point p of A not in A (Art. 3–4(I)). Let $(p_1, p_2, \ldots)$ be a sequence on A converging to p and defined as in the proof of Theorem 12. The sets $(S_1, S_2, \ldots)$, defined exactly as in the proof of Theorem 11, cover A, but no finite subset of them covers A, contradicting its compactness.

THEOREM 13. **A compact subset A of a metric space S is bounded.**

Proof. Otherwise, for a point p of S and each $n > 0$, there is a point of A at distance greater than n from p. Therefore the spherical n-neighborhoods of p ($n = 1, 2, 3, \ldots$) are a covering of A containing no finite covering, contradicting its compactness.

THEOREM 14 (THE HEINE-BOREL THEOREM). **A subset A of euclidean n-space E^n is compact if and only if it is closed and bounded.**

This is a standard theorem of analysis, whose proof is readily accessible in the literature. (See Exercise 66.)

THEOREM 15. **The topological product $A \times B$ of two compact spaces is compact.**

Proof. Let $\{\sigma\}$ be an open covering of $A \times B$, and let $\{\alpha\}$ and $\{\beta\}$ be bases for A and B. For fixed $x \in A$, let $\{\tau_x\}$ be the set of all products $\alpha \times \beta$ such that $x \in \alpha$ and $\alpha \times \beta \subset \sigma$ for at least one σ. Then $B \subset \cap \{\beta \mid \alpha \times \beta \in \{\tau_x\}\}$, and, since B is compact, there exists a finite subset of $\{\tau_x\}$, such that B is contained in the union of the corresponding sets of $\{\beta\}$. For each such finite subset of $\{\tau_x\}$, x is in $\cup \alpha$, which is open, since it is a finite intersection of open sets. The corresponding finite union $\cup \{\tau_x\}$ covers $(\cap \alpha) \times B$.

Since the set of all such finite intersections, $\cap \alpha$, taken for every $x \in A$, is a covering of A, and A is compact, a finite subset, say of n of them, covers A. Then n choices of corresponding finite coverings of B, followed by finitely many choices from $\{\sigma\}$ containing the sets τ thereby determined, yield a finite covering of $A \times B$ by members of $\{\sigma\}$.

THEOREM 16. **A continuous function $f : A \to R$, where A is compact and R is the real number system, assumes a largest and a smallest value.**

Proof. By Theorem 10, $f(A)$ is compact. Hence, by Theorem 13 and the corollary to Theorem 12 (interpreting R as E^1), $f(A)$ is bounded and closed. But a closed, bounded set of real numbers contains a largest and a smallest number, and Theorem 16 follows.

THEOREM 17. **A compact subset A of a metric space (S, ρ) is of finite diameter.**

Proof. By Theorem 15, $A \times A$ is compact. The metric ρ maps

Proof. By Theorem 15, $A \times A$ is. compact. The metric ρ maps $A \times A$ continuously into R (Exercise 67), and Theorem 17 follows from Theorem 16.

THEOREM 18. **If A and B are compact subsets of a metric space S, then there exist points $a \in A$ and $b \in B$ such that $\rho(a, b) = \rho(A, B)$.**

A proof can be given (Exercise 55) along the lines of the proof of Theorem 17.

(*C*) If $A \subset E^n$, $B \subset E^n$ are closed and one of them bounded, the conclusion of Theorem 18 holds.

(*D*) Let $\Phi = \{f\}$ be the set of all continuous mappings of a compact space A into a metric space (T, ρ). Then $\rho(f(p), g(p))$ is continuous in p on the compact set A. Hence, by Theorem 16, ρ assumes a maximum value. Let

$$(3.34) \qquad \varphi(f, g) = \max_{p \in A} \rho(f(p), g(p)).$$

THEOREM 19. **The function φ defined by (3.34) is a metric on Φ.**

Proof. This is a generalization of Theorem 9 and its proof. If f and g are the same mapping, that is $f(p) = g(p)$ for all $p \in A$, using the notation of (E), then $\varphi(f, g) = 0$ and conversely. The symmetry of φ follows from that of ρ. By Theorem 16, there is a point $p_1 \in A$, such that $\varphi(f, h) = \rho(f(p_1), h(p_1))$. For that point, by the triangle axiom, $\rho(f(p_1), g(p_1)) + \rho(g(p_1), h(p_1)) \geq \rho(f(p_1), h(p_1)) = \varphi(f, h)$. But $\varphi(f, g) \geq \rho(f(p_1), g(p_1))$ and $\varphi(g, h) \geq \rho(g(p_1), h(p_1))$. Hence $\varphi(f, g) + \varphi(g, h) \geq \varphi(f, h)$, completing the proof.

(*E*) The metric space (Φ, φ) is called the **space of mappings $A \to T$.**

EXERCISES

50. Define an open covering of the set $x^2 + y^2 < 1$ in the (x, y)-plane which contains no finite covering.

51. Define a continuous function on the set $x^2 + y^2 < 1$ which has neither an upper nor a lower bound.

52. Prove Statements (B).

53. Prove the corollary to Theorem 10.

54. In the proof of Theorem 11, why can no finite subset of $(S_1, S_2, \dots)$ cover S?

55. Prove Theorem 18.

56. Prove result (C).

57. Using the example of $A : xy \geq 1$ and $B : xy \leq -1$ in E^2, show that the hypothesis that A or B be bounded is necessary in (C).

3–8. Brouwer Dimension; The Lebesgue Number

An η-**covering**, or covering of **mesh** η, of a compact metric space (S, ρ) is a covering $\{A\}$ of S such that each of the sets of $\{A\}$ is of diameter less than η.

(A) *For any η, a compact metric space S admits a finite open [closed]* η-*covering.* In the open case, a finite subcovering of the covering by all spherical η'-regions for any $\eta' < \eta$ is an example. In the closed case, the set of closures of regions of an open η-covering is an example.

Let $\{A\}$ be a covering of a set S. The **order** of $\{A\}$ is the largest natural number ν, if such a number exists, with the property that some collection of ν of the sets $\{A\}$ has a non-vacuous intersection. If no such ν exists, $\{A\}$ is of **infinite order**. A finite covering is obviously of finite order, having the number of sets in the covering as a largest possible value. In general, as η gets smaller, the number of sets in a finite η-covering of a metric space will increase without limit. We will see, however, that it is possible, for a large class of spaces, to impose an upper bound on the order, independently of η.

The closure $\bar{A}$ of a bounded open region A of euclidean n-space E^n is compact, by Theorem 14. In Art. 6–3 we will show that (1) for any $\eta > 0$, there exists a finite closed η-covering of $\bar{A}$ of order $n + 1$, and (2) for η sufficiently small, there exists no finite closed η-covering of $\bar{A}$ of order less than $n + 1$.

(B) The property just stated motivates the following definition, due to L. E. J. Brouwer.* Let S be a compactum, and ρ a metric on S. Then S has **(Brouwer) dimension** $n = \dim S$ if (1) for each $\eta > 0$, S admits a finite closed η-covering of order $n + 1$, and (2) for $\eta > 0$ sufficiently small, S admits no finite closed η-covering of order less than $n + 1$. If these conditions are not fulfilled for any integer n, the **(Brouwer) dimension** of S is infinite: $\dim S = \infty$.

LEMMA 3. **The dimension $\dim S$ is independent of the metric used in the definition.**

Proof of Lemma. Let ρ_1 and ρ_2 be two metrics on S. For a number $\eta_1 > 0$ and a point $p \in S$, let $\sigma_1(p)$ be the spherical η_1-neighborhood (Art. 3–6) of p in terms of the metric ρ_1 and let $\rho^*(p)$ be the distance from p to $S - \sigma_1(p)$ in terms of the metric ρ_2.

(C) Then $\rho^*(p)$ is a positive continuous function on S and therefore (Exercise 60) has a positive minimum value

$$(3.35) \qquad \eta_2 = \min_{p \in S} \rho^*(p).$$

By definition of η_2, $\sigma_1(p)$ contains the η_2-neighborhood $\sigma_2(p)$ of p in terms of the metric ρ_2 for each $p \in S$.

(D) It is now a simple matter to complete the proof, by showing that $\dim S$ as defined in terms of ρ_1 equals $\dim S$ as defined in terms of ρ_2 (Exercise 61).

THEOREM 20. **The Brouwer dimension of a compactum S is a topological property.**

* "Beweis der Invarianz der Dimensionszahl," *Mathematische Annalen*, 70 (1911), pp. 161–165.

Proof. Let $h : S \to T$ be a homeomorphic mapping of S. Let ρ be a metric on S and ρ_0 the metric carried over to T by h (Art. 3–6(E)). Then η-neighborhoods on S, and their respective intersections relative to ρ, are mapped by h onto η-neighborhoods on T and their respective intersections relative to ρ_0. Theorem 20 now follows readily, with the aid of Lemma 3.

THEOREM 21. **A definition of** dim S **equivalent to Definition** (B) **is obtained by replacing "closed" by "open" throughout** (B).

Proof. Theorem 21 is equivalent (Exercise 62) to the following lemma.

LEMMA 4. **If, for some integer** $\nu > 0$ **and each number** $\eta > 0$, S **admits a closed** η**-covering of order** ν, **then it admits an open** η**-covering of order** ν; **and if it admits an open** η**-covering of order** ν, **then it admits a closed** η**-covering of order** ν.

Proof of Lemma. Part I. Given the first hypothesis, let η be a positive number, let $\zeta = \eta/2$, and let $\{A\} = (A_1, \ldots, A_m)$ be a closed ζ-covering of S of order ν. For each A_i, let B_i denote the union of all intersections disjoint from A_i of subsets of the covering $\{A\}$. If B_i is vacuous, let $\rho_i = 1$. Otherwise, let $\rho_i = \rho(A_i, B_i)$. Let $\delta = \frac{1}{2} \min (\zeta, \rho_1, \ldots, \rho_m)$, and let $\sigma_i(A_i)$ be the set of all points each at distance less than δ from A_i $(i = 1, \ldots, m)$.

(E) The regions $\sigma_i(A_i)$ $(i = 1, \ldots, m)$ are an open η-covering of S of order ν (Exercise 63).

Part II. We will say that an open covering $\{\sigma\}$ of S is obtained from an open covering $\{\alpha\}$ of S by shrinking an element $\alpha \in \{\alpha\}$, if $\{\sigma\}$ is obtained from $\{\alpha\}$ by substituting for α an open set σ for which $\bar{\sigma} \subset \alpha$. This is easily seen to be possible, given $\{\alpha\}$ and an arbitrary $\alpha \in \{\alpha\}$, since $S - \alpha$ and the part of α not covered by $\{\alpha\} - (\alpha)$ are disjoint closed subsets of S.

From a given open η-covering $\{\alpha\} = (\alpha_1, \ldots, \alpha_m)$ of order ν, let $\{\sigma\} = (\sigma_1, \ldots, \sigma_m)$ be obtained by successively shrinking $(\alpha_1, \ldots, \alpha_m)$. Then $\{\bar{\sigma}\} = (\bar{\sigma}_1, \ldots, \bar{\sigma}_m)$ is a closed covering of order ν, or less, since the order of a covering cannot increase when its respective elements are replaced by sets contained in them. This completes a proof of Lemma 4.

From $\{\bar{\sigma}\}$ a second closed η-covering $\{\bar{\tau}\} = (\bar{\tau}_1, \ldots, \bar{\tau}_m)$ of order $\leq \nu$, and with certain useful properties, is obtained as follows: (1) τ_1 is the subset of S not covered by $(\bar{\sigma}_2, \ldots, \bar{\sigma}_m)$. (2) Once $(\tau_1, \ldots, \tau_{j-1})$ are defined, τ_j is defined as the subset of $S - \bar{\tau}_1 \cup \cdots \cup \bar{\tau}_{j-1}$ not covered by $(\bar{\sigma}_{j+1}, \ldots, \bar{\sigma}_m)$. (See Exercise 64.)

(*F*) The closed η-covering $(\bar{\tau}_1, \ldots, \bar{\tau}_m)$ has the following properties: (1) each element $\bar{\tau}_i$ is the closure of an open set τ_i $(i = 1, \ldots, m)$; (2) the open sets $(\tau_1, \ldots, \tau_m)$ are disjoint, that is, $i \neq j \Rightarrow \tau_i \cap \tau_j = \emptyset$. A closed covering with properties (1) and (2) is called a **simple** covering.

(*G*) As a corollary to the above proof, a compact metric space of dimension n admits, for any $\eta > 0$, a finite closed simple η-covering of order $n + 1$.

THEOREM 22 (LEBESGUE'S LEMMA). **Let** $\{A\} = (A_1, \ldots, A_m)$ **be a closed covering of a compact metric space** (S, ρ). **Then, there exists a number** $\lambda > 0$ **so small that if a set** $B \subset S$ **with** diam $B < \lambda$ **intersects each of the sets** $(A_{i_1}, \ldots, A_{i_j})$ **then** $A_{i_1} \cap A_{i_2} \cap \cdots \cap A_{i_j} \neq \emptyset$.

Proof. Assume the contrary. Then for each positive integer n there exists a non-vacuous set $B_n \subset S$ where (1) diam $B_n < 1/n$ and (2) the subcollection $\mathfrak{A}_n$ of $\{A\}$ intersected by B_n has a vacuous intersection. Since there are only $2^m - 1$ non-vacuous subcollections of $\{A\}$, some one of them must be repeated infinitely often in the sequence $\mathfrak{A}_1, \mathfrak{A}_2, \ldots$. Suppose $(A_{i_1}, \ldots, A_{i_j}) = \mathfrak{A}_{n_1} = \mathfrak{A}_{n_2} = \cdots$. Let $(p_1, p_2, \ldots)$ be a set of points and $k_2, k_3, k_4, \ldots$ a sequence of integers such that $p_1 \in B_{n_1}$ and $p_i \in B_{n_{k_i}} - (p_1, \ldots, p_{i-1})$ $(i = 2, 3, \ldots)$ (Exercise 65). By Theorem 11, there exists a limit point p of the set $(p_1, p_2, \ldots)$. Each neighborhood of p then contains infinitely many of the sets $B_{n_{k_i}}$, hence a point from each of the sets $(A_{i_1}, \ldots, A_{i_j})$. The latter being closed, $p \in A_{i_1} \cap \cdots \cap A_{i_j}$, contradicting (2) above, and establishing the theorem.

(*H*) Any number λ satisfying Theorem 22 for given $\{A\}$ is called a **Lebesgue** number of $\{A\}$.

EXERCISES

58. Given a positive $\eta < \frac{1}{2}$, define, for the unit disk $x^2 + y^2 \leq 1$, a finite closed η-covering of order 3.

59. Give a positive $\eta < \frac{1}{2}$, define, for the unit circle $x^2 + y^2 = 1$, a finite open η-covering of order 2.

60. Prove (*C*).

61. Carry through the argument suggested in (*D*).

62. Establish that Lemma 4 is equivalent to Theorem 21.

63. Prove (*E*).

64. Show that $\{\bar{\tau}\}$ is obtainable from $\{\alpha\}$ by m shrinkings, also that $\{\bar{\tau}\}$ has properties (1) and (2) in (*F*).

65. In the proof of Theorem 22, show that $(p_1, p_2, \ldots)$ and $k_2, k_3, \ldots$ exist as described.

66. Prove that a subset A of euclidean n-space E^n is closed if and only if it contains its limit points.

67. Prove that if A is a metric space, the metric ρ maps $A \times A$ continuously into the real number system.

4

Complexes

A **topological space** was defined in Chapter 3 as a set S of **points** together with a collection $\{\tau\}$ of **open** subsets of S, subject to certain axioms. Thus a foundation was laid for set-theoretic topology.

In this chapter, we similarly lay a foundation for combinatorial topology, commencing with a definition of a **complex** as a collection K of **simplexes** subject to appropriate structural conditions.

4–1. Linear and Convex Subspaces of E^n

To avoid undesirable repetition, we remark that all the geometric objects defined or discussed in this section are understood to be in a euclidean n-space $E = E^n$, with a coordinate system $(x) = (x_1, \ldots, x_n)$. The **dimension number** n is merely required to be high enough, in each case, for a definition or statement to have significance. For brevity, we will use the term **dimension** instead of dimension number. It is to be emphasized, however, that we have not yet established any relationship between the term **dimension**, as used in this chapter, and the **Brouwer dimension** defined in Art. 3–8.

The simplest general equations defining a **line** in E^n are of the form

$$(4.1) \qquad x_i = a_i + b_i t \qquad (i = 1, \ldots, n)$$

where the parameter t has the arithmetical continuum, interpreted as a t-axis, for its domain, and where at least one of the numbers b_i is not zero. Equations (4.1) map the t-axis into E, carrying $t = 0$ into $(a) = (a_1, \ldots, a_n)$ and $t = 1$ into $(a_1 + b_1, \ldots, a_n + b_n)$. The line $p_0 p_1$, where p_0 and p_1 have the coordinates $p_0 : (a_{01}, \ldots, a_{0n})$ and $p_1 : (a_{11}, \ldots, a_{1n})$, can therefore be defined by

$$(4.2) \qquad x_i = a_{0i} + (a_{1i} - a_{0i})t$$
$$= a_{0i}(1 - t) + a_{1i}t \qquad (i = 1, \ldots, n).$$

Much of the later work is simplified by the use of a parameter

$t_0 = 1 - t$, which, if we write t_1 for t, converts (4.2) into the following definition of the line $p_0 p_1$, also to be denoted by $\Lambda(p_0, p_1)$:

$$(4.3) \qquad \Lambda(p_0, p_1): \begin{cases} \text{(a)} \ \ x_i = a_{0i} t_0 + a_{1i} t_1 & (i = 1, \ldots, n) \\ \text{(b)} \ \ t_0 + t_1 = 1. \end{cases}$$

The condition that some $b_i \neq 0$ in (4.1) is converted into the condition that p_0 and p_1 be distinct points.

(A) A subspace Λ of E is **linear** if $p_j \in \Lambda$ $(j = 0, 1)$ implies $\Lambda(p_0, p_1) \subset \Lambda$; that is, Λ contains the entire line through any two of its points.

The segment $[p_0 p_1]$, which we will also denote by $\Gamma(p_0, p_1)$, is analytically defined as follows:

$$(4.4) \qquad \Gamma(p_0, p_1): \begin{cases} \text{(a)} \ \ x_i = a_{0i} t_0 + a_{1i} t_1 & (i = 1, \ldots, n) \\ \text{(b)} \ \ t_0 + t_1 = 1 \\ \text{(c)} \ \ t_j \geq 0 & (j = 0, 1). \end{cases}$$

(B) A subset Γ of E is **convex** if $p_j \in \Gamma$ $(j = 0, 1)$ implies $\Gamma(p_0, p_1) \subset \Gamma$.

In the case of a single point, we make the definitions (Exercise 1)

$$(4.5) \qquad \Lambda(p_0) = \Gamma(p_0) = p_0.$$

For a subspace S of E, (1) the **linear space** $\Lambda(S)$ **determined by** S will mean the minimal linear subspace of E which contains S and (2) the **convex hull** $\Gamma(S)$ of S will mean the minimal convex set containing S. In other words, (1) $\Lambda(S) \supset S$ and no linear space which is a proper subset of $\Lambda(S)$ contains S and (2) $\Gamma(S) \supset S$ and no convex set which is a proper subset of $\Gamma(S)$ contains S.

(C) Equivalent definitions are as follows (Exercise 4): $\Lambda(S)$ is the intersection of all linear spaces containing S, and $\Gamma(S)$ is the intersection of all convex sets containing S.

(D) It is easy to verify that Definitions (4.3) and (4.4) generalize as follows to an arbitrary finite subset $(p_0, \ldots, p_k)$ in place of (p_0, p_1):

$$(4.6) \quad \Lambda(p_0, \ldots, p_k): \begin{cases} \text{(a)} \ \ x_i = a_{0i} t_0 + \cdots + a_{ki} t_k & (i = 1, \ldots, n) \\ \text{(b)} \ \ t_0 + \cdots + t_k = 1, \end{cases}$$

$$(4.7) \quad \Gamma(p_0, \ldots, p_k): \begin{cases} \text{(a)} \ \ x_i = a_{0i} t_0 + \cdots + a_{ki} t_k & (i = 1, \ldots, n) \\ \text{(b)} \ \ t_0 + \cdots + t_k = 1 \\ \text{(c)} \ \ t_j \geq 0 & (j = 0, \ldots, k). \end{cases}$$

EXERCISES

1. Show that if $p_0 = p_1$, the defining conditions of $\Lambda(p_0, p_1)$ and of $\Gamma(p_0, p_1)$ both yield the single point $p_0 = p_1$.

2. Show that (a) in E^2 and E^3, the definitions of $\Lambda(p_0, p_1)$ and $\Gamma(p_0, p_1)$ agree with the usual *line* and *line-segment* of plane and solid geometry; (b) in E^n, linear spaces are convex.

3. Which of the following sets are convex and which linear? Justify your answers: (a) The set $|x_i| \leq 1$ $(i = 1, \ldots, n)$. (b) The set $|x_i| \geq 1$ $(i = 1, \ldots, n)$. (c) The part of E^n where all coordinates are positive. (d) The part of E^n where exactly one coordinate is negative. (e) The locus $\Sigma_{i=1}^n x_i = 1$. (f) The locus $\Sigma_{i=1}^n x_i^2 = 1$.

4. Show that (a) the intersection of any collection of convex sets is convex, (b) the intersection of any collection of linear subspaces of E is linear. Hence justify Statement (C).

5. Let $n = 3$ and let $p_0, p_1,$ and p_2 be the points $p_0 : (0, 0, 0)$, $p_1 : (1, 0, 0)$, and $p_2 : (1, 2, 0)$. Write out (4.6) and (4.7), then verify that they define the (x_1, x_2)-plane and the closure of the triangular region $p_0 p_1 p_2$.

6. Discuss (4.6) and (4.7) for the case $n = 3$ and the triple of collinear points $p_0 : (0, 0, 0)$, $p_1 : (1, 0, 0)$, $p_2 : (-1, 0, 0)$.

7. Show that the conditions (4.6) define a linear space.

8. Show that conditions (4.7) define a convex set.

4–2. Dimension Numbers in E^n

(A) If $k + 1$ is the smallest number of points whereby a given linear subspace $\Lambda \subset E^n$ can be determined, then k is the **dimension number** or **(numerical) dimension** of Λ. The existence of such a number k is a consequence of Lemma 2 below. We will call Λ a k-**plane** (short for k-**dimensional hyperplane**). The agreement of numerical dimension with Brouwer dimension (Art. 3–8) will be established later (Art. 6–3).

LEMMA 1. **Euclidean n-space E^n is n-dimensional.**

Proof of Lemma. In the first place (Exercise 9), E^n is the linear space determined by a particular set of $n + 1$ points. It remains to show that E^n is not the linear space determined by a set $(p_0, p_1, \ldots, p_k)$ of points where $k < n$. This amounts to showing (Exercise 10) that if $k < n$, then there exists a point of E^n not on the locus Λ defined by (4.6).

We will assume a number of basic properties of determinants and matrices which the reader can readily find in the literature. Among the most fundamental is that a system of equations

$$(4.8) \qquad y_i = y_i^0 + \sum_{j=1}^n a_{ji} x_j \qquad (i = 1, \ldots, n)$$

can be solved in the form

(4.9) $$x_j = x_j^0 + \sum_{i=1}^{n} b_{ij}y_i \qquad (j = 1, \ldots, n)$$

if and only if the determinant $|a_{ji}|$ is not zero.

It is a straightforward procedure to generalize the basic concepts and results of plane and solid geometry to higher dimensions. We present a few essential generalizations now and introduce others as needed.*

(B) Equations (4.8) can be interpreted as a transformation of coordinates in E^n, from the given system (x) to (y), and (4.9) is then the inverse transformation. In general, the euclidean distance formula

(4.10) $$\rho^2((a_1, \ldots, a_n), (b_1, \ldots, b_n)) = \sum_{i=1}^{n} (a_i - b_i)^2$$

defined in terms of x-coordinates, is transformed into a more general quadratic expression in terms of y-coordinates.

THEOREM 1. **The euclidean distance formula is preserved by the transformation (4.8) if and only if the matrix** (a_{ji}) **is unit-orthogonal, that is,**†

(4.11) $$\sum_{h=1}^{n} a_{hi}a_{hj} = \delta_{ij} = \begin{cases} 0 \text{ if } i \neq j \\ 1 \text{ if } i = j \end{cases} \qquad (i, j = 1, \ldots, n).$$

We refer to the literature ([S–S], for example) for readers unfamiliar with this result. Alternatively, we suggest that the reader verify the result for $n = 2$ and 3, then develop his own general proof.

(C) If the matrix (a_{ji}) is unit-orthogonal, then (y) is a **rectangular cartesian system**. Thus (x), in particular, is such a system. If (a_{ji}) is not unit-orthogonal, (y) is a **skew coordinate system**. In either case, (4.8) and (4.9) are **affine transformations**. An (**affine**) **coordinate system** in E^n is a coordinate system obtainable from the original system (x) by an affine transformation.

(D) According to convenience, we interpret a **point** $x = (x_1, \ldots, x_n)$ as an ordered set of n real numbers or else as a **vector** x with components $(x_1, \ldots, x_n)$ and length $(x_1^2 + \cdots + x_n^2)^{\frac{1}{2}}$. In the latter interpretation, we use **vector addition** $x + x' = (x_1 + x_1', \ldots, x_n + x_n')$. The **unit point (vector) on the** x_j**-axis**, in terms of Kronecker deltas, is

(4.12) $$e_j = (\delta_{1j}, \delta_{2j}, \ldots, \delta_{nj}) \qquad (j = 1, \ldots, n).$$

---

* For a more detailed discussion, see [S–S].

† The symbol δ_{ij} in (4.11) is the **Kronecker delta**, defined as 1 when the subscripts are equal and 0 for unequal subscripts.

The **(coordinate)** $(x_{i_1}, \ldots, x_{i_h})$-**plane** is defined by $x_j = 0$ $(j \neq i_1, \ldots, i_h)$. It is a coordinate axis if $h = 1$.

(E) If (y) is a rectangular cartesian system, and θ is the angle between vectors y, y' of unit length, then $\cos \vartheta = \Sigma_{i=1}^n y_i y_i'$ (Exercise 13).

(F) To give another useful interpretation to (4.8) and (4.9), let (x) be a coordinate system in E^n and let (y) be a coordinate system in a second euclidean n-space E_0^n. Then (4.8) defines a **linear*** **homeomorphism** $\lambda : E^n \to E_0^n$ and (4.9) defines its inverse λ^{-1}. This homeomorphism is uniquely determined, among linear homeomorphisms, by the requirement that the origin, or 0 vector, in the x-system map onto $y^0 = (y_1^0, \ldots, y_n^0)$ in the y-system and the unit vector e_j of the x-system map onto $y^0 + a_j$ where $a_j = (a_{j1}, \ldots, a_{jn})$ $(j = 1, \ldots, n)$.

In E^n, with the coordinate system (x), let q_0 be the origin and let $q_1, \ldots, q_k$ be a set of k points $(k \leq n)$. Let the x-coordinates of q_j be denoted by $(b_{j1}, \ldots, b_{jn})$ $(j = 1, \ldots, k)$.

LEMMA 2. **The space** $\Lambda_0^k = \Lambda(q_0, \ldots, q_k)$ **is k-dimensional if and only if the n-by-k matrix** (b_{ji}) **is of rank k** (Exercise 14).

If (b_{ji}) is of rank k, the plane $\Lambda_0^k = \Lambda(q_0, \ldots, q_k)$ can be defined parametrically by the equations (Exercise 14)

$$(4.13) \qquad \Lambda_0^k : x_i = \sum_{j=1}^k b_{ji} u_j \qquad (i = 1, \ldots, n)$$

and $(u_1, \ldots, u_k)$ can be interpreted as a coordinate system on Λ_0^k, with origin q_0 and with q_j as unit point on the u_j-axis.

(G) The coordinate system $(u_1, \ldots, u_k)$ on Λ_0^k is rectangular cartesian, in terms of the metric of E^n, if and only if $\Sigma_{i=1}^n b_{hi} b_{ji} = \delta_{hj}$ $(h = 1, \ldots, k; j = 1, \ldots, k)$ (Exercise 15). This means that then and only then will $[\Sigma_{i=1}^k (u_i' - u_i'')^2]^{\frac{1}{2}}$ equal the distance $[\Sigma_{i=1}^n (x_i' - x_i'')^2]^{\frac{1}{2}}$ between two points u', u'' on Λ_0^k.

EXERCISES

9. Let q_0 be the origin and q_i the unit point on the x_i-axis $(i = 1, \ldots, n)$ in E^n. Prove that $E = \Lambda(q_0, q_1, \ldots, q_n)$.

10. Show that $\Lambda(p_0, p_1, \ldots, p_k)$ cannot contain the origin and the unit points on all the axes in E^n if $k < n$.

11. Show that the determinant of a unit-orthogonal matrix equals $+1$ or -1.

12. If (y) is a skew coordinate system, given by (4.8), with inverse (4.9), what is the distance formula in terms of (y)?

13. Establish Statement (E). Obtain an analogous formula for a skew system.

14. (a) Prove Lemma 2. (b) Establish (4.13), using (4.6).

15. Establish Statement (G).

---

* That is, a homeomorphism mapping lines onto lines.

4-3. Barycentric Coordinates

An exceptionally useful tool in combinatorial topology is a system of barycentric coordinates, defined below.

(A) Suppose the n-by-k matrix (a'_{ji}) $(j = 1, \ldots, k;\ i = 1, \ldots, n)$ is of rank k. Then, just as in the case of Λ_0^k in Lemma 2, the locus Λ^k parametrically defined as follows is k-dimensional.

$$(4.14) \qquad \Lambda^k : x_i = a'_{0i} + \sum_{j=1}^{k} a'_{ji} t_j \qquad (i = 1, \ldots, n).$$

Also, as above, $(t_1, \ldots, t_k)$ can be interpreted as a coordinate system on Λ^k. This defines the general k-plane $\Lambda^k \subset E^n$, by contrast with Λ_0^k, which is special in that it contains the origin.

(B) Equations (4.14) can also be interpreted as defining a linear homeomorphism between Λ^k and a euclidean k-space E^k, in which $(t_1, \ldots, t_k)$ is a coordinate system.

Equations (4.14) are simplified by the use of

$$(4.15) \qquad t_0 = 1 - (t_1 + \cdots + t_k) \Rightarrow \sum_{i=0}^{k} t_i = 1$$

and of the notation

$$(4.16) \quad a_{0i} = a'_{0i} \qquad a_{ji} = a'_{0i} + a'_{ji} \qquad (i = 1, \ldots, n; j = 1, \ldots, k).$$

(C) In terms of $(t_0, \ldots, t_k)$ and the a_{ji}, Eqs. (4.14) reduce precisely to Eqs. (4.6), so that

$$(4.17) \qquad \Lambda^k = \Lambda(p_0, p_1, \ldots, p_k).$$

One calls $(t_0, \ldots, t_k)$ the **barycentric coordinates on Λ^k relative to** $(p_0, \ldots, p_k)$. In terms of them, the p's have the coordinates $p_j : (\delta_{j0}, \ldots, \delta_{jk})$, using Kronecker deltas $(j = 0, \ldots, k)$.

LEMMA 3. **The set of all k-planes in E^n is the set of all images of a euclidean k-space E^k under linear homeomorphisms mapping E^k into E^n.**

Proof of Lemma. This follows directly from (B). We note that two different homeomorphisms may yield the same plane.

(D) *An important advantage of the barycentric system* $(t_0, t_1, \ldots, t_k)$ *is that it is invariant under affine transformations of coordinates in the space E^n.* In other words, the barycentric coordinates, relative to $(p_0, p_1, \ldots, p_k)$, of a point on Λ^k depend only on $(p_0, p_1, \ldots, p_k)$, and are not changed (Exercise 18) if the (x)-system is replaced by the (y)-system, in the notation of (4.8) and (4.9).

Since (4.14) defines a k-plane if and only if the matrix (a'_{ji}) is of rank k, it follows from (4.16) that (4.6) defines a k-plane if and only if the matrix

$$(4.18) \quad \begin{pmatrix} (a_{11} - a_{01}) & \cdots & (a_{k1} - a_{01}) \\ \cdot & & \cdot \\ \cdot & & \cdot \\ \cdot & & \cdot \\ (a_{1n} - a_{0n}) & \cdots & (a_{kn} - a_{0n}) \end{pmatrix}$$

is of rank k, hence (Exercise 19) if and only if the matrix

$$(4.19) \quad \begin{pmatrix} a_{01} & a_{11} & \cdots & a_{k1} \\ \cdot & \cdot & & \cdot \\ \cdot & \cdot & & \cdot \\ \cdot & \cdot & & \cdot \\ a_{0n} & a_{1n} & \cdots & a_{kn} \\ 1 & 1 & \cdots & 1 \end{pmatrix}$$

is of rank $k + 1$.

(*E*) If $\Lambda^k = \Lambda(p_0, p_1, \ldots, p_k)$ is a k-plane and if $p_{k+1} \in E^n - \Lambda^k$, then $\Lambda(p_0, p_1, \ldots, p_{k+1})$ is a $(k + 1)$-plane (Exercise 20). Thus the concept of k-planes in E^n could be developed recurrently with respect to increasing values of k.

(*F*) If $E^n = \Lambda(p_0, \ldots, p_n)$, then $\Gamma(p_0, \ldots, p_n)$ contains inner points (Exercise 22).

EXERCISES

16. What is the locus defined in E^3 by the equations $x_1 = 1 - 4t_1 - 2t_2$, $x_2 = 10t_1 + 5t_2$, $x_3 = -2t_1 - t_2$?

17. Using barycentric coordinate systems, write equations for (a) the line containing $p_0 : (3, 4)$ and $p_1 : (4, -3)$ in E^2, (b) the 2-plane in E^4 containing $p_0 : (-1, 3, 2, 0)$, $p_1 : (1, 5, 2, -4)$, and $p_2 : (4, -5, 4, -3)$. Verify that these points determine a 2-plane.

18. Prove Statement (*D*).

19. Show that the rank of the matrix (4.18) is less by 1 than that of (4.19).

20. Prove result (*E*). Also show that if $(q_0, \ldots, q_k)$ is a set of points such that $\Lambda(p_0, \ldots, p_k) = \Lambda(q_0, \ldots, q_k)$, and if $q_{k+1} \in \Lambda(p_0, \ldots, p_{k+1}) - \Lambda(p_0, \ldots, p_k)$, then $\Lambda(q_0, \ldots, q_{k+1}) = \Lambda(p_0, \ldots, p_{k+1})$.

21. Show that if $\Lambda^k = \Lambda(p_0, \ldots, p_k) = \Lambda(q_0, \ldots, q_k)$, then the barycentric coordinates on Λ^k relative to $(q_0, \ldots, q_k)$ and to $(p_0, \ldots, p_k)$, respectively, are expressible linearly and homogeneously in terms of one another.

22. Prove result (*F*).

4–4. Simplexes

The points $p_0, p_1, \ldots, p_k$ in E^n $(k \leq n)$ are said to be **(linearly) independent** if $\Lambda(p_0, p_1, \ldots, p_k)$ is a k-plane. Even if no two of the points p_i coincide, $\Lambda(p_0, p_1, \ldots, p_k)$ could be a j-plane for any $j \in (1, 2, \ldots, k)$ (see Exercises 25, 26). If $p_0, p_1, \ldots, p_k$ are independent, they determine an **(open)** k**-simplex**, s^k, analytically defined by

$$(4.20) \qquad s^k = p_0 p_1 \cdots p_k : \begin{cases} \text{(a)} \quad x_i = \sum_{j=0}^{k} a_{ji} t_j \qquad (i = 1, \ldots, n) \\ \text{(b)} \quad \sum_{j=0}^{k} t_j = 1 \\ \text{(c)} \quad t_j > 0 \qquad (j = 0, 1, \ldots, k) \end{cases}$$

where $(a_{j1}, \ldots, a_{jn})$ are the x-coordinates of p_j $(j = 0, 1, \ldots, k)$. Comparing (4.7), we see that $\bar{s}^k$, to be called a **closed** k**-simplex**, is given by

$$(4.21) \qquad \bar{s}^k = \Gamma(p_0, p_1, \ldots, p_k).$$

(*A*) The unmodified term k-**simplex** will always mean **open simplex**. If $k > 0$, the points of s^k are the **inner points** of $\bar{s}^k$, and $\bar{s}^k - s^k$ is the **boundary** of s^k or of $\bar{s}^k$. It should be noted that s^k is not an open subset of E^n, unless $k = n$. However, s^k is an open subset of $\Lambda^k = \Lambda(p_0, \ldots, p_k)$ and $\bar{s}^k - s^k$ is its boundary, relative to Λ^k, where Λ^k is regarded as a subspace of E^n with the induced topology. The **vertices** of $s^k = p_0 \ldots p_k$ are $(p_0, \ldots, p_k)$.

(*B*) For the first few values of k, we have (Exercise 24): (1) $s^0 = p_0$, a point; (2) $s^1 = p_0 p_1$, a finite linear interval, that is, a segment without its end points; (3) $s^2 = p_0 p_1 p_2$, a plane triangular region; (4) $s^3 = p_0 p_1 p_2 p_3$, the interior of a tetrahedron. The symbol s^{-1} (a (-1)-**simplex**) will be interpreted as the vacuous set.

(*C*) A **boundary** j-**simplex of** $s^k = p_0 \ldots p_k$ means either s^{-1} or a simplex $s^j = q_0 q_1 \ldots q_j$ where $(q_0, q_1, \ldots, q_j)$ is a proper subset of $(p_0, \ldots, p_k)$ $(j = 0, \ldots, k - 1)$. A **face** of s^k means a boundary simplex or s^k itself. Each point of $\bar{s}^k$ is on a unique face of s^k (Exercise 27). The total number of faces of s^k is 2^{k+1}, of which the number of j-dimensional faces (to be called j-**faces**) equals the binomial coefficient $C_{k+1,j+1}$ $(j = -1, \ldots, k)$.

An alternative recurrent definition of s^k, equivalent to the above, is as follows: A 0-**simplex** is a point, $s^0 = p_0$, and its **boundary simplex** is the vacuous (-1)-simplex, s^{-1}. Assume, for a non-negative integer $j < n$, that a j-**simplex**, $s^j = p_0 p_1 \ldots p_j$, and its **boundary** i-**simplexes** $(i = -1, 0, \ldots, j - 1)$ have been defined in such a way that (1) $s^j \subset \Lambda^j \subset E^n$ for some j-plane Λ^j, (2) s^j is an open set relative to Λ^j, (3) $\bar{s}^j - s^j$ is the union of the boundary simplexes of s^j. Given a point $p_{j+1} \in E^n - \Lambda^j$, the $(j + 1)$-simplex

$$(4.22) \qquad s^{j+1} = s_j p_{j+1} = p_0 p_1 \cdots p_{j+1}$$

is the set of all points each on a 1-simplex $p_{j+1} p$ as p ranges over s^j.

The **boundary simplexes** of s^{j+1} are (1) the 0-simplex p_{j+1}, (2) s^j and its boundary simplexes, (3) the $(i + 1)$-simplexes $p_{j+1}s^i$ as s^i ranges over the boundary simplexes of s^j. The closed simplex $\bar{s}^{j+1}$ is the union of the segments $[p_{j+1}p]$ as p ranges over $\bar{s}^j$.

Etymologically, the term **barycenter** suggests center of gravity. In E^n, with the rectangular cartesian coordinate system $(x_1, \ldots, x_n)$, imagine a particle of mass w_j at the point $p_j : (a_{j1}, \ldots, a_{jn})$ $(j = 0, 1, \ldots, k)$ and let $W = w_0 + \cdots + w_k$. The formula for the center of gravity $(\bar{x}_1, \ldots, \bar{x}_n)$, generalized, is

(4.23) $$\bar{x}_i = \frac{1}{W} \sum_{j=0}^{k} w_j a_{ji} = \sum_{j=0}^{k} t_j a_{ji} \qquad (i = 1, \ldots, n)$$

where $t_j = w_j/W \Rightarrow \Sigma_{j=0}^{k} t_j = 1$. This suggests a "physical" reason for the invariance of barycentric coordinates (Art. 4–3(D)).

(D) Let the vertices $(p_0, \ldots, p_m)$ of an m-simplex s^m be partitioned into two complementary sets $(p_{i_0}, \ldots, p_{i_k})$ and $(p_{j_0}, \ldots, p_{j_{m-k-1}})$. Let $s^k = p_{i_0} \ldots p_{i_k}$ and $s^{m-k-1} = p_{j_0} \ldots p_{j_{m-k-1}}$. Then s^k is defined as follows, in terms of the barycentric coordinates $(t_0, \ldots, t_m)$ relative to $p_0, \ldots, p_m$:

(4.24) $$s^k : \begin{cases} t_j = 0 & (j = j_0, \ldots, j_{m-k-1}) \\ t_i > 0 & (i = i_0, \ldots, i_k) \end{cases} \Biggr\} \Rightarrow \sum_{h=0}^{k} t_{i_h} = 1.$$

It follows that $(t_{i_0}, \ldots, t_{i_k})$ are barycentric coordinates on s^k relative to $(p_{i_0}, \ldots, p_{i_k})$. The faces s^k and s^{m-k-1} are **opposite faces** of s^m, and we will use such notation as

(4.25) $$s^m = s^k s^{m-k-1} = p_{i_0} \ldots p_{i_k} s^{m-k-1}, \text{ and so on.}$$

(E) Now let $(u) = (u_0, \ldots, u_k)$ and $(v) = (v_0, \ldots, v_k)$ be barycentric coordinates, relative to $(p_0, \ldots, p_k)$ and $(q_0, \ldots, q_k)$ respectively on two k-planes $\Lambda_1^k = \Lambda^k(p_0, \ldots, p_k)$ and $\Lambda_2^k = \Lambda^k(q_0, \ldots, q_k)$. Let $\lambda : \Lambda_1^k \to \Lambda_2^k$ be the mapping such that $q = \lambda(p)$ if and only if the (v)-coordinates of q equal the (u)-coordinates of p. *Then* (Exercise 28) λ *is a linear homeomorphism uniquely determined, among linear homeomorphisms of* Λ_1^k *onto* Λ_2^k, *by the conditions* $p_j \to q_j$ $(j = 0, \ldots, k)$. We will frequently be interested in the restriction $\lambda \,|\, s^k$ where $s^k = p_0 \ldots p_k$.

EXERCISES

23. In E^4, let p_0, p_1, p_2 be defined as in Exercise 17b above. Find the x-coordinates of (a) the center of gravity of three particles of equal masses at p_0, p_1, and p_2; (b) the point on $s^2 = p_0 p_1 p_2$ with barycentric coordinates $(\frac{1}{2}, \frac{1}{2}, 0)$. Show that these two points are collinear with p_2.

24. Prove all parts of (B) for the case $E^n = E^3$.

25. In the plane E^2, define $\Gamma(S)$ analytically and describe it geometrically where S consists of (a) the two points $(1, 1)$ and $(-1, -1)$; (b) the three points $(1, 1)$, $(2, 2)$, and $(3, 3)$; (c) the points $(0, 0)$, $(1, 0)$, $(0, 1)$; and (d) the points $(1, 1)$, $(1, -1)$, $(-1, 1)$, $(-1, -1)$.

26. Show that $\Gamma(p_0, p_1, p_2, p_3)$, where the p's are four different points of E^3, is the closure of one and only one of the following: (a) a linear interval, (b) a plane triangular region, (c) a plane quadrilateral region, (d) the interior of a tetrahedron.

27. Prove the last two sentences of (C).

28. Establish the italicized part of (E).

4–5. Complexes

Simplexes are the building blocks .for the structures, known as **complexes**, with whose topological properties we will be mainly concerned. The 1-**complexes** include the linear graphs of Chapter 1, and the 2-**complexes** include the surfaces of Chapter 2. In general, a 2-**complex** can be described as a collection $\{s\}$ of simplexes of dimensions ≤ 2 such that (1) $\{s\}$ contains at least one 2-simplex; (2) $\{s\}$ contains all boundary faces of each of its members; and (3) if $s^j \in \{s\}$ and $s^k \in \{s\}$, then the intersection $\bar{s}^j \cap \bar{s}^k$ is the closure of a common face of s^j and s^k.

Boxlike building blocks, square and cubical for example, might seem more natural and, indeed, can be advantageously used for many topological purposes. However, simplexes have many advantages stemming from the fact that a j-simplex is the convex hull of the smallest number of points, $j + 1$, of a euclidean space, whose convex hull can be j-dimensional.

(A) A formal definition of a **finite** m-**complex** $K^m = \{s\}$ in E^n is as follows: It is a set of disjoint simplexes

$$(4.26) \qquad \{s\} = (s^{-1}) \cup \{s^0\} \cup \{s^1\} \cup \cdots \cup \{s^m\}$$

consisting of singleton (s^{-1}) and some finite sets of k-simplexes

$$(4.27) \qquad \{s^k\} = (s_1^k, \ldots, s_{\alpha_k}^k) \qquad (k = 0, 1, \ldots, m)$$

with the following properties: (1) each face* of a simplex of the set $\{s\}$ is a simplex of $\{s\}$ and (2) $\alpha_m > 0$. In this definition, m can be any integer ≥ -1. If $m = -1$, K^{-1} consists of (s^{-1}) alone.

(B) An m-complex K^m contains at least 2^{m+1} simplexes, since by (2) it contains at least one m-simplex and all its faces (see Art. 4–4(C)). Furthermore, $\alpha_j \geq C_{m+1, j+1}$. The collection of all the faces of an m-simplex is the simplest example of an m-complex.

---

* Singleton (s^{-1}), the vacuous (-1)-dimensional simplex, is included for the sake of Property (1) and to simplify the statements of other properties and results.

(C) Occasionally we will be concerned with infinite complexes. An **infinite complex** K^m in E^n is defined exactly as in (A), except that (1) $\{s^k\} = (s_1^k, s_2^k, \ldots)$ is denumerably infinite and (2) each point of E^n has some neighborhood intersecting only a finite subset of $\{s\}$.

(D) We will write $s^h < s^k$ or $s^k > s^h$ to symbolize the relationship of s^h being a boundary simplex of s^k (implying $h < k$), and we will then refer to (s^h, s^k) as **incident** simplexes. We will write $s^h \leq s^k$ or $s^k \geq s^h$ to signify that s^h is a face of s^k, which is consistent with $s^h = s^k$.

Thus the symbols $(<, >, \leq, \geq)$ express relationships among simplexes, as well as among real numbers.

(E) Consider a set A and a relation $<$. It is said that $<$ **orders** A if (1) for any two elements a and a' of A, exactly one of the relations $a < a'$, $a' < a$, $a = a'$ holds; (2) $a < a'$ and $a' < a''$ imply $a < a''$. It is said that $<$ **partially orders** A under the same conditions modified by changing "exactly one" to "at most one" in (1). If $<$ orders [partially orders] A, it will be said that $\leq$, meaning $<$ or $=$, also **orders** [**partially orders**] A. Equivalent formulations of $a < a'$, $a \leq a'$ are $a' > a$, $a' \geq a$, respectively.

EXERCISE

29. Show that the simplexes of a complex $\{s\}$ are partially ordered by $<$, but that they are not ordered by this relation.

4–6. Polyhedra; Topological Complexes

If L is a set of simplexes, then $|L|$ will denote their point-set union (the set of all points each on at least one of them), regardless of whether or not L is a complex.

(A) If K is a complex, $|K|$ is called a **polyhedron**, **finite** or **infinite** according as K is finite or infinite, and K is a **triangulation** of $|K|$. We will frequently use such notation as $P = |K|$ for a polyhedron. A given polyhedron P admits infinitely many triangulations, if its dimension is positive.

A finite polyhedron is a compactum, since it is a closed bounded subset of E^n (Chapter 3, Theorem 14).

(B) It is instructive to interpret $K = \{s\}$ as a topological space whose elements are the simplexes $\{s\}$. To accomplish this, we define a subset $L \subset K$ of the simplexes $\{s\}$ as **closed** if L contains each face of each of its simplexes; that is, if $(s \in L, \ t < s) \Rightarrow t \in L$. This is equivalent to the statement that L is a complex. We then call L a **subcomplex** of K.

(C) A set $L \subset K$ of the simplexes $\{s\}$ is **open** if it is the complement of a closed set. *This is equivalent* (Exercise 33) *to the condition*

$(s \in L, t > s) \Rightarrow t \in L$, *which says that* L *contains each simplex which has a face in* L.

LEMMA 4. **Relative to** $|K|$, **the subset** $|L| \subset |K|$ **is closed if and only if** L **is a closed subset of** K **and is open if and only if** L **is an open subset of** K.

Outline of Proof. The closure of a simplex $s^k \in K$, interpreted as a point set, is $\bar{s}^k$. Its closure as a subset of K consists of all the faces of s^k, and they have $\bar{s}^k$ for their union. The closure of $|L|$ is therefore the point-set union of the closures of the simplexes of L, and the closure of L as a subset of K consists of all the faces of its simplexes. This leads to the part of Lemma 4 relating to $|L|$ and L being closed. The other part follows because open sets are the complements of closed sets.

(*D*) If K^m is an m-complex, then, for any $k \in (-1, 0, \ldots, m)$, the set of all the simplexes of K^m of dimensions $\leq k$ is a complex K^k, called the k-**skeleton** of K^m. In the notation of Art. 4–5(*A*), $K^k = (s^{-1}) \cup \{s^0\} \cup \cdots \cup \{s^k\}$. It is a subcomplex of K^m.

(*E*) The 1-skeleton K^1 of K^m, minus any isolated vertices, is a linear graph. A path on K^1 is defined as in Art. 1–2, and so is the concept of **connectedness**. We say that K^m is **connected** if K^1 is connected. If $p \in \{s^0\}$ is a vertex of K^m, hence of K^1, then the subgraph of K^1 consisting of all vertices, plus incident edges, which can be joined to p by paths is a **component** K^1_0 of K^1. The simplexes of K^m each having vertices on a component K^1_0 of K^1 constitute a **component** K^m_0 of K^m. A component of K^m is a maximal connected subcomplex of K^m.

(*F*) Now suppose K^m finite, and let $(K_1, \ldots, K_{\gamma_0})$ be its components. Then $|K_i|$ is a component of $|K^m|$ and is a **connected polyhedron** (Exercise 34), in the sense that each pair of points on $|K^m_i|$ can be joined by a broken line on $|K^m_i|$. Each component of a complex K^m is a subcomplex and is both open and closed.

(*G*) Later (Art. 6–9(*E*)) it will be seen that a polyhedron $P = |K^m|$ is connected if and only if it has no proper non-vacuous subset which is both open and closed.

A **topological polyhedron** means a space Π homeomorphic to a polyhedron $P = |K^m|$ in a euclidean space E. A **topological** k-**simplex** means a space σ^k homeomorphic to a k-simplex $s^k \subset E$. Consider a particular homeomorphism $h : P \to \Pi$, and let $K = \{s\}$ be a triangulation of P, so that $P = |K|$. If

(4.28) $\sigma^k = h(s^k)$ where $s^k \in \{s\}$,

then σ^k is a topological k-simplex on Π. The aggregate $\Re = \{\sigma\}$ of such topological simplexes is a **topological complex**, and its point-set union is $|\Re| = \Pi$. We refer to $\Re$ as a **triangulation** of Π.

A simplex $s^k \subset E$, as defined in Art. 4–4, will be called a **linear simplex** when it is important to distinguish it from a topological simplex. Similarly, K will be described as a **linear (simplicial) complex** to distinguish it from the topological complex $\mathfrak{K}$, and $P = |K|$ will be called a **simplicial polyhedron** to distinguish it from the topological polyhedron $\Pi = |\mathfrak{K}|$. When either the meaning is clear from the context or a statement applies to both cases, the modifying adjectives will be omitted.

(H) We remark, for later reference, that a triangulation $\mathfrak{K} = \{\sigma\}$ of a topological polyhedron Π is defined by a homeomorphism $h : P \to \Pi$ and a triangulation K of P. The concepts of **face**, **boundary face**, and **incidence relation**, symbolized by $<$, are carried over by h from K to $\mathfrak{K}$. So are the concepts of **connectedness**, **components**, and so on.

EXERCISES

30. Let Π be the convex hull in E^3 of the six vertices $p_0 : (0, 0, 0), p_1 : (1, 0, 0)$, $p_2 : (1, 1, 0)$, $q_0 : (0, 0, 1)$, $q_1 : (1, 0, 1)$, $q_2(1, 1, 1)$. Show that the 3-simplexes $p_0q_0q_1q_2$, $p_0p_1q_1q_2$, $p_0p_1p_2q_2$ and their faces are a complex K^3 with Π for its point-set union.

31. In the complex K^3 of the preceding exercise give the smallest closed and open subsets of simplexes (a) containing the 1-simplex p_0q_2, (b) containing the 2-simplex $p_0q_1q_2$.

32. Let $\Pi = S_1^2 \cup S_2^2$, where S_1^2 and S_2^2 are the spheres of radius 1 about the points $(2, 0, 0)$ and $(-2, 0, 0)$ in an E^3. Show that Π is a topological polyhedron with S_1^2 and S_2^2 as components and that S_i^2, as a subspace of Π, is both open and closed.

33. Establish the italicized sentence in (C).

34. Demonstrate result (F).

4-7. Abstract and Generalized Complexes

An **abstract k-simplex** is a set of $k + 1$ points, symbolized thus: $\mathfrak{s}^k = (p_0, p_1, \ldots, p_k)$ or $p_0p_1 \ldots p_k$. The form $p_0p_1 \ldots p_k$ will be used only where confusion with a linear simplex is unlikely or immaterial. A 0-simplex is also called a **vertex**. A subset of $\mathfrak{s}^k$ is a **face** of $\mathfrak{s}^k$, and a proper subset is a **proper** or **boundary face**.

Let S be an arbitrary point set. An **abstract complex** is a collection $\mathfrak{K} = \{\mathfrak{s}\}$ of abstract simplexes such that the 0-simplexes of $\mathfrak{K}$ are the points of S, and each face of an element of $\mathfrak{K}$ is an element of $\mathfrak{K}$. We describe $\mathfrak{K}$ as **finite** if S is finite, and **denumerable** if S is denumerable. We describe $\mathfrak{K}$ as m-**dimensional** if it contains an m-simplex but no $(m + 1)$-simplex, hence no n-simplex for any $n > m$. *This does not define a geometric dimension, since an m-simplex is a finite point set.*

To suggest the generality of abstract complexes, note that the collection of all triples of points, together with all pairs, singletons, and the vacuous set in E^2 or, for that matter, on E^1 is an abstract 2-complex.

The relations $<$ and $\leq$ are defined for abstract complexes just as for linear and topological simplicial complexes, and $<$ partially orders the elements of an abstract complex.

Abstract complexes originated as abstractions of simplicial polyhedral complexes. Indeed, if K is a simplicial complex, we obtain from it an abstract complex $\Re$ by letting S be the set of all vertices of K and defining an **abstract k-simplex of $\Re$** as the vertices $(p_0, p_1, \ldots, p_k)$ of a k-simplex of K.

(A) We will refer to $\Re$, just defined, as the **abstract complex of K**, and we will call K, or $|K|$, a **simplicial**, or **polyhedral**, **realization of $\Re$**. We prove, in the next section, that an arbitrary abstract complex $\Re$ admits a simplicial realization in a euclidean space E if $\Re$ is denumerable and each of its 0-simplexes is incident with only a finite set of 1-simplexes.

(B) **Algebraic topology** consists of (1) an algebraic theory directly concerned with abstract (or more general) complexes, (2) theorems to the effect that various results of this algebraic theory have topological significance for realizations of such complexes, and (3) the use of mappings to apply the algebraic theory to topological spaces more general than topological polyhedra.

(C) A collection $A = \{\alpha\}$ of objects is called a **generalized complex** if it satisfies the following conditions:

(1) With each $\alpha \in A$ is associated a non-negative integer k, the **dimension** of $\alpha = \alpha^k$, and α^k is called an **abstract k-cell**.

(2) The set A is partially ordered by a relation $<$, such that $\alpha^j < \alpha^k \Rightarrow j < k$.

It is obvious that generalized complexes are more general than abstract complexes. In order to make effective use of them, one must impose restrictions in addition to the defining conditions. We have given Definition (C) to round out our collection of definitions with the most general one that appears useful.

4–8. Realizations of Abstract Complexes

THEOREM 2. **Let $\Re = \{s\}$ be a denumerable abstract m-complex, each of whose vertices is incident with only a finite set of 1-simplexes. Then $\Re$ admits a linear simplicial realization in a euclidean n-space E^n, for n sufficiently large.**

Proof. Case 1 ($\Re$ is finite). We treat this case separately, because it is particularly useful and simple.

Let $p_0, p_1, \ldots, p_N$ be the vertices of $\Re$. In an E^N, consider a linear N-simplex $\tau = q_0 q_1 \cdots q_N$. Let $\{t\}$ be the set of faces of τ defined by the condition that a face $t^k = q_{i_0} q_{i_1} \cdots q_{i_k}$ of τ belongs to $\{t\}$ if and only if the correspondingly numbered set of p's, namely $p_{i_0} \cdots p_{i_k}$ is a simplex of $\Re$. It is a simple matter to verify that $K = \{t\}$ is a realization of $\Re$.

(A) The realization K of $\Re$ just defined, that is, its realization as a subcomplex of the faces of an N-simplex τ where $N + 1$ is the number of vertices of $\Re$, will be called a **natural realization** of $\Re$. It is unique, given τ, up to a renumbering of the vertices. A barycentric coordinate system $(u) = (u_0, u_1, \ldots, u_N)$ on τ affords a **natural coordinate system**, unique up to a permutation, on K. If $p \in t^k \in K$ and $t^k = q_{i_0} q_{i_1} \cdots q_{i_k}$, then $(u_{i_0}, u_{i_1}, \ldots, u_{i_k})$ are all positive at p and are a barycentric coordinate system on t^k. All the other u's are zero on t^k.

Case 2 ($\Re$ *is not necessarily finite*). The following argument proves Theorem 2 in all its generality and, incidentally, yields the following subsidiary result.

COROLLARY. **The value $n = 2m + 1$ is sufficiently large in Theorem 2.**

The following lemma contains the heart of the proof.

LEMMA 5. **It is possible to define an infinite set of points $\{q\} = q_0, q_1, q_2, \ldots$ in a euclidean space E^n ($n > 0$) in such a way that**

(1) **Each set of $k + 1$ of the points $\{q\}$ determines a linear k-simplex, provided $k \leq n$.**

(2) **The x_1-coordinate of q_i equals i ($i = 0, 1, 2, \ldots$).**

Proof of Lemma. As the basic step of a recurrent argument, let q_0 be the origin in E^n. The following hypothesis, read for $j = 0$, is fulfilled.

Hypothesis. For some non-negative integer j, the points $q_0, q_1, \ldots, q_j$ have been so defined in E^n as to satisfy Conditions (1) and (2) of the lemma with $\{q\}$ replaced by $(q_0, q_1, \ldots, q_j)$.

Then, as a consequence of the hypothesis, if $1 \leq k \leq n$ each subset of $(k + 1)$ of the points $(q_0, \ldots, q_j)$ determines a k-plane.

(B) A k-plane determined by a subset of $(q_0, \ldots, q_j)$ intersects the $(n - 1)$-plane $x_1 = j + 1$ in a $(k - 1)$-plane, and the collection of all such $(k - 1)$-planes of intersection for all values of k satisfying $1 \leq k \leq n - 1$ does not cover the $(n - 1)$-plane $x_1 = j + 1$ (Exercise 37).

As a consequence of (B), it is possible to define q_{j+1} as some point such that (1) $x_1 = j + 1$ and (2) each subset of $k + 2$ of the points $(q_0, \ldots, q_{j+1})$ is linearly independent if $1 \leq k \leq n - 1$ and hence so is each set of $k + 1$ of these points if $1 \leq k \leq n$. Thus the hypothesis is verified with $j + 1$ in place of j. Lemma 5 follows.

Now let $p_0, p_1, p_2, \ldots, p_N$ or $p_0, p_1, p_2, \ldots$ be the vertices of $\Re$ according as $\Re$ is finite or infinite. Let $n = 2m + 1$, and let $\{q\}$ satisfy Lemma 5. Let K denote the set $\{t\}$ of all k-simplexes $t^k = q_{i_0} q_{i_1} \cdots q_{i_k}$ ($k = 0, 1, \ldots, m$) such that $s^k = p_{i_0} p_{i_1} \cdots p_{i_k}$ is an abstract k-simplex of $\Re$. We will refer to each pair t^k and s^k as a pair of **corresponding** simplexes. If $\Re$ is finite, then q_{N+1}, q_{N+2}, ... are not used.

LEMMA 6. **(a) The set $K = \{t\}$ is a linear m-complex (Art. 4–6) in E^n. (b) If (s^j, t^j) and (s^k, t^k) are two pairs of corresponding simplexes then $s^j < s^k$ if and only if $t^j < t^k$.**

Proof of Lemma. Let $s_1 = q_{i_0} \ldots q_{i_j}$ and $s_2 = q_{h_0} \ldots q_{h_k}$ be two simplexes of K and let r be the number of distinct vertices in the set $(q_{i_0}, \ldots, q_{i_j}, q_{h_0}, \ldots, q_{h_k})$. Then $r \leq j + k + 2 \leq 2m + 2 = n + 1$. Hence, by Lemma 5, these distinct vertices determine a linear $(r-1)$-simplex c^{r-1}, generally not an element of K, which has s_1, s_2 for faces. A proof of Lemma 6, hence of Theorem 2 and corollary, in the finite case is now easy to complete (Exercise 38).

To complete the argument for the infinite case, it suffices to show that a sufficiently small neighborhood of $p \in E^n$ intersects only a finite collection of the simplexes of K. But if k is an integer exceeding the x_1-coordinate of p and σ is a neighborhood of p of diameter less than 1, then σ can intersect only those simplexes, finite in number, each having a vertex in the set $(q_0, q_1, \ldots, q_k)$. The simplexes with no vertices in this set are all on the subspace $x_1 \geq k + 1$ of E^n.

(C) **Two complexes $K = \{s\}$ and $L = \{t\}$, whether linear, polyhedral, or abstract (and they need not both be of the same kind), are isomorphic if there exists a 1–1 onto mapping $\varphi : \{s\} \to \{t\}$ which preserves incidence relations; that is, $s^j < s^k \Leftrightarrow \varphi(s^j) < \varphi(s^k)$. Such a mapping is an isomorphism.**

EXERCISES

35. Let $\Re$ be the abstract complex of the 1-complex K^1 whose vertices are the vertices of a square and whose edges are the edges and one diagonal of the square. Draw a figure showing a realization of $\Re$ as a subcomplex of the faces of a 3-simplex.

36. Write out, and illustrate with figures, the proof of Theorem 2, Case 2, for $m = 1$, $n = 3$, thus showing that an abstract 1-complex has a realization as a linear graph in E^3, with line segments for edges.

37. Prove (B).

38. For the case where $\Re$ is finite, complete the proof of Lemma 6 and deduce Theorem 2, with corollary.

4–9. Isomorphisms and Homeomorphisms

THEOREM 3. **Let $\varphi : \{s\} \to \{t\}$ be an isomorphism between two linear simplicial complexes, $K = \{s\}$ and $L = \{t\}$. Then there exists**

one and only one linear homeomorphism,[*] $f : |K| \to |L|$ **such that** f **maps each** $s \in \{s\}$ **linearly onto** $\varphi(s)$.

Proof. Let the vertices of K and L be so numbered $(p_1, p_2, \ldots)$ and $(q_1, q_2, \ldots)$ that $q_i = \varphi(p_i)$ $(i = 1, 2, \ldots)$. If $s^k = p_{i_0} \ldots p_{i_k}$ is a simplex of K, then $t^k = q_{i_0} \ldots q_{i_k}$ is the simplex $t^k = \varphi(s^k)$. By Art. 4–4(E), there exists a unique linear homeomorphism mapping $\bar{s}^k$ onto $\bar{t}^k$ so that $p_{i_h} \to q_{i_h}$ $(h = 0, \ldots, k)$. It will be described as the homeomorphism **induced** by φ on $\bar{s}^k$. It is easy to verify that $s^j < s^k$ implies that the homeomorphism induced by φ on $\bar{s}^j$ is a restriction of that induced by φ on $\bar{s}^k$. Since each point p of $|K|$ is on a unique simplex s of $\{s\}$, it has a unique image, which we denote by $\lambda(p)$, on $|L|$, where $\lambda(p)$ is the image of p under the homeomorphism induced on s by φ. The mapping λ defined by $q = \lambda(p)$, $p \in |K|$, is a homeomorphism satisfying Theorem 3. Its one-to-one-ness follows from the fact that its inverse λ^{-1} can be defined just as λ was defined, using φ^{-1} in place of φ. Its continuity on $|K|$ follows, by a straightforward though perhaps somewhat tedious argument, from its continuity on each closed simplex $\bar{s} \in \{\bar{s}\}$.

THEOREM 4. **Two topological polyhedra** Π_1 **and** Π_2 **are homeomorphic if and only if they admit isomorphic triangulations.**

Proof. By Art. 4–6(H), a triangulation $\Re_1$ of Π_1 is defined by a homeomorphism $h : P \to \Pi_1$ and a triangulation K of P. If $h_1 : \Pi_1 \to \Pi_2$ is a homeomorphism, then $h_1 h : P \to \Pi_2$ and K define a triangulation $\Re_2$ of Π_2 isomorphic to $\Re_1$.

Now suppose Π_1 and Π_2 admit isomorphic triangulations $\Re_1$ and $\Re_2$. This means that there exist linear complexes K_1 and K_2 and homeomorphisms $h_i : |K_i| \to \Pi_i$ $(i = 1, 2)$ which induce isomorphisms $\varphi_i : K_i \to \Re_i$. If $\varphi : \Re_1 \to \Re_2$ is an isomorphism, then $\varphi_2^{-1} \varphi \varphi_1$ is an isomorphism $K_1 \to K_2$. Hence, by Theorem 3, there exists a homeomorphism $\lambda : |K_1| \to |K_2|$. But $h_2 \lambda h_1^{-1}$ is then a homeomorphism $\Pi_1 \to \Pi_2$ and Theorem 4 is proved.

4–10. Simplicial Mappings

Let $\Re = \{s\}$ and $\mathfrak{L} = \{t\}$ be two abstract complexes and let $\Re^0$ and $\mathfrak{L}^0$ be their 0-skeletons; that is, their respective sets of vertices.

Consider a mapping $\varphi_0 : \Re^0 \to \mathfrak{L}^0$ of the vertices of $\Re$ into those of $\mathfrak{L}$. It is not required that φ_0 be either one-to-one or onto.

The mapping $\varphi_0 : \Re^0 \to \mathfrak{L}^0$ is **simplicial** if the image $\varphi_0(p_0, \ldots, p_k)$ of a k-simplex $s^k = (p_0, \ldots, p_k)$ of $\Re$ is a simplex $t^j = (q_0, \ldots, q_j)$ of $\mathfrak{L}$. The notation does not imply that q_i is the image of p_i, but

---

[*] Such a homeomorphism is frequently described as **piecewise linear.**

$(q_0, \ldots, q_j)$ is merely the set of distinct points among the images $\varphi_0(p_i)$ $(i = 0, \ldots, k)$.

(A) *It follows that a simplicial mapping* $\varphi_0 : \Re^0 \to \Omega^0$ *has a natural extension into a mapping* $\varphi : \Re \to \Omega$. We will also describe φ as simplicial.

THEOREM 5. **Suppose $\Re$ and Ω satisfy the hypotheses of Theorem 2, so that they have linear realizations K and L. Let $\varphi : \Re \to \Omega$ be a simplicial mapping. Then there exists a unique linear mapping $\lambda : |K| \to |L|$ which maps the realization of $\mathfrak{s}^k \in \Re$ onto the realization of $\varphi(\mathfrak{s}^k) \in \Omega$.**

Proof. We will interpret $\Re$ and Ω as the abstract complexes of K and L, so that the same symbols can be used for the vertices of K and $\Re$ and L and Ω. We will use the same symbol φ to denote the mapping $\{s\} \to \{t\}$ determined by $\varphi : \Re \to \Omega$.

LEMMA 7. **Let $s^k = p_0 \ldots p_k$ be a simplex of K, and let $t^j = q_0 \ldots q_j$ be its image, $t^j = \varphi(s^k)$. For each vertex q_h of t^j let $\pi_h = \varphi^{-1}(q_h)$, the subset of $(p_0, \ldots, p_k)$ mapping onto q_h. There exists a unique linear mapping $\lambda : s^k \to t^j$ such that $\lambda(\pi_h) = q_h$ $(h = 0, \ldots, j)$.**

Proof of Lemma. Let $(u_0, \ldots, u_k)$ and $(v_0, \ldots, v_j)$ be the barycentric coordinates on $\bar{s}^k$ and $\bar{t}^j$ relative to $(p_0, \ldots, p_k)$ and $(q_0, \ldots, q_j)$, respectively.

(B) A mapping λ satisfying the lemma is defined as follows (Exercise 40). We will say that the coordinate u_i is **associated** with p_i $(i = 0, \ldots, k)$. Then λ maps a point $(u_0, \ldots, u_k)$ onto the point $(v_0, \ldots, v_j)$ where v_h is the sum of the u's associated with the vertices in the set $\pi_h = \varphi^{-1}(q_h)$; that is,

$$(4.29) \qquad v_h = \sum_{p_i \in \pi_h} u_i \qquad (h = 0, \ldots, j).$$

We will refer to λ as the mapping **induced** by φ.

The remainder of the proof of Theorem 5 follows along the same lines as that of Theorem 3. In fact, Theorem 3 deals with the special case of Theorem 5 where the simplicial mapping φ is an isomorphism.

EXERCISES

39. Discuss the mapping λ of Statement (B) geometrically in the case $k = 3$, $j = 2$.

40. Prove (A) and (B).

4–11. Barycentric Subdivisions

Combinatorial topology is concerned with abstract complexes (or with generalized complexes) rather than with their realizations. It is through such realizations or, more generally, through mappings into topological spaces, that combinatorial topology is applied to set-theoretic problems.

For the most satisfactory interplay between combinatorial and set-theoretic methods, it would be desirable to define **combinatorial equivalence** so that abstract complexes with realizations (Theorem 2) are combinatorially equivalent if and only if their realizations are homeomorphic. However, no **combinatorial criterion*** has been discovered† whereby we can determine, in general, whether the realizations of two such abstract complexes are homeomorphic. The methods actually used to apply combinatorial results to topological spaces depend on **subdivisions** of triangulations, especially **barycentric subdivisions**, which we proceed to define and discuss. (See Art. 4–12(G) below.)

(A) Let $\Re$ and $\Re_1$ be two triangulations of the same topological polyhedron, so that $\Pi = |\Re| = |\Re_1|$. Then $\Re_1$ is a **subdivision** of $\Re$ if and only if each simplex of $\Re_1$ is on a simplex of $\Re$. It follows that each simplex $\sigma \in \Re$ is the union of the simplexes of $\Re_1$ which intersect σ.

The only subdivision of a 0-complex K^0 is K^0 itself, which is accordingly defined as the first barycentric subdivision of K^0. Now let m be a positive integer, let $K^m = \{s\}$ be a linear simplicial m-complex, and suppose the **first barycentric subdivision** K_1^{m-1} defined for the $(m-1)$-skeleton K^{m-1} of K^m. The boundary B^{m-1} of an m-simplex $s^m \in K^m$ is then covered by a subcomplex B_1^{m-1} of K^{m-1}. Let p be the **barycenter** of s^m; that is, the point all of whose barycentric coordinates relative to the vertices of s^m equal $1/(m+1)$. The **first barycentric** subdivision of $\bar{s}^m$ then consists of (1) the vertex p, (2) the complex B_1^{m-1}, and (3) the simplexes pt^j (see (4.25) for notation) for $t^j \in B_1^{m-1}$. The **first barycentric subdivision** K_1^m of K^m is the union of the first barycentric subdivisions of its closed m-simplexes. It is easy to verify that K_1^m is a linear simplicial m-complex and is a subdivision of K^m. (See Fig. 4–1.) This completes a recurrent definition of the **first barycentric subdivision** of a linear simplicial m-complex K^m, with respect to increasing values of m.

The νth **barycentric subdivision** of K^m is the first barycentric subdivision of its $(\nu-1)^{\text{th}}$ barycentric subdivision, a definition recurrent in $\nu = 1, 2, 3, \ldots$. The 0th **barycentric subdivision** of K^m is K^m. The term **barycentric subdivision** without the numerical adjective ν^{th} will mean the first barycentric subdivision.

---

* Such a criterion would have to be expressible in terms of the incidence relations among the simplexes of a complex.

† (Added in proof.) While this book was in preparation, A. A. Markov showed ("The Unsolvability of the Problem of Homeomorphism," *Doklady Akad. Nauk SSSR* **121** (1958), pp. 218–220) that no such criterion can be discovered.

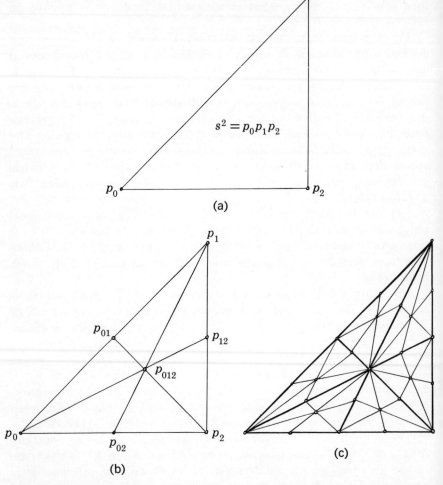

Fig. 4–1. The first two barycentric subdivisions of $\bar{s}^2$. (a) $K^2 =$ the faces of s^2; (b) K_1^2; (c) K_2^2.

(B) Let $s^m = p_0 p_1 \ldots p_m$ and let $p_{i_0 i_1 \ldots i_j}$ be the barycenter of the face $p_{i_0} p_{i_1} \ldots p_{i_j}$ of s^m (Fig. 4–1b). Note that $p_{i_0 \ldots i_j} = p_{r_0 \ldots r_j}$ if $(r_0, \ldots, r_j)$ is a permutation of $(i_0, \ldots, i_j)$. A typical m-simplex of the barycentric subdivision of $\bar{s}^m$ is then

(4.30) $$s^m_{i_0 \ldots i_m} = p_{i_0} p_{i_0 i_1} p_{i_0 i_1 i_2} \cdots p_{i_0 \ldots i_m}$$

where $(i_0, \ldots, i_m)$ is a permutation of $(0, 1, \ldots, m)$. The barycentric subdivision of $\bar{s}^m$ is the set of all the faces of the $(m + 1)!$ m-simplexes $s^m_{i_0 i_1 \ldots i_m}$.

THEOREM 6. **On the m-plane Λ^m of $s^m = p_0 p_1 \ldots p_m$, let $(u_0, \ldots, u_m)$**

be the barycentric coordinate system relative to $(p_0, \ldots, p_m)$. Then $s^m_{i_0 \ldots i_m}$ is defined by the following inequalities:

(4.31) $$s^m_{i_0 \ldots i_m} : u_{i_0} > u_{i_1} > \cdots > u_{i_m}.$$

Proof. The following lemma will be used.

LEMMA 8. **The barycentric coordinates $(v_0, \ldots, v_m)$ on Λ^m relative to $p_{i_0}, p_{i_0 i_1}, \ldots, p_{i_0 \ldots i_m}$ are related to $(u_0, \ldots, u_m)$ as follows:**

(4.32) $$u_{i_j} = \sum_{h=j}^{m} \frac{v_h}{h+1} \qquad (j = 0, \ldots, m).$$

To establish this lemma, it is sufficient to make the simple verification that Eqs. (4.32) yield the correct u-coordinates for the point $p_{i_0 \ldots i_h}$, $h \in (0, \ldots, m)$, when we substitute $v_h = 1$ and let all the other v's be zero. For (1) we know that the u's are expressible linearly in terms of the v's (Exercise 21), and (2) the coefficients in (4.32) must be correct for each h in order to give correct results when $v_h = 1$ and $v_k = 0$ $(k \neq h)$.

To complete the proof of Theorem 6 it is sufficient to show (Exercise 43) that the defining conditions $v_j > 0$ $(j = 0, 1, \ldots, m)$ of $s^m_{i_0 i_1 \ldots i_m}$ are equivalent to $u_{i_j} > u_{i_{j-1}}$ $(j = 1, \ldots, m)$.

COROLLARY TO THEOREM 6. **Each k-simplex t^k of the barycentric subdivision of $\bar{s}^m$ is definable by a set of conditions of the form (4.31) with all but k of the symbols $>$ replaced by $=$, and t^k is the common face of all the m-simplexes (4.31) from which its defining conditions can be thus obtained.**

THEOREM 7. **If each m-simplex of K^m is of diameter less than d, then each simplex of its νth barycentric subdivision K_ν is of diameter less than $[m/(m+1)]^\nu d$.**

Proof. The following two lemmas will be used.

LEMMA 9. **Let $q \in \bar{s}^k$, where s^k is a linear k-simplex, and let p be a point on $\bar{s}^k$ such that $\rho(q, p) = \max\limits_{r \in \bar{s}^k} \rho(q, r)$. Then p is a vertex of s^k.**

Proof of Lemma. Let s^j be the face of s^k containing p. If $j > 0$, let $p'p''$ be a segment on $\bar{s}^j$ through p, with its end points on $\bar{s}^j - s^j$. Then (Exercise 45), either $\rho(q, p') > \rho(q, p)$ or $\rho(q, p'') > \rho(q, p)$. This contradiction of the definition of p and q implies $j = 0$, which means that p is a vertex.

COROLLARY. **Suppose $\rho(p, q) = \operatorname{diam} s^k$ in Lemma 9. Then pq is an edge of s^k.**

LEMMA 10. **Let $d = \operatorname{diam} s^m$ and let $x = \rho(q, r)$, where qr is a 1-simplex of the barycentric subdivision S^m_1 of $\bar{s}^m$. Then $x \leq dm/(m+1)$, with equality only if $m = 1$.**

Proof of Lemma. For $m = 1$, $x = d/2$, verifying the lemma. Assume the lemma with $m - 1$ in place of m. Then each edge x of S_1^m not incident with the barycenter q_0 of s^m is an edge to which the inductive hypothesis applies for some face of s^m. Hence $x \leq d(m - 1)/m < dm/(m + 1)$. Consider, finally, an edge pq_0 of S_1^m, $x = \rho(p, q_0)$. By Lemma 9, if such an edge maximizes x, p is a vertex p_j of s^m. The barycentric coordinate u_j on s^m associated with p_j equals 1 at p_j, $1/(m + 1)$ at q_0, and 0 at the barycenter q_j of the face of s^m opposite p_j. Since p_j, q_0, q_j are collinear (Exercise 46), and since u_j is proportional to the distance from q_j along $q_j p_j$, it follows that $\rho(q_0, p_j) = m\rho(q_j, p_j)/(m + 1)$. But $\rho(q_0, p_j) = x$; and $\rho(q_j, p_j) < d$, by the corollary to Lemma 9. This implies Lemma 10.

Theorem 7 now follows (Exercise 47).

(C) As a consequence of Theorem 7, there exists, for each $\varepsilon > 0$, an integer ν so large that each simplex of K_ν is of diameter less than ε. We will then say that K_ν is **of mesh** ε.

EXERCISES

41. On a finite m-complex K^m with vertices $(p_1, \ldots, p_N)$ let $(u_1, \ldots, u_N)$ be the natural coordinate system as defined in Art. 4–8(A). Show that $u_j = \max(u_1, \ldots, u_N)$ defines the union of the closed simplexes incident with p_j on the barycentric subdivision K_1^m of K^m.

42. Carry through the suggested proof of Lemma 8.

43. Carry through the suggested completion of the proof of Theorem 6.

44. With the aid of the corollary to Theorem 6, show that each point of $\bar{s}^m$ is on one and only one simplex of the barycentric subdivision of $\bar{s}^m$.

45. In the proof of Lemma 9, show that $\rho(q, p') > \rho(q, p)$ or $\rho(q, p'') > \rho(q, p)$.

46. Show that q_0, q_j, and p_j are collinear in the proof of Lemma 10.

47. Deduce Theorem 7 from Lemmas 10 and 9, and the corollary to Lemma 9.

4–12. General Polyhedral Complexes

It is frequently convenient to consider polyhedral complexes which are structures of "cells" that are not simplexes; for example, the surface of a cube with square faces, or of a dodecahedron with pentagonal faces.

In E^n, with a coordinate system $(x) = (x_1, \ldots, x_n)$, an **open half-space** and a **closed half-space** are defined by inequalities, thus:

(4.33)

$$\text{Open half-space: } \sum_{i=1}^{n} a_i x_i + a_0 > 0,$$

$$\text{Closed half-space: } \sum_{i=1}^{n} a_i x_i + a_0 \geq 0,$$

where at least one of the numbers $(a_1, \ldots, a_n)$ is not zero.

(A) A **convex open polyhedral** n-**cell** c^n in E^n is a non-vacuous bounded set which is the intersection of a finite collection of open half-spaces, and $\bar{c}^n$ is a **convex closed polyhedral** n-**cell**.

Consider the intersection

$$(4.34) \qquad \bar{c} : \sum_{i=1}^{n} a_{ij}x_i + a_{0j} \geq 0 \qquad (j = 1, \ldots, m)$$

of a finite set of closed half-spaces, and let $E^k = \Lambda(\bar{c})$. If $\bar{c}$ is vacuous, we will denote $\Lambda(\bar{c}) = \emptyset$ by E^{-1}. If $\bar{c}$ is a single point, $k = 0$.

(B) If $k > 0$, let (y) be a coordinate system in E^n such that E^k is the $(y_1, \ldots, y_k)$-plane. The transformation from (x) to (y) carries (4.34) into a system

$$(4.35) \qquad \bar{c}^k = \bar{c} : \begin{cases} \sum_{i=1}^{k} b_{ij}y_i + b_{0j} \geq 0 & (j = 1, \ldots, m') \\ y_h = 0 & (h = k+1, \ldots, n) \end{cases}$$

such that

$$(4.36) \qquad c^k : \begin{cases} \sum_{i=1}^{k} b_{ij}y_i + b_{0j} > 0 & (j = 1, \ldots, m') \\ y_h = 0 & (h = k+1, \ldots, n) \end{cases}$$

is non-vacuous. If c^k is a bounded set, it is a **convex open polyhedral** k-**cell**, and $\bar{c}^k$ is a convex closed polyhedral k-cell, to be referred to, for brevity, as merely a **cell** c^k or $\bar{c}^k$, respectively.

(C) The **boundary** of c^k is $\bar{c}^k - c^k$. It falls naturally into convex j-cells $(j < k)$, called **faces** of c^k, defined by replacing some of the signs $>$ in the defining relations of c^k by $=$. If this be done for all possible subsets of the defining relations, then all the faces are obtained, including the vacuous c^{-1}, some of them possibly in several different ways. Thus c^k is reckoned as one of its own faces. See Exercise 49 for the simplicial case.

While the replacement of $>$ by $=$ leads to a system formally different from (4.34), note that $\lambda = 0$ is equivalent to the pair of relations $\lambda \geq 0$ and $\lambda \leq 0$.

A **finite polyhedral** m-**complex** C^m in E^n means a finite set $\{c\}$ of convex polyhedral j-cells $(j \leq m)$, including at least one m-cell, where (1) every face of a member of $\{c\}$ is a member of $\{c\}$ and (2) any two members of $\{c\}$ intersect in a common face, which of course may be vacuous.

If each cell of C^m is a simplex, C^m is a simplicial complex.

(D) Let C^m and C_1^m be two finite polyhedral m-complexes which coincide as point sets, $|C^m| = |C_1^m|$. Then C_1^m is a **subdivision of** C^m if and only if each cell of C_1^m is on a cell of C^m. A subdivision each of whose cells is a simplex is called a **simplicial subdivision**.

THEOREM 8. **A finite polyhedral m-complex C^m admits a simplicial subdivision.**

Proof. We prove Theorem 8 by giving a specific subdivision which will be useful in Chapter 6.

The k-**skeleton** of C^m means the polyhedral subcomplex C^k consisting of the cells of C^m of dimensions $\le k$.

Hypothesis. For some positive $k < m$, C^k has a simplicial subdivision C_1^k, which contains as a subcomplex all the simplicial cells of C^k (compare Exercise 49).

For $k = 1$, this hypothesis is fulfilled, and $C_1^1 = C^1$, since all polyhedral 1-complexes are simplicial.

If all cells of C^{k+1} are simplicial, let $C_1^{k+1} = C^{k+1}$. If not, let c^{k+1} be an arbitrary non-simplicial cell of C^{k+1}. The boundary $\bar{c}^{k+1} - c^{k+1}$ is covered by a subcomplex B_1^k of C_1^k. Let p be the barycenter* of c^{k+1}, and let $\{pB_1^k\}$ be the set of all the simplexes ps^j for $s^j \in B_1^k$.

(E) The set of all the faces of the simplexes $\{pB_1^k\}$ is a simplicial subdivision of $\bar{c}_1^{k+1}$. If each non-simplicial cell of C^{k+1} is thus subdivided, a simplicial subdivision C_1^{k+1} of C^{k+1} is obtained, which satisfies the hypothesis with $k + 1$ in place of k.

(F) The above process, repeated for $k = 1, \ldots, m - 1$, leads to a simplicial subdivision C_1^m of C^m, which we will call its **minimal central subdivision,** it being **minimal** in the sense that only the non-simplicial cells are subdivided in passing from C^m to C_1^m.

(G) Two complexes are **combinatorially equivalent** if they can be subdivided into isomorphic complexes.

THEOREM 9. **A topological polyhedron Π is a compact space if and only if it admits a finite triangulation. If it admits a finite triangulation, it does not admit an infinite triangulation.**

Proof. Let $\mathfrak{K} = \{\sigma\}$ be a triangulation of Π. The **star** Σ_i of a vertex σ_i^0 is the union of all the (topological) simplexes of $\mathfrak{K}$ incident with σ_i^0. The set $\{\Sigma\} = (\Sigma_1, \Sigma_2, \ldots)$ of all such stars is an open covering of Π. If $\mathfrak{K}$ is infinite, $\{\Sigma\}$ is an infinite covering admitting no finite subcovering, so that Π is not compact.

Now suppose $\mathfrak{K}$ finite. Then Π is homeomorphic to $P = |K|$ where K is a linear simplicial realization of $\mathfrak{K}$ in some euclidean space E. As a closed bounded subset of E, P is compact (Chapter 3, Theorem 14); hence (Chapter 3, Theorem 10) so is Π. The last conclusion of Theorem 9 now becomes obvious.

* That is, the point $x_j = (1/h) \sum_{i=1}^{h} a_{ij}$ $(j = 1, \ldots, n)$, where $q_i : (a_{i1}, \ldots, a_{in})$ $(i = 1, \ldots, h)$ are the vertices of c^{k+1}.

EXERCISES

48. Draw diagrams illustrating the minimal central subdivision (a) where $m = 2$ and C^2 consists of the faces of a square 2-cell $c^2 = p_1p_2p_3p_4$ and a 2-simplex $s^2 = p_0p_1p_2$, (b) where $m = 3$ and C^3 is the set of all faces of a cube.

49. Show that (a) a cell c^n in E^n is an n-simplex if it is definable by $n + 1$ inequalities $\sum_{i=1}^{n} a_{ij}x_i + a_{0j} > 0$, and (b) that the faces of c^n, as defined in (C) above, are the same as its faces in terms of the definition in Art. 4–4(C).

50. Prove Statement (E).

51. Let Π be the unit segment $0 \leq x \leq 1$ and let it be subdivided using the points $x = 0$ and $1/n$ ($n = 1, 2, \ldots$) as 0-simplexes and the intervals $1/(n + 1) < x < 1/n$ ($n = 1, 2, \ldots$) as 1-simplexes. This yields an infinite subdivision of the compact space Π. Why does it not contradict Theorem 9?

5

Homology and Cohomology Groups

Algebraic topology, to which we now turn, has the homology theory of complexes as its most important and fundamental part.

5–1. Chains, Cycles, and Bounding Cycles

Throughout this chapter, attention is confined to finite simplicial complexes, which may be linear, topological, or abstract. In statements applicable to all of these three types, we will use the terms **simplex** and **complex** without modifier.

The algebraic part of combinatorial topology employs **oriented** simplexes and complexes. The distinction between a k-simplex and an oriented k-simplex generalizes that between a segment p_0p_1 and a directed segment $\overrightarrow{p_0p_1} = -\overrightarrow{p_1p_0}$. Indeed, we **orient** a 1-simplex $s^1 = p_0p_1$ by associating $+1$ with one of the permutations of p_0p_1 and -1 with the other; for example:

(5.1)
$$(+1)s^1 = +s^1 = +p_0p_1,$$
$$(-1)s^1 = -s^1 = -p_0p_1 = +p_1p_0.$$

We refer to p_0 and p_1 as the **initial** and **terminal** points respectively of $+p_0p_1$ and represent $+s^1$ by the vector $\overrightarrow{p_0p_1}$ (Fig. 5–1b).

(A) The arrangements of the $k + 1$ vertices of a k-simplex $s^k = p_0p_1 \ldots p_k$ (Art. 3–2(B)) can be separated into the even permutations and the odd permutations of the arrangement $(p_0, p_1, \ldots, p_k)$. The association of s^k with either of these two classes of permutations is an **oriented k-simplex** and may be denoted by s^k, in which case the association of s^k with the other class is denoted by $-s^k$.

In the case $k = 2$, for example, we use the notation

(5.2) $+s^2 = p_0p_1p_2 = p_1p_2p_0 = p_2p_0p_1,$

and

(5.3) $-s^2 = p_1p_0p_2 = p_0p_2p_1 = p_2p_1p_0 = -p_0p_1p_2,$ etc.

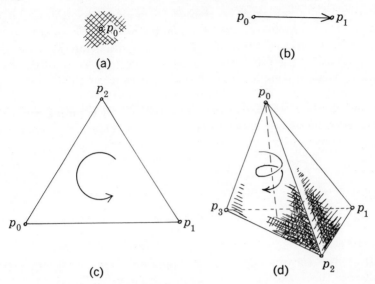

Fig. 5–1. Oriented j-simplexes $(j = 0, 1, 2, 3)$. (a) $+ s^0 = + p_0$; (b) $+s^1 = p_0p_1$; (c) $+s^2 = p_0p_1p_2 = p_1p_2p_0 = p_2p_0p_1$; (d) $+s^3 = p_0p_1p_2p_3 = p_0p_2p_3p_1$, etc.

Note that the even permutations assign one sense of description to the boundary of s^2, and the odd ones assign to it the opposite sense (Fig. 5–1c). Thus, intuitively, one may think of a 2-simplex as being oriented either clockwise or counterclockwise.

In three dimensions also, a fairly simple intuitive interpretation of orientation is possible. Suppose the "oriented 3-simplex"

$$(5.4) \qquad\qquad +s^3 = +p_0p_1p_2p_3$$

is such that a right-handed screw with head at p_0 would be driven into the face $p_1p_2p_3$ by a rotation in the sense of the cyclic permutation $p_1p_2p_3$ (Fig. 5–1d). It is easy to verify that if $p_{i_0}p_{i_1}p_{i_2}p_{i_3}$ is an even permutation of $p_0p_1p_2p_3$, then a right-handed screw with head at p_{i_0} would be driven into the opposite face by a rotation in the sense of $p_{i_1}p_{i_2}p_{i_3}$. For an odd permutation, representing $-s^3$, a left-handed screw would have this property. Thus oriented 3-simplexes can be interpreted as either "right-handed" or "left-handed." Otherwise expressed, a 3-simplex $+s^3$ with a right-handed [left-handed] orientation has the property that if $p_{i_0}p_{i_1}p_{i_2}p_{i_3} = +s^3$ then the 2-simplex $+s^2 = p_{i_1}p_{i_2}p_{i_3}$ appears to be oriented clockwise [counterclockwise] when viewed from p_{i_0}.

Since there is a unique permutation of a single point, we **orient** a 0-simplex $s^0 = p$ by writing either $+s^0 = +p$ and $-s^0 = -p$ or $+s^0 = -p$ and $-s^0 = +p$. We generally let $+s^0 = +p$.

A simplicial complex K is **oriented** when an orientation is assigned to each of its simplexes. Since each k-simplex $s^k \in K$ admits two different orientations, there are 2^α ways of orienting K where $\alpha = \Sigma_{i=0}^m \alpha_i$, and α_i is the number of its i-simplexes. In spite of the use of the term **oriented complex**, one should bear in mind that the 2^α orientations of K are not different complexes but different orientations of the same complex. Orientations are a tool for discovering properties of complexes, much as a coordinate system in analytic geometry is a device to facilitate the analysis of geometric properties.

The positive simplexes of an oriented m-complex will conventionally be denoted as follows, with s^k instead of $+s^k$ when it is clear that oriented simplexes are meant:

$$(5.5) \qquad K = \{s\} = \bigcup_{k=0}^{m} \{s^k\}$$

where $\{s^k\} = (s_1^k, \ldots, s_{\alpha_k}^k)$ (the positive k-simplexes of K).

(*B*) In the terminology of the Appendix (Art. A–4), let $\{s^k\}$ be regarded as the initial basis for the integral module $[s^k] = [s_1^k, \ldots, s_{\alpha_k}^k]$, which will be called the (**integral**) k-**chain group** $\mathfrak{C}_k$. An element of $\mathfrak{C}_k$ is then a linear form

$$(5.6) \qquad C^k = \sum_{i=1}^{\alpha_k} a_i s_i^k \qquad (a_i \text{ an integer}),$$

and is called an (**integral**) k-**chain**. If $k = -1$ or if $k > m$, $\mathfrak{C}_k$ reduces to a null set $\emptyset$. If $D^k = \Sigma_{i=1}^{\alpha_k} b_i s_i^k$, then $C^k + D^k = \Sigma_{i=1}^{\alpha_k} (a_i + b_i) s_i^k$.

We next define, for each k-chain C^k, a $(k-1)$-chain called the **boundary chain**, or simply the **boundary**, of C^k, and denoted by ∂C^k.

Consider an oriented k-simplex

$$(5.7) \qquad t^k = +q_0 q_1 \cdots q_k.$$

By omitting a vertex q_i from the symbol $q_0 q_1 \cdots q_k$ we obtain a symbol, which we denote by $q_0 \cdots \hat{q}_i \cdots q_k$, for the face of t^k opposite q_i. It will prove convenient to orient that face thus

$$(5.8) \qquad t_i^{k-1} = (-1)^i q_0 \cdots \hat{q}_i \cdots q_k.$$

In the case $k = 2$, for example,

$$(5.9) \qquad \begin{array}{ll} t^2 = q_0 q_1 q_2, & t_0^1 = \hat{q}_0 q_1 q_2 = q_1 q_2, \\ t_1^1 = q_0 \hat{q}_1 q_2 = -q_0 q_2, & t_2^1 = q_0 q_1 \hat{q}_2 = q_0 q_1, \end{array}$$

and the edges form a clockwise or counterclockwise circuit, corresponding to the orientation of t^2 (Fig. 5–2b).

(*C*) We define the **boundary** (**chain**) of t^k as the $(k-1)$-chain

$$(5.10) \qquad \partial t^k = \sum_{i=0}^{k} t_i^{k-1},$$

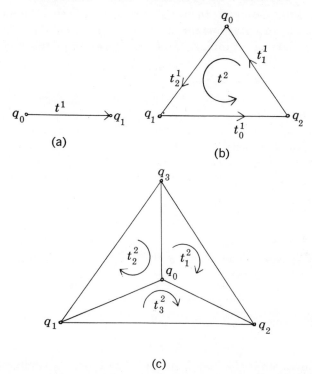

Fig. 5-2. Oriented simplexes t^k and boundary chains ∂t^k. (a) $\partial t^1 = q_1 - q_0$; (b) $\partial t^2 = t_0^1 + t_1^1 + t_2^1$; (c) $\partial t^3 = \Sigma_{i=0}^{3} t_i^2$ (looking down on vertex q_0).

a definition justified by the following result. See Fig. 5-2 for the first few dimensions.

LEMMA 1. **The chain ∂t^k depends only on the orientation of t^k, not on the particular permutation in (5.7).**

Proof of Lemma. A transposition of q_j and q_{j+1} has the following effects: (1) It changes the sign of t^k. (2) It changes the sign of t_i^{k-1} $(i \neq j, j+1)$. (3) It replaces $(t_j^{k-1}, t_{j+1}^{k-1})$ by $(-t_{j+1}^{k-1}, -t_j^{k-1})$ respectively (Exercise 1). It thus changes the sign of ∂t^k. Since an even permutation is the product of an even number of transpositions, the lemma follows. As a corollary,

$$(5.11) \qquad\qquad \partial(-t^k) = -\partial t^k.$$

(*D*) Let t^{k-1} be an oriented face of an oriented k-simplex t^k. Then t^{k-1} has the orientation **induced** by t^k, and t^k has the orientation **induced** by t^{k-1} if t^{k-1} appears with the coefficient $+1$ in ∂t^k. The $(k-1)$-faces of t^k are **coherently oriented** if each has the orientation induced by t^k or else each has the opposite orientation, induced by $-t^k$.

An orientation assigned to a $(k-1)$-face of t^k uniquely determines coherent orientations for all the $(k-1)$-faces of t^k (Exercise 2).

The **boundary** of an integral k-chain expressed in the form (5.6) is

$$(5.12) \qquad \partial C^k = \partial \sum_{i=1}^{\alpha_k} a_i s_i^k = \sum_{i=1}^{\alpha_k} a_i\, \partial s_i^k = \sum_{j=1}^{\alpha_{k-1}} b_j s_j^{k-1},$$

where the coefficient b_j of s_j^{k-1} is $\Sigma_{i=1}^{\alpha_k} a_i \varepsilon_{ij}$ with $\varepsilon_{ij} = 0,\ +1,$ or -1 according as s_j^{k-1} and s_i^k are not incident, incident with induced orientations, or incident with opposite orientations.

(E) *Since, as a result of* (5.12), $\partial(C^k + D^k) = \partial C^k + \partial D^k$, *the boundary operator has the important interpretation as a homomorphism* (Art. A–2)

$$(5.13) \qquad \partial : \mathfrak{C}_k \to \mathfrak{C}_{k-1}$$

of the k-chain group into the $(k-1)$-chain group. The kernel (Art. A–2(C)) of ∂ consists of those k-chains whose boundaries are null. They are called k-**cycles**:

$$(5.14) \qquad \partial C^k = \emptyset \Leftrightarrow C^k \text{ is a } k\text{-cycle,}$$

and the subgroup

$$(5.15) \qquad \mathfrak{Z}_k \subset \mathfrak{C}_k$$

consisting of them is the k-**cycle group**. For $k = 0$, we define ∂C^k as $\emptyset$.

(F) To motivate the above definitions geometrically, consider first a path $\pi = q_0 q_1 \ldots q_\nu$ on a complex K, where $t_i^1 = q_{i-1} q_i\, (i = 1, \ldots, \nu)$ is an edge of K, with the indicated orientation. By the **chain** of π we mean the 1-chain $C(\pi) = \Sigma_{i=1}^\nu t_i^1$. Since $\partial t_i^1 = q_i - q_{i-1}$, it follows that

$$(5.16) \qquad \partial C(\pi) = \partial \sum_{i=1}^\nu q_{i-1} q_i = \sum_{i=1}^\nu (q_i - q_{i-1}) = q_\nu - q_0,$$

which is the terminal point of the path minus the initial point. If the path is closed, $q_\nu = q_0$, then $\partial C(\pi) = \emptyset$, so that the chain of a closed path is a cycle. (See Exercise 3.)

THEOREM 1. **A bounding chain ∂C^{k+1} is a k-cycle. That is,**

$$(5.17) \qquad \partial\partial C^{k+1} = \emptyset, \text{ the null } (k-1)\text{-cycle.}$$

Proof. Since ∂ is a linear* operator, it is sufficient to establish (5.17) for $C^{k+1} = s^{k+1}$. In particular, it suffices to show that an arbitrary face s^{k-1} of s^{k+1} does not appear in $\partial\partial s^{k+1}$. Let s^{k+1} be written in the form $s^{k+1} = p_0 p_1 s^{k-1}$. The only terms in ∂s^{k+1} giving rise to $\pm s^{k-1}$ in $\partial\partial s^{k+1}$ are $+p_1 s^{k-1}$ and $-p_0 s^{k-1}$, which lead to $+s^{k-1} - s^{k-1} = \emptyset$.

---

* This means that $\partial(C^k + D^k) = \partial C^k + \partial D^k$.

LEMMA 2.   **The bounding k-cycles constitute a subgroup $\mathfrak{F}_k$ of the cycle group $\mathfrak{Z}_k$.**

Proof of Lemma. The lemma follows without difficulty from the fact that $C_i^k = \partial C_i^{k+1}$ $(i = 1, 2)$ implies $C_1^k \pm C_2^k = \partial(C_1^{k+1} \pm C_2^{k+1})$, so that the sum and the difference of two bounding cycles is a bounding cycle.

(G) The work of this article generalizes easily from integral chains to chains of the form

$$(5.18) \qquad C^k = \sum_{i=1}^{\alpha_k} g_i s_i^k$$

where $g_i \in \mathfrak{G}$, an arbitrary abelian group. This leads to the concepts of (1) the k-chain group $\mathfrak{C}_k(\mathfrak{G})$, (2) the k-cycle group $\mathfrak{Z}_k(\mathfrak{G})$, and (3) the bounding k-cycle group $\mathfrak{F}_k(\mathfrak{G})$. The group $\mathfrak{C}_k(\mathfrak{G})$ is isomorphic to the direct product (Art. A–3(A)) $\mathfrak{G} \times \cdots \times \mathfrak{G}$ (α_k factors). In this book, we restrict ourselves to integral chains, for which $\mathfrak{G} = \mathbf{Z}$, the additive group of the integers and, where explicitly stated, to chains mod 2, where $\mathfrak{G} = \mathbf{Z}_2$ (Art. A–1(B)).

EXERCISES

1. Verify Statements (1) to (3) in the proof of Lemma 1 with the aid of the substitutions $p_i = q_i$ $(i \neq j, j + 1)$, $p_j = q_{j+1}$, $p_{j+1} = q_j$, $s^k = p_0 \cdots p_k$.

2. Prove the last sentence of (D).

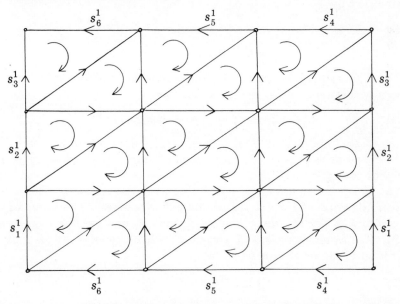

Fig. 5–3. The torus as an oriented complex.

3. Show that a 1-cycle can be expressed as a sum of chains of simple closed paths, which may intersect in sets of common vertices.

4. In the triangulation of the torus shown in Fig. 5–3, let all 2-simplexes be oriented clockwise and show that Σs_i^2 is a 2-cycle. Then reverse the orientation of just one of the 2-simplexes and find $\partial \Sigma s_i^2$.

5. Write out $\partial\partial t^3$ and $\partial\partial t^4$, where $t^3 = q_0 q_1 q_2 q_3$ and $t^4 = q_0 q_1 q_2 q_3 q_4$. Show that they reduce to $\emptyset$.

6. Let K^2 consist of the oriented faces of a 2-simplex $s^2 = p_0 p_1 p_2$ together with three oriented 1-simplexes $p_2 p_3$, $p_3 p_4$, $p_4 p_2$ and their vertices. Discuss the homomorphisms ∂ of (5.13) for $k = 0, 1, 2$.

7. Reassign notation and orientations to some of the simplexes s_i^1 so as to convert Fig. 5–3 into a triangulation of the Klein bottle (Chapter 2, Exercise 18). Show that Σs_i^2 (Exercise 4 above) is not a cycle.

8. Show that Σs_i^2 in the preceding exercise is a cycle mod 2. Find a non-bounding 1-cycle.

5–2.   Homology Groups of Finite Simplicial Complexes

The kth **homology group** $\mathfrak{H}_k = \mathfrak{H}_k(K)$ of a finite oriented complex is the factor group (Art. A–2(B))

(5.19) $$\mathfrak{H}_k = \mathfrak{Z}_k / \mathfrak{F}_k$$

where $\mathfrak{Z}_k$ and $\mathfrak{F}_k$ are, respectively, the k-cycle group and the bounding k-cycle group.

The fact that a k-chain C^k is the boundary of some chain will be symbolized by

(5.20) $$C^k \sim \emptyset \Leftrightarrow \exists\, C^{k+1} \text{ such that } C^k = \partial C^{k+1}$$

$$\Leftrightarrow C^k \in \mathfrak{F}_k.$$

(A) The symbol $\sim$ (read **is homologous to**) will be used, more generally, between two k-chains, as follows:

(5.21) $$C_2^k \sim C_1^k \Leftrightarrow C_2^k - C_1^k \sim \emptyset \Rightarrow \partial C_2^k = \partial C_1^k.$$

While (5.20) implies that C^k is a cycle, (5.21) does not imply that C_1^k and C_2^k are cycles. As indicated, it does imply that $C_2^k - C_1^k$ is a cycle, or that $\partial C_2^k = \partial C_1^k$.

(B) It is easy to see that $\sim$ is an equivalence relation. The corresponding equivalence classes are **homology classes**. The homology classes of k-cycles are the cosets of $\mathfrak{Z}_k$ mod $\mathfrak{F}_k$ and are the elements of $\mathfrak{H}_k$. The homology class of a cycle Z will be denoted by $[Z]$. By definition of factor groups (Art. A–2),

(5.22) $$[Z_1^k] + [Z_2^k] = [Z_1^k + Z_2^k].$$

(C) Since $\mathfrak{H}_k$ is a finitely generated (abelian) additive group (see

Art. A–3), it is uniquely expressible as a direct product (or direct sum)

$$(5.23) \qquad \mathfrak{H}_k = \mathfrak{B}_k \times \mathfrak{T}_k \qquad (\text{or } \mathfrak{B}_k + \mathfrak{T}_k)$$

where (1) $\mathfrak{B}_k$ is a free abelian group with β_k generators for some $\beta_k \geq 0$ and (2) $\mathfrak{T}_k$ is the direct product of a set, possibly vacuous, of finite cyclic groups whose orders $\tau_1^k, \ldots, \tau_{\rho_k}^k$ have the property that $\tau_{\rho_k}^k > 1$ and τ_{i+1}^k divides τ_i^k $(i = 1, \ldots, \rho_k - 1)$.

(D) The number β_k of generators of $\mathfrak{B}_k$ is the kth **Betti number** of K, and $\mathfrak{B}_k$ is the kth **Betti group** of K. The orders τ_i^k $(i = 1, \ldots, \rho_k)$ of the cyclic subgroups of $\mathfrak{T}_k$ are the kth **torsion coefficients** of K and $\mathfrak{T}_k$ is the kth **torsion group** of K.

(E) A set $(C_1^k, \ldots, C_r^k)$ of k-cycles of a complex K are (1) **linearly independent** if and only if

$$(5.24) \qquad \sum_{i=1}^{r} a_i C_i^k = \emptyset \Rightarrow a_i = 0 \qquad (i = 1, \ldots, r),$$

that is, no non-trivial linear combination of them equals the null k-chain; (2) **homology-independent** (an abbreviation for **linearly independent with respect to homology**) if and only if

$$(5.25) \qquad \sum_{i=1}^{r} a_i C_i^k \sim \emptyset \Rightarrow a_i = 0 \qquad (i = 1, \ldots, r),$$

that is, no non-trivial linear combination of them is a bounding k-cycle.

THEOREM 2. **The kth Betti number β_k of K equals the number of k-cycles in a maximal set of homology-independent k-cycles of K.**

Proof. Let $\mathfrak{H}_k$ be expressed as a direct sum of $\mathfrak{T}_k$ and some infinite cyclic groups Z_i $(i = 1, \ldots, \beta_k)$. If $[C^k]$ is a homology class in $\mathfrak{T}_k$, then, since all elements of $\mathfrak{T}_k$ are of finite order, some multiple mC^k $(m > 0)$ of C^k bounds. Hence C^k is not in any homology-independent set. If $[G_i]$ generates Z_i $(i = 1, \ldots, \beta_k)$ then no two cycles of $[mG_i]$ and $[nG_i]$, for integers m and n, are homology-independent, since their respective multiples by n and m are homologous.

To complete the proof, note that the cycles G_i $(i = 1, \ldots, \beta_k)$ are homology-independent.

COROLLARY 1. **The mth Betti number of an m-complex K equals the number of m-cycles in a maximal set of linearly independent m-cycles of K.**

The only $(m + 1)$-chain of K is the null chain. Therefore the only bounding m-cycle is the null cycle. Hence homology independence and linear independence mean the same thing for m-cycles.

COROLLARY 2. **An m-complex has no m^{th} torsion coefficients.**

THEOREM 3. **The kth homology group of a complex is the same as that of its $(k + 1)$-skeleton.**

Proof. The group $\mathfrak{H}_k$ is determined by the incidence relations between the k-simplexes and the $(k + 1)$-simplexes, which are the same on the $(k + 1)$-skeleton as on the entire complex.

THEOREM 4. **The kth homology group of a complex K is the direct product (or sum) of the kth homology groups of the components $(K_1, \ldots, K_\beta)$ of K. (See Art. 4–6(E).)**

Proof. If C is a chain on K, then $C = C_1 + \cdots + C_\beta$, where C_j, to be called a **component** of C, is the part of C into which simplexes of K_j enter $(j = 1, \ldots, \beta)$. It is easy to verify that C is a cycle if and only if each C_j is a cycle.

Consider a $(k + 1)$-chain $C^{k+1} = \Sigma_{j=1}^{\beta} C_j^{k+1}$. Its boundary is

$$(5.26) \qquad C^k = \partial C^{k+1} = \sum_{j=1}^{\beta} \partial C_j^{k+1} = \sum_{j=1}^{\beta} C_j^k$$

where $C_j^k = \partial C_j^{k+1}$. Thus the components of a bounding cycle C^k on K are bounding cycles on the components of K. Conversely, a linear combination of bounding cycles on the components of K is a bounding cycle on K. Thus the aggregate of a class of sets of generators, one set for the kth homology class of each of the components of K, is a set of generators of $\mathfrak{H}_k(K)$, and each homology relation among cycles of K is a consequence of homology relations among cycles of $K_1, \ldots, K_\beta$. Theorem 4 follows with the aid of Art. A–3.

EXERCISES

9. Let K^2 consist of the oriented boundary faces of an octahedron. Show that $p_1 p_2 + p_2 p_3 \sim p_1 p_4 + p_4 p_3$ where the $p_i p_j$ in the relation are 1-simplexes of K^2.

10. Find the Betti numbers β_1 and β_0 of the 1-skeleton of the complex consisting of the faces of a 3-simplex.

5–3. Some Lower-dimensional Cases

THEOREM 5. **The 0th Betti number of a complex K equals the number of its components.**

Proof. The **Kronecker index** of a 0-chain $C^0 = \Sigma_{i=1}^{\alpha_0} a_i s_i^0$ means the sum $\Sigma_{i=1}^{\alpha_0} a_i$ of its coefficients. We employ two lemmas.

LEMMA 3. **The Kronecker index of a bounding 0-chain C^0 is zero.**

Proof of Lemma. Let $C^1 = \Sigma_{i=1}^{\alpha_1} b_i s_i^1$ be a 1-chain such that $C^0 = \partial C^1$. If s_j^0 is the initial vertex of s_i^1 and s_k^0 the terminal vertex, then the term $\partial(b_i s_i^1) = b_i s_k^0 - b_i s_j^0$ contributes $b_i - b_i = 0$ to the Kronecker index. This being a typical contribution, the Kronecker index is zero.

COROLLARY. If $(C_1^0, \ldots, C_\beta^0)$ are the components of a bounding 0-chain (proof of Theorem 4), then the Kronecker index of C_j^0 is zero $(j = 1, \ldots, \beta)$.

LEMMA 4. If K is connected, $\mathfrak{H}_0(K)$ is the free cyclic group.

Proof of Lemma. Since K is connected, there exists a path π_i from s_1^0 to s_i^0 $(i = 1, \ldots, \alpha_0)$. But the chain C_i^1 of π_i then has the boundary $\partial C_i^1 = s_i^0 - s_1^0$ (see Art. 5–1(F)). Hence $s_i^0 \sim s_1^0$. It follows that

$$(5.27) \qquad \sum_{i=1}^{\alpha_0} a_i s_i^0 \sim \sum_{i=1}^{\alpha_0} a_i s_1^0 = k s_1^0$$

where k is the Kronecker index of C^0. As a consequence of Lemma 3, $k s_1^0 \sim k' s_1^0$ if and only if $k = k'$. Thus the chain s_1^0 is a complete set of homology-independent 0-chains, and the lemma follows from Art. 5–2(C), (D) and Theorem 2.

COROLLARY. **Two 0-chains on a connected complex are homologous if and only if their Kronecker indices are equal.**

Theorem 5 now follows from Lemma 4 and Theorem 4.

(A) Two 0-chains C^0 and D^0 on a complex are homologous if and only if the Kronecker indices of their respective components C_j^0 and D_j^0 $(j = 1, \ldots, \beta)$ are equal (Exercise 11).

(B) There exist no 0th coefficients of torsion for any complex (Exercise 12).

THEOREM 6. **The first Betti number β_1 of a connected linear graph K^1 equals the cyclomatic number (Art. 1–3) $\beta_1 = \alpha_1 - \alpha_0 + 1$. For a linear graph with β_0 components,**

$$(5.28) \qquad \beta_1 = \alpha_1 - \alpha_0 + \beta_0.$$

Proof. By Corollary 1 to Theorem 2, linear and homology dependence are equivalent for 1-cycles on K^1. Therefore, by Art. 1–3, $\beta_1 = \mu = \alpha_1 - \alpha_0 + 1$, in the connected case. Equation (5.28) follows from Theorem 4 in the case where K^1 has β_0 components.

EXERCISES

11. Prove (A).
12. Prove (B).

5–4. Homology Groups of a Surface

Let K^2 be a triangulation of the closure of a convex plane region R bounded by a polygon π. Later, we will identify some of the edges of π in pairs, so as to obtain a polygonal representation of a surface M, and the triangulation of M so obtained will be called K^*.

LEMMA 5. **The 2-simplexes of K^2 can be so numbered $\{s^2\} = (s_1^2, \ldots, s_{\alpha_2}^2)$ that the point set**

$$(5.29) \qquad\qquad \bar{R}_j = \bigcup_{i=1}^{j} \bar{s}_i^2$$

is, for each $j \in (1, \ldots, \alpha_2)$, the closure of a region R_j bounded by a simple closed polygon π_j.

Proof of Lemma. Geometrically, the lemma means that the complex K^2 can be built up, one closed 2-simplex at a time, so that the growing subcomplex at each stage covers the interior and boundary of a simple closed polygon. Let s_1^2 be arbitrarily chosen from $\{s^2\}$. Suppose, for some positive integer $k < \alpha_2$, that the 2-simplexes $s_1^2, \ldots, s_k^2$ have been so defined that the lemma holds for $j = 1, \ldots, k$. To complete the proof, we need only select as $\bar{s}_{k+1}^2$ a 2-simplex of K^2 whose intersection with $\bar{R}_k$ is either a single 1-simplex or the union of two 1-simplexes, but not a 1-simplex and the opposite vertex (Exercise 14).

Let K_j^2 denote the subcomplex of K^2 consisting of $(s_1^2, \ldots, s_j^2)$ and their boundary simplexes. A 1-simplex of K_j^2 will be called a **boundary** or an **inner** 1-simplex thereof, according as it is on π_j or on R_j; that is, according as it is incident with one or two 2-simplexes of K_j^2. The subcomplex of K_j^2 on π_j will be called the **boundary complex B_j of K_j^2.**

Now let the 2-simplexes $\{s^2\}$ all be oriented clockwise, and let each boundary 1-simplex of K_j^2 have the orientation induced by the 2-simplex of K_j^2 incident with it. This orients K^2, since each of its 1-simplexes is a boundary simplex of some K_j^2.

(A) As a direct consequence of Lemma 5 and the orientation just defined, the boundary of the chain $C_j^2 = \Sigma_{i=1}^{j} s_i^2$ is the sum of the boundary 1-simplexes of K_j^2.

LEMMA 6. **Let C^1 be a 1-chain on K^2 whose boundary ∂C^1 is on the boundary complex B of K^2. Then C^1 is homologous (Art. 5–2(A)) to some 1-chain D^1 on B.**

Proof of Lemma. We will pass from C^1 to D^1 by adding to C^1 the boundaries of certain 2-chains. The addition to C^1 of such null-homologous 1-chains keeps us, by definition, within the homology class of C^1. Our proof will be recurrent.

Hypothesis. For some positive integer $k < \alpha_2$, there exist integers $(a_1, \ldots, a_k)$ such that, for each $j \in (1, \ldots, k)$, no inner 1-simplex of K_j^2 appears in the chain

$$(5.30) \qquad\qquad C_j^1 = C^1 + \sum_{i=1}^{j} a_i \, \partial s_i^2.$$

The hypothesis is automatically fulfilled for $k = 1$, since there exist no inner 1-simplexes of K_1^2, which consists of the faces of s_1^2.

Figure 5–4 shows two possibilities for the relationship of s_{k+1}^2 and B_k. In either case, let a_{k+1} equal the multiplicity with which s^1 appears in C_k^1. Then, since s^1 has multiplicity -1 in ∂s_{k+1}^2, it does not

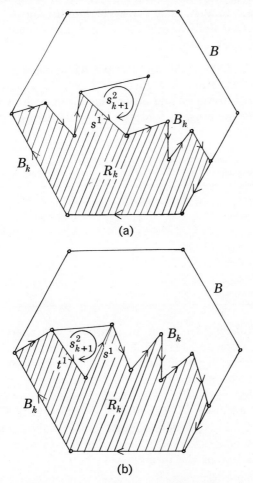

(a)

(b)

Fig. 5–4. The 2-simplex s_{k+1}^2 and the boundary complex B_k. (a) s_{k+1}^2 having just one edge s^1 on B_k; (b) s_{k+1}^2 having two edges on B_k.

appear in $C_{k+1}^1 = C_k^1 + a_{k+1} \partial s_{k+1}^2$. This takes care of the case shown in Fig. 5–4a. For the case in Fig. 5–4b, we show that t^1 cannot appear in C_{k+1}^1. For if t^1 appeared without s^1, then the initial vertex of s^1 would appear in ∂C_{k+1}^1, contradicting the fact that (Art. 5–2(A)) $\partial C_{k+1}^1 = \partial C^1$, which is on B. The recurrency leads to a chain $D^1 = C_{a_2}^1$ satisfying the lemma.

COROLLARY 1. **If C^1 is a cycle, then** (Exercise 15)

$$(5.31) \qquad D^1 = mB \qquad \text{where} \qquad B = \partial \sum_{i=1}^{\alpha_2} s_i^2.$$

COROLLARY 2. **The first homology group of K^2 consists of the null element alone; that is, every 1-cycle bounds on K^2 or, otherwise expressed, the first Betti number of K^2 is 0 and K^2 has no first torsion coefficients** (Exercise 16).

THEOREM 7. **Let K^* be an oriented triangulation of the standard polygonal representation of a surface M (Art. 2–4, Lemma 3). Then K^* has the Betti numbers and torsion coefficients shown in the following table, corresponding to the possible structures of M listed in the left column:**

A Sphere with	β_0	β_1	β_2	Torsion Coefficients
$h \geq 0$ handles	1	$2h$	1	None
$q > 0$ crosscaps	1	$q - 1$	0	A first torsion coefficient $\tau^1 = 2$
$h \geq 0$ handles, $r > 0$ contours	1	$2h + r - 1$	0	None
$q > 0$ crosscaps, $r > 0$ contours	1	$q + r - 1$	0	None

Proof. Corollary 2 to Theorem 2 implies that there are no second torsion coefficients and Art. 5–3(B) does the same for 0th torsion coefficients. Since M is connected, $\beta_0 = 1$ by Theorem 5.

The rest of the above table will be established with the aid of Lemma 6, which applies to the present case, with suitable modifications to take account of identifications of certain 1-cells of B in pairs. Let $A_1, \ldots, A_\nu$ denote these 1-cells, cyclically numbered and oriented in the clockwise sense. An identification of two 1-cells can be expressed in one of the forms

$$(5.32) \qquad \text{(a) } A_i = A_j, \qquad \text{(b) } A_i = -A_j,$$

which will be taken to imply the identification of corresponding points under the linear homeomorphism between A_i and A_j or $-A_j$. Let K^* be the complex obtained from K^2 of Lemma 6 as a result of these identifications. Let A_i^* be the 1-cell of K^* corresponding to the 1-cell A_i of K^2, taken with the orientation of A_i. Then

$$(5.33) \text{ (a) } A_i = A_j \Rightarrow A_i^* = A_j^*, \qquad \text{(b) } A_i = -A_j \Rightarrow A_i^* = -A_j^*.$$

Now (compare Lemma 6, Corollary 1)

$$(5.34) \qquad \partial \sum_{i=1}^{\alpha_2} s_i^2 = B = \sum_{i=1}^{\nu} A_i^*,$$

where $\Sigma_{i=1}^{\nu} A_i^*$ can be reduced by substitutions suggested by (5.33).

In the case of the sphere with h handles, represented by the symbol $A_1 B_1 A_1^{-1} B_1^{-1} \ldots A_h B_h A_h^{-1} B_h^{-1}$, (5.34) reduces to

$$(5.35)$$
$$\partial \sum_{i=1}^{\alpha_2} s_i^2 = A_1^* + B_1^* - A_1^* - B_1^* + \cdots + A_h^* + B_h^* - A_h^* - B_h^* = \emptyset.$$

Similarly, for the other standardized forms (Art. 2–4),

$$\text{(a)} \quad \partial \sum_{i=1}^{\alpha_2} s_i^2 = \sum_{i=1}^{q} 2C_i^* = 2 \sum_{i=1}^{q} C_i^* \quad (q > 0 \text{ crosscaps}),$$

$$(5.36)\ \text{(b)} \quad \partial \sum_{i=1}^{\alpha_2} s_i^2 = \sum_{i=1}^{r} D_i^* \qquad\qquad (h \geq 0 \text{ handles}, r > 0 \text{ contours}),$$

$$\text{(c)} \quad \partial \sum_{i=1}^{\alpha_2} s_i^2 = 2 \sum_{i=1}^{q} C_i^* + \sum_{i=1}^{r} D_i^* \quad (q > 0 \text{ crosscaps}, r > 0 \text{ contours}).$$

Let B^* be the complex of those cells of K^* which were obtained from cells of B.

LEMMA 7. **Each 1-cycle on K^* is homologous to a 1-cycle on B^*, hence to a 1-cycle of the form**

$$\text{(a)} \quad \sum_{i=1}^{h} (a_i A_i^* + b_i B_i^*) + \sum_{i=1}^{r} d_i D_i^* \qquad (h \geq 0 \text{ handles}, r \geq 0 \text{ contours}), \text{ or}$$
$$(5.37)$$
$$\text{(b)} \quad \sum_{i=1}^{q} c_i C_i^* + \sum_{i=1}^{r} d_i D_i^* \qquad (q > 0 \text{ crosscaps}, r \geq 0 \text{ contours}).$$

Proof of Lemma. We first note that, since K^* was obtained from K^2 by identifications of certain 1-cells of B by pairs, the given 1-cycle C^1 might, *without* the said identifications, become a 1-chain with boundary on B. Nevertheless, it is easily seen from Lemma 6 that C^1 is homologous on K^* to some cycle C on B^*. Since the only 1-cells of B^* in Case (a) are the A_i^*, B_i^*, and D_i^*, and the only ones in Case (b) are the C_i^* and D_i^*, it follows that the lemma is true.

LEMMA 8. **Each bounding 1-cycle on K^* is homologous to a multiple of**

$$\text{(a)} \quad B_0 = \sum_{i=1}^{r} D_i^* \qquad\qquad (h \geq 0 \text{ handles}, r \text{ contours}), \text{ or}$$
$$(5.38)$$
$$\text{(b)} \quad B_1 = 2 \sum_{i=1}^{q} C_i^* + \sum_{i=1}^{r} D_i^* \qquad (q > 0 \text{ crosscaps}, r \text{ contours}),$$

and each multiple of B_0 or B_1 bounds.

Proof of Lemma. By Lemma 7, each bounding 1-cycle on K^* is homologous to a bounding 1-cycle all of whose 1-cells are on B^*.

(B) If the boundary of $C^2 = \Sigma_{i=1}^{\alpha_2} e_i s_i^2$ is on B^*, then all the co-efficients e_i are equal (Exercise 18).

The lemma now follows with the aid of (5.36b, c).

COROLLARY 1. **Let B^* be the subcomplex of K^* on the boundary of the polygonal representation. In the case of a sphere with $h > 0$ handles and no contours, the only bounding 1-cycle on B^* is the null cycle, which is the boundary of $m \Sigma_{i=1}^{\alpha_2} s_i^2$ for each $m \in Z$.**

COROLLARY 2. **For a sphere with $q > 0$ crosscaps and no contours, the only bounding 1-cycles on B^* are $2m \Sigma_{i=1}^q C^* = \partial m \Sigma_{i=1}^{\alpha_2} s_i^2 \ (m \in Z)$.**

COROLLARY 3. **For a sphere with $h \geq 0$ handles and no contours, $\Sigma_{i=1}^{\alpha_2} s_i^2$ and all its multiples are the only 2-cycles. For the other surfaces, the only 2-cycle is the null cycle.**

From Corollary 3, the values of β_2 in Theorem 7 are deduced. By Corollary 1 and Lemma 7 the 1-cycles $(A_1^*, B_1^*, \ldots, A_h^*, B_h^*)$ are a maximal set of homology-independent 1-cycles in the case $h \geq 0$, $r = 0$, so that $\beta_1 = 2h$. In the case $h \geq 0, r > 0$, we see from (5.36b) and Lemmas 7 and 8 that there is a single homology relation, $\Sigma_{i=1}^r D_i^* \sim \emptyset$, among $(A_1^*, B_1^*, \ldots, A_h^*, B_h^*, D_1^*, \ldots, D_r^*)$ on which all other homology relations depend, so that $\beta_1 = 2h + r - 1$. In the case $q > 0, \ r = 0$, all homology relations among cycles of the form $\Sigma_{i=1}^q c_i C_i^*$ depend on $2 \Sigma_{i=1}^q C_i^* \sim \emptyset$. Hence $x \Sigma_{i=1}^q C_i^* + \Sigma_{i=1}^{q-1} c_i C_i^*$ yields one cycle from each homology class as $x = 0, 1$ and the c's range independently over the integers. Accordingly, the first homology group is the direct sum of a cyclic group of order 2 and $q - 1$ free cyclic groups, so that there is a torsion coefficient $\tau^1 = 2$, and the first Betti number is $\beta_1 = q - 1$. In the case $q > 0, r > 0$, there are only the relations $m(2 \Sigma_{i=1}^q C_i^* + \Sigma_{i=1}^r D_i^*) \sim \emptyset \ (m \in Z)$ among the cycles $(C_1^*, \ldots, C_q^*, D_1^*, \ldots, D_r^*)$, so that $\beta_1 = q + r - 1$.

EXERCISES

13. Let K^2 be a triangulation of the annulus $1 \leq x^2 + y^2 \leq 4$ into six 2-simplexes and their boundary faces. Show that each 1-cycle on K^2 is homologous to some 1-cycle on the circle $x^2 + y^2 = 1$.

14. Complete the proof of Lemma 5.

15. Prove Corollary 1 to Lemma 6. *Suggestion*: Show that if $D^1 = \Sigma_{i=1}^b a_i t_i^1$ where $(t_i^1, \ldots, t_b^1)$ are the boundary 1-simplexes of K^2, and if $\partial D^1 = \emptyset$, then all the coefficients a_i are equal.

16. Prove Corollary 2 to Lemma 6.

17. In the notation of (5.30) and (5.31), give a 2-chain of which C^1 is the boundary, for the case where C^1 is a cycle.

18. Prove (B) by showing that, under a contrary assumption, some inner 1-simplex of the polygonal representation appears on ∂C^2.

19. Figure 5–5 shows a disk with two holes in it, along with a particular triangulation. Show that the 1-cycles which are the sums of the 1-simplexes on

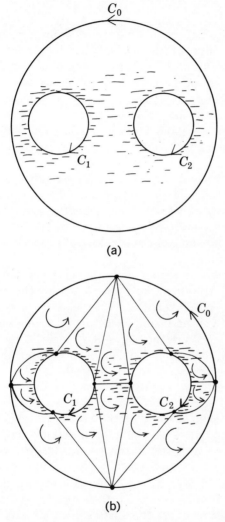

(a)

(b)

Fig. 5–5. A surface and a triangulation of it.

C_0, C_1, C_2 are in different homology classes, but that these 1-cycles are not homology-independent.

20. For the same triangulation, show that the homology classes represented by C_1 and C_2 generate $\mathfrak{H}_1$; that is, that any other homology class equals a linear combination of them.

5–5. Surface Topology

THEOREM 8. **Two closed surfaces are homeomorphic if and only if they have the same Betti numbers.**

Outline of Proof. In the first place, by Theorem 7, orientable closed surfaces ($r = 0$) are distinguished from non-orientable closed surfaces by the value of the second Betti number, $\beta_2 = 1$ and 0, respectively. The orientability class being thus determined, one can deduce the number of handles h or of crosscaps q in a standard representation from $\beta_1 = 2h$ or $q - 1$, respectively.

Theorem 8 is still not proved, however, for the Betti numbers were deduced from a standard representation, and we have not shown that the same numbers would result from an arbitrary polygonal representation.

(A) Theorem 8 will follow in all its generality from the work in Chapter 6, as will the following statement. *Two surfaces with contours are homeomorphic if and only if they have the same number r of contours, the same orientability class, and the same first Betti number β_1.* In order to bring out some of the topological properties of surfaces, we assume these results.

A convex polygonal region R bounded by a polygon P can be triangulated by introducing as 1-simplexes all the chords joining a vertex p of P to other vertices. This leads to a complex $K = \{s\}$ covering R where (1) the 0-simplexes $\{s^0\}$ of K are the vertices of P; (2) its 1-simplexes $\{s^1\}$ are the edges of P and the chords from p; (3) its 2-simplexes are the triangular regions into which the chords from p separate R. We will take K to be oriented.

Now let K be converted into a different surface K_0 by the identification in pairs of some of its 1-simplexes on B and, of course, the induced identification of some of the vertices (Arts. 2–1, 2–2). But then $\{t\}$, denoting $\{s\}$ with the identifications, is not a complex, because some pairs of closed 2-simplexes intersect in more than the closure of a single common face. For example, in the case where P is a quadrilateral (Fig. 5–6a), $K = \{s\}$ consists of two 2-simplexes, five 1-simplexes, and four 0-simplexes, to be numbered and oriented as indicated. We now convert the surface into a torus by the identifications $s_2^1 = s_4^1$, $s_3^1 = s_5^1$. Then (Fig. 5–6b) $K_0 = \{t\}$ consists of two 2-simplexes, $t_1^2 = s_1^2$, $t_2^2 = s_2^2$; three 1-simplexes, $t_1^1 = s_1^1$, $t_2^1 = s_2^1 = s_4^1$, $t_3^1 = s_3^1 = s_5^1$, and one 0-simplex, $t^0 = s_i^0$ ($i = 1, 2, 3, 4$). Since t_1^2 and t_2^2 have all their faces in common, $\{t\}$ does not satisfy the definition of a complex. If, however, each simplex of $\{t\}$ is subjected to its second barycentric subdivision (Fig. 5–6c), the resulting set of simplexes is a complex. So is the simpler subdivision shown in Fig. 5–3 above.

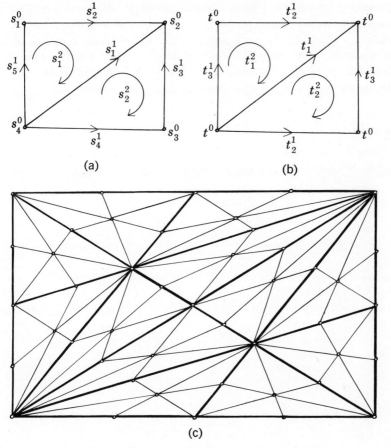

(a)   (b)

(c)

Fig. 5–6. Subdivisions of a rectangle and a torus.

(B) In the general case, the set of simplexes obtained from $\{t\}$ by subjecting each simplex of $\{t\}$ to its second barycentric subdivision is a simplicial complex (Exercise 23).

THEOREM 9. **Let K be a triangulation of a surface M, and let α_j be the number of j-simplexes of K. Then, in the notation of Theorem 7,**

$$(5.39)\quad \alpha_0 - \alpha_1 + \alpha_2 = \beta_0 - \beta_1 + \beta_2 = \begin{cases} 2 - 2h - r & (h \geq 0, r \geq 0) \\ 2 - q - r & (q > 0, r \geq 0). \end{cases}$$

Proof. Consider the standard polygonal representation of M in the orientable case, as given in (2.6a). It is easy to verify that there are $\alpha_0^* = 1 + r$ vertices, $\alpha_1^* = 2h + 2r$ edges, and $\alpha_2^* = 1$ region, the interior of the polygonal representation. One can pass to an arbitrary triangulation of K by a sequence of steps each consisting of either (1) introducing a vertex which divides an edge into two edges or (2) introducing a new edge, perhaps in the form of a broken line, which divides a region into two regions. Each step adds one unit each either to the number of edges and the number of vertices or to the number of edges and the number of regions, and hence does not affect the value of the quantity $\alpha_0 - \alpha_1 + \alpha_2$. Therefore, at each stage,

$$\begin{aligned}
\alpha_0 - \alpha_1 + \alpha_2 &= \alpha_0^* - \alpha_1^* + \alpha_2^* \\
(5.40) \qquad &= 1 + r - 2h - 2r + 1 = 2 - 2h - r \\
&= \beta_0 - \beta_1 + \beta_2.
\end{aligned}$$

The non-orientable case can be similarly proved (Exercise 24).

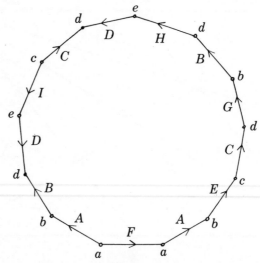

Fig. 5–7. The polygon $FAECGBHDC^{-1}IDB^{-1}A^{-1}$.

(C) Given a polygonal representation, not necessarily in standard form, for a surface M, it is possible to deduce its standard form from its orientability class, its number of edges α_1^*, its number of vertices α_0^*, and its number of contours (see (D) below), which can easily be counted with the aid of a diagram of the representation.

We illustrate (C) by carrying out the described process for the symbol

$$(5.41) \qquad \pi = FAECGBHDC^{-1}IDB^{-1}A^{-1} \qquad \text{(Fig. 5–7).}$$

It is non-orientable because D appears twice with the same super-script. In the diagram, the same letter is used for all copies of a set of identified vertices, since they count as a single vertex. A count yields $\alpha_0^* = 5$, $\alpha_1^* = 9$, and there is just one region, so that $\alpha_2^* = 1$. The contours are made up of free edges. Since the end points of F are identified, F represents a contour. The edges $EIH^{-1}G$ represent a four-edged contour, from b to c along E, thence along I to e, along H^{-1} to d, and back to b along G. Since this exhausts the free edges, $r = 2$. Substituting in (5.39) for the non-orientable case (compare (5.40)), we find

$$(5.42) \qquad \alpha_0^* - \alpha_1^* + \alpha_2^* = 5 - 9 + 1 = -3 = 2 - q - 2,$$

so that $q = 3$. Thus (5.41) represents a sphere with three crosscaps and two contours, so it is reducible to $C_1 C_1 C_2 C_2 C_3 C_3 K_1 D_1 K_1^{-1} K_2 D_2 K_2^{-1}$.

(*D*) The contour number r is the number of closed curves which can be traced along the free edges of a polygonal representation.

(*E*) The number $N = \alpha_0 - \alpha_1 + \alpha_2$ is the (**Euler-Poincaré**) **characteristic** of an arbitrary 2-complex K^2. *If $|K^2|$ is a closed manifold, then $|K^2|$ is determined topologically by its orientability class and its characteristic N.* For, since $r = 0$ for a closed manifold, K^2 is a sphere with $h = \frac{1}{2}(2 - N)$ handles if orientable and with $q = 2 - N$ crosscaps if non-orientable.

(*F*) Each even integer not exceeding 2 is the characteristic of some orientable closed surface. Each integer not exceeding 1 is the characteristic of some non-orientable closed surface. There is just one closed surface of characteristic 2, the sphere, and just one of each odd characteristic ≤ 1. For each even characteristic ≤ 0 there are just two closed surfaces: one orientable and one non-orientable.

(*G*) The **genus** of a closed surface is $g = h$ (the handle number) or $g = q$ (the crosscap number). *A closed surface is topologically characterized by its orientability class and its genus.*

EXERCISES

21. Show that two surfaces with contours can have the same Betti numbers without being homeomorphic.

22. Show that the first barycentric subdivision of K_0 in Fig. 5–6b is not a complex.

23. Prove (*B*).

24. Complete the proof of Theorem 9 by dealing with the non-orientable case.

25. In (5.41), replace the second D by D^{-1} and use the illustrated method for deducing the standard form.

26. Characterize each of the following by finding its orientability class, its contour number, and its handle number or crosscap number, as appropriate: (a) $ABCDA^{-1}EFC^{-1}GF^{-1}H$, (b) $AEAFDCGBD^{-1}HC^{-1}B^{-1}$.

27. Find the orientability class and characteristic of (a) $ABACBC$, (b) $ACA^{-1}C^{-1}DD$, (c) $ABACB^{-1}C^{-1}$.

28. Find the orientability class and genus of (a) $ABCDDEBAC^{-1}E^{-1}$, (b) $ADCACD^{-1}B^{-1}$, (c) $ABA^{-1}CB^{-1}C$.

29. Find the Euler-Poincaré characteristic, contour number, orientability class, and standard form for the following surfaces: (a) $ABCADBEFC^{-1}G$, (b) $ABCCA^{-1}DEB^{-1}ED$, (c) $ABCACB$.

30. (a) Two square regions have their edges matched in pairs as suggested by $ACB^{-1}D^{-1}$ and $ADB^{-1}C^{-1}$. Characterize the resulting surface. (b) Do the same for two pentagonal regions $ABCDE$ and $AD^{-1}BE^{-1}C$.

31. A sphere with three twisted handles (see Figs. 2–22 and 2–23) is equivalent to a sphere with how many crosscaps?

32. To what form $H(h, r)$ or $C(q, r)$ is each of the following equivalent: (a) $A_1A_2 \ldots A_kA_1^{-1}A_2^{-1} \ldots A_k^{-1}$?   (b) $A_1A_2 \ldots A_kA_k^{-1}A_{k-1}^{-1} \ldots A_1^{-1}$?   (c) $A_1A_2 \ldots A_kA_1A_2 \ldots A_k$?

33. Figure 5–8 shows a disk with a simple bridge, a twisted bridge, and a double bridge, the terminology being clarified by the figure. Prove the following statements:

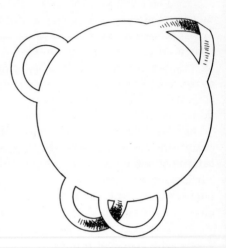

(a) A sphere with $r > 0$ contours and h handles is equivalent to a disk with $r - 1$ simple bridges and h double bridges.

(b) A sphere with $r > 0$ contours and q crosscaps is equivalent to a disk with $r - 1$ simple bridges and q twisted bridges.

This problem uses terminology and states results to be found in Kerékjártó [K_2]. Note that it gives a method whereby one can make a model, free from self-penetrations, for any surface having a boundary.

Fig. 5–8. Simple, twisted, and double bridges.

34. The same as Exercise 29 for the surface represented by a disk with three double bridges and three twisted bridges.

35. The same for the surface represented by a disk with a double bridge modified (a) by putting a twist in one of the two bands composing it, (b) by putting a twist in each of these bands.

36. The same for a Moebius band with a handle.

37. Show the equivalence of the following: (a) a sphere with one crosscap and t twisted handles (Fig. 2-23); (b) a sphere with one crosscap and t ordinary handles; (c) a sphere with $2t + 1$ crosscaps.

38. Show that a sphere with $x > 1$ twisted handles and y ordinary handles is equivalent to a sphere with $x + y$ twisted handles.

39. Describe, as spheres with handles or crosscaps, all closed surfaces (a) with characteristic -6; (b) with characteristic $1 - 2k$.

5–6.   Pseudomanifolds

In E^m, with coordinate system $(x_1, \ldots, x_m)$, consider an oriented simplex $s^m = +p_0p_1 \ldots p_m$. Let $(a_{j1}, \ldots, a_{jm})$ be the coordinates of p_j $(j = 0, \ldots, m)$, and let $\Delta(s^m)$ be the determinant

(5.43) $\Delta(s^m) = |1 \ a_{j1} \ a_{j2} \ \ldots \ a_{jm}|$ $(j = 0, \ldots, m)$.

The statement that $p_0, p_1, \ldots, p_m$ are linearly independent is equivalent to the statement that $\Delta(s^m) \neq 0$ (Chapter 4, Lemma 2, and Art. 4–3). Reversing the orientation of s^m reverses the sign of $\Delta(s^m)$. That is, $\Delta(s^m) = -\Delta(-s^m)$, a consequence of the fact that an odd permutation of vertices of s^m corresponds to an odd permutation of the rows of $\Delta(s^m)$.

(A) Two oriented m-simplexes s^m and t^m in E^m have **like** (= **similar**) or **unlike** orientations according as $\Delta(s^m)$ and $\Delta(t^m)$ agree or disagree in algebraic sign. The whole space E^m (or any region of E^m) is **oriented** when one m-simplex s^m in it is oriented. All other oriented m-simplexes are then described as **positively** or **negatively** oriented, according as they are oriented like or unlike s^m.

(B) The selection of a coordinate system also serves to **orient** E^m or any region of E^m, each oriented s^m in such region being described as **positively** or **negatively** oriented according as $\Delta(s^m) > 0$ or $\Delta(s^m) < 0$.

(C) Let $(p_1, \ldots, p_m)$, but not p_0, be given, and suppose $(p_1, \ldots, p_m)$ determine an $(m - 1)$-simplex. Let $p : (x) = (x_1, \ldots, x_m)$ be an arbitrary point, let $s_x^m = +pp_1 \ldots p_m$, and let $\Delta(x)$ denote $\Delta(s_x^m)$. Then $p \in \Lambda(p_1, \ldots, p_m)$, which is the $(m - 1)$-plane of $p_1, \ldots, p_m$ (Art. 4–1), if and only if $\Delta(x) = 0$. Hence $\Lambda : \Delta(x_1, \ldots, x_m) = 0$ is an equation for $\Lambda = \Lambda(p_1, \ldots, p_m)$. Therefore Λ separates E^m into two parts (Exercise 44), called the **half-spaces** $\Delta(x) > 0$ and $\Delta(x) < 0$. These are the loci of a point $p : (x)$ such that the orientation of $pp_1 \ldots p_m$ is positive and negative, respectively.

LEMMA 9. **If (a) $s^m = ps^{m-1}$ and $t^m = qs^{m-1}$ are oriented alike and (b) $\Lambda(s^{m-1})$ separates p from q, then s^m and t^m induce opposite orientations on s^{m-1}** (Exercise 45).

Thus far, we have discussed orientations of m-simplexes in an E^m. We turn now to oriented m-simplexes in an E^n $(n > m)$.

(D) Consider, in E^n $(n > m)$, two oriented m-simplexes $s^m = ps^{m-1}, t^m = qs^{m-1}$ such that $\bar{s}^m \cap \bar{t}^m = \bar{s}^{m-1}$. Guided by Lemma 9, we say that s^m and t^m have **like** (= **similar**) or **unlike** orientations according as they induce opposite or equal orientations on s^{m-1}.

(E) A rectilinear simplicial m-complex M in E^n is called a (**closed**) m-**pseudomanifold** if (1) each $(m - 1)$-simplex of M is incident with exactly two m-simplexes and (2) any two m-simplexes of M can be used as first and last members of a sequence of such m-simplexes, consecutive members having a common $(m - 1)$-dimensional face. If M satisfies (1) and (2) with the exception that each member of a non-vacuous subset $\{\beta^{m-1}\}$ of its $(m - 1)$-simplexes is incident with a corresponding single m-simplex, then M is an m-**pseudomanifold with boundary** B, where B is the complex consisting of all the faces of the simplexes $\{\beta^{m-1}\}$. We describe two m-simplexes of M as **adjacent** to each other if they have a common $(m - 1)$-dimensional face. We say that M is **orientable** or **non-orientable** according as it is or is not possible to orient all its m-simplexes so that if two m-simplexes are adjacent, they are oriented alike.

A pseudomanifold M is **coherently oriented** if it is oriented so that (1) every two adjacent m-simplexes are oriented alike and (2) each $(m - 1)$-simplex of the boundary B of M, considered vacuous if M is closed, has the orientation induced by the incident m-simplex.

LEMMA 10. **An m-pseudomanifold M can be coherently oriented if and only if it is orientable. In such case, exactly two coherent orientations are possible. If $s^m \in M$, each of the two possible orientations of M is determined by one of the two possible orientations of s^m. If M has a boundary B and $s^{m-1} \in B$, an orientation of s^{m-1} similarly determines an orientation of M, and conversely.**

This lemma follows directly from the definitions.

(F) By the **chain** of an oriented m-complex K^m, with oriented m-simplexes s_i^m ($i = 1, \ldots, \alpha_m$), we mean the chain $C^m(K^m) = \Sigma_{i=1}^{\alpha_m} s_i^m$.

LEMMA 11. **If M is a coherently oriented m-pseudomanifold, then $\partial C^m(M) = C^{m-1}(B)$, where B is the possibly vacuous boundary of M.**

For, if an $(m - 1)$-simplex s^{m-1} of M is incident with two m-simplexes s^m and t^m of M, then s^{m-1} appears on $\partial(s^m + t^m)$ with coefficient 0, and s^{m-1} appears with coefficient 0 on ∂r^m for any r^m not incident with s^{m-1}. If an $(m - 1)$-simplex is on B it appears with coefficient 1 in $\partial C^m(M)$, by definition of **coherent orientation**.

LEMMA 12. **Let M be an m-pseudomanifold whose simplexes of all dimensions $k \neq m - 1$ are arbitrarily oriented. If $s^{m-1} \in M$ is incident with two similarly oriented m-simplexes, let it be arbitrarily oriented. If $s^{m-1} \in M$ is incident with two m-simplexes with unlike orientations, let s^{m-1} have the common induced orientation and let K^{m-1} be the oriented complex consisting of the faces of the latter $(m - 1)$-simplexes. Let each $(m - 1)$-simplex of B have the orientation induced by the incident m-simplex of M. Then**

$$(5.44) \qquad \partial C^m(M) = 2C^{m-1}(K^{m-1}) + C^{m-1}(B).$$

The proof of Lemma 11 with obvious modifications establishes Lemma 12 (Exercise 47).

THEOREM 10. **If M is a closed orientable m-pseudomanifold, then**

$$(5.45) \qquad \mathfrak{H}_0(M) \approx \mathfrak{H}_m(M) \approx \text{the free cyclic group,}$$

where $\approx$ is the isomorphism relation.

Proof. In the case of $\mathfrak{H}_0$, this follows from the connectedness of M. For $\mathfrak{H}_m$, it follows from the facts that (1) the chain $C^m(M)$ is a cycle if M is coherently oriented (Lemma 11), (2) each m-cycle on M is a multiple of $C^m(M)$, and (3) no m-cycle $\neq \emptyset$ can bound, since the only $(m + 1)$-chain on an m-complex is $\emptyset$.

THEOREM 11. **If M is a closed non-orientable m-pseudomanifold, then its mth Betti number is $\beta_m = 0$ and it has an $(m - 1)^{\text{th}}$ torsion coefficient equal to 2 (Exercise 49).**

EXERCISES

40. In Definition (B) let $m = 2$. Suppose, in E^2, that a clockwise rotation through $\pi/2$ takes the positive x_1-axis into the positive x_2-axis. Show that Definition (B) then means that clockwise oriented 2-simplexes are positively oriented.

41. Triangulate a Moebius strip into the faces of three 2-simplexes, orient them, showing them in a diagram, and apply Lemma 12, indicating on the diagram the 1-chains which are involved.

42. (a) Show that Definition (A) implies that two 2-simplexes in E^2 are oriented alike if and only if both are oriented clockwise or both counterclockwise. (See Exercise 40 above.) (b) Interpret the definition for $m = 1$.

43. Expand $\Delta(x)$, in Statement (C), by minors so as to put $\Delta(x) = 0$ into the form of a linear equation in (x).

44. Show that Λ in Statement (C) separates E^m into at least two parts, by showing that a curve from a point where $\Delta(x) < 0$ to a point where $\Delta(x) > 0$ must pass through a point where $\Delta(x) = 0$. Show that if $\Delta(a)$ and $\Delta(b)$ are of like sign, then $\Delta(x)$ is not zero on the segment ab.

45. Deduce Lemma 9 from (C).

46. (a) Show that a 2-sphere with two of its points identified is a pseudomanifold. (d) Do the same for an arbitrary surface S with arbitrary identifications among the vertices of a triangulation of S.

47. Prove Lemma 12.

48. Let c^k be a convex polyhedral k-cell (Art. 4–12). Show that each linear simplicial subdivision of $\bar{c}^k$ (Chapter 4, Theorem 8) is an orientable k-pseudomanifold, with a boundary consisting of the subcomplex on $\bar{c}^k - c^k$.

49. Prove Theorem 11.

5–7. Homology Bases and Incidence Matrices

Let $K = \{s\}$ be a finite oriented m-complex. Using the notation of (5.5), let the boundary chain of s_j^{k+1} be written in the form

$$(5.46) \qquad \partial s_j^{k+1} = \sum_{i=1}^{\alpha_k} \varepsilon_{ij}^k s_i^k \qquad (j = 1, \ldots, \alpha_{k+1}).$$

(A) If s_i^k is not incident with s_j^{k+1}, then $\varepsilon_{ij}^k = 0$. If $s_i^k < s_j^{k+1}$, (Art. 4–5(D)), then $\varepsilon_{ij}^k = +1$ or -1. In the former case, s_i^k has the orientation induced by s_j^{k+1} (Art. 5–1(D)). The number ε_{ij}^k is the **incidence number of** s_i^k **and** s_j^{k+1}.

The kth **incidence matrix** of K is the matrix

$$(5.47) \quad J_k = (\varepsilon_{ij}^k) = \begin{array}{c|ccc} & (s_1^{k+1}) & \cdots & (s_{\alpha_{k+1}}^{k+1}) \\ \hline (s_1^k) & \varepsilon_{11}^k & \cdots & \varepsilon_{1\alpha_{k+1}}^k \\ \cdot & \cdot & & \cdot \\ \cdot & \cdot & & \cdot \\ \cdot & \cdot & & \cdot \\ (s_{\alpha_k}^k) & \varepsilon_{\alpha_k 1}^k & \cdots & \varepsilon_{\alpha_k \alpha_{k+1}}^k \end{array} \qquad (k = 0, 1, \ldots, n-1)$$

where (s_i^k) and (s_j^{k+1}) are used to label the rows and columns.

Now let $\{C^{k+1}\} = (C_1^{k+1}, \ldots, C_{\alpha_{k+1}}^{k+1})$ and $\{C^k\} = (C_1^k, \ldots, C_{\alpha_k}^k)$ be arbitrary bases for $\mathfrak{C}_{k+1}$ and $\mathfrak{C}_k$, respectively. Since $\{C^k\}$ is a base for the k-chains, the boundary ∂C_i^{k+1} of C_i^{k+1} can be uniquely expressed in the form

$$(5.48) \qquad \partial C_j^{k+1} = \sum_{i=1}^{\alpha_k} \eta_{ij}^k C_i^k \qquad (j = 1, \ldots, \alpha_{k+1}).$$

The kth incidence matrix of K for $\{C^{k+1}\}$, $\{C^k\}$ is

$$(5.49) \quad J_k(\{C^{k+1}\}, \{C^k\}) = (\eta_{ij}^k) = \begin{array}{c|ccc} & (C_j^{k+1}) \\ \hline & \cdot \\ & \cdot \\ (C_i^k) & \cdots \quad \eta_{ij}^k \quad \cdots \\ & \cdot \\ & \cdot \\ & \cdot \end{array}$$

(B) *A characteristic property of incidence matrices is that the boundary of the chain C_j^{k+1} labeling a column is the chain $\Sigma_{i=1}^{\alpha_k} \eta_{ij}^k C_i^k$ in which the chains labeling the rows appear with the respective elements in the column as coefficients.*

Our next objective is to show how bases can be selected for the chain groups so as to simplify the corresponding incidence matrices as much as possible and to put them into a canonical form. Exercises 50–54 illustrate the general procedure for 1-complexes.

THEOREM 12. **Let** $(J_0, \ldots, J_{m-1})$ **be the incidence matrices corresponding to arbitrary bases** $\{C^k\}$ **for** $\mathfrak{C}_k$ ($k = 0, \ldots, m$). **Then, in terms of matrix products** (see Art. A–3),

$$(5.50) \qquad J_{k-1} J_k = O_k$$

where O_k **is the null matrix (each element is zero) of** α_{k-1} **rows and** α_{k+1} **columns.**

Proof. Applying the boundary operator twice, and using the formulations (5.48) and (5.49) for $k = (0, \ldots, m)$, we find

$$(5.51) \quad \partial\partial C_j^{k+1} = \sum_{i=1}^{\alpha_k} \eta_{ij}^k \partial C_i^k = \sum_{i=1}^{\alpha_k}\sum_{h=1}^{\alpha_{k-1}} \eta_{ij}^k \eta_{hi}^{k-1} C_h^{k-1} = \sum_{h=1}^{\alpha_{k-1}} \left(\sum_{i=1}^{\alpha_k} \eta_{hi}^{k-1} \eta_{ij}^k \right) C_h^{k-1}$$

$$(j = 1, \ldots, \alpha_{h+1}).$$

The coefficient of C_h^{k-1} (in parentheses in (5.51)) is the element in row h, column j of $J_{k-1} J_k$. Since $\partial\partial C^{k+1}$ is the null cycle (Theorem 1), the present theorem follows.

(*C*) Indeed, (5.50) is a way of formulating the general property $\partial\partial C^{k+1} = \emptyset$.

THEOREM 13. **It is possible to choose bases for the chain groups** $\mathfrak{C}_0, \mathfrak{C}_1, \ldots, \mathfrak{C}_m$ **in terms of which the incidence matrices have the form**

$$(5.52) \quad J_k^* = \begin{bmatrix} \overset{\alpha_{k+1}-\gamma_k \text{ columns}}{} & \begin{matrix} \tau_1^k & & 0 \\ & \ddots & \\ 0 & & \tau_{\gamma_k}^k \end{matrix} \\ \hline \mathbf{0} & \mathbf{0} \end{bmatrix} \begin{matrix} (k = 0, 1, \ldots, m-1) \\ \\ \alpha_k - \gamma_k \text{ rows} \end{matrix}$$

where the τ'**s are positive integers, with** τ_i^k **divisible by** τ_{i+1}^k.

Proof. The matrices J_k^* will be called the **normal** or **normalized** **incidence matrices** of K. In the Appendix, the matrix (e_{ij}) of Eqs. (A.29) having m rows and n columns is normalized into a form exactly like (5.52) save that the submatrix of the τ's appears in the upper left corner instead of the upper right (Appendix, Theorem 5). Property (5.50) is impossible with the J's normalized as in the Appendix. Rows can, however, be permuted and columns can be permuted (Art. A–3(*E*)(*F*)) to obtain such forms as (5.52).

The simultaneous normalizing of the matrices $(J_0, \ldots, J_{m-1})$ into $(J_0^*, J_1^*, \ldots, J_{m-1}^*)$ differs from the normalizing of the single matrix in the Appendix because (1) the labels for the columns of J_{k-1} are also the same as the labels for the rows of J_k for an arbitrary set of bases $\{C^h\}$ ($h = 0, \ldots, m$) and hence (2) an alteration of the columns of J_{k-1} entails a corresponding alteration of the rows of J_k.

(*D*) Starting with a base $(C_1^k, \ldots, C_{\alpha_k}^k)$ for $\mathfrak{C}_k$, we define certain elementary changes of base, and note the effects on the incidence matrices:

(1) Replacing C_i^k by $D_i^k = -C_i^k$ corresponds to changing all signs in the ith column of J_{k-1} and the ith row of J_k.

(2) Replacing C_h^k, C_j^k by $D_h^k = C_j^k$, $D_j^k = C_h^k$ corresponds to interchanging columns h and j in J_{k-1}, rows h and j in J_k.

(3) Replacing U_h^k by $V_h^k = U_h^k + rU_j^k$ for some integer r and some $j \neq h$ corresponds to making the replacements

$$\text{(new col } h) = \text{(old col } h) + r(\text{col } j) \quad \text{in } J_{k-1},$$
$$\text{(new row } j) = \text{(old row } j) - r(\text{row } h) \quad \text{in } J_k.$$

Parts (1) and (2) of (D) are trivial to verify. Part (3) results from $\partial V_h^k = \partial U_h^k + r\partial U_j^k$ and the fact that if $\partial U_g^{k+1} = \Sigma_{i=1}^{\alpha_k} \eta_{ig}^k U_i^k$, then $\partial U_g^{k+1} = \Sigma_{i \neq h,j} \eta_{ig}^k U_i^k + \eta_{hg}^k V_h^k + (\eta_{jg}^k - r\eta_{hg}^k)U_j^k$.

(E) The matrix J_0 is the incidence matrix of a linear graph, the 1-skeleton K^1 of K. As such, it can be normalized into a form J_0^*, like (5.52), in which each $\tau_i^0 = 1$ (Exercise 54).

In accordance with (D), operations on the columns of J_0 during its normalization (see Art. A–3) involve corresponding operations on the rows of J_1. Let J_1' be the incidence matrix into which J_1 is thus carried.

Hypothesis. For some $h > 0$, it is possible to select bases for the chain groups $\mathfrak{C}_0, \ldots, \mathfrak{C}_m$ for which the incidence matrices are $(J_0^*, \ldots, J_{h-1}^*, J_h', J_{h+1}, \ldots, J_{m-1})$. Here the starred matrices are of the form (5.52), while $J_{h+1}, \ldots, J_{m-1}$ are the matrices for the initial bases $\{s^h\}, \ldots, \{s^m\}$.

For $h = 1$, the conditions of the hypothesis are fulfilled by the definitions of J_0^* and J_1' with the corresponding new bases for $\mathfrak{C}_0$ and $\mathfrak{C}_1$.

LEMMA 13. The last γ_{h-1} rows of J_h' consist entirely of zeros.

Proof of Lemma. If a non-zero element η appeared in the jth of the last γ_{h-1} rows of J_h', then the product matrix $J_{h-1}^* J_h'$ would contain the element $\tau_j^{h-1}\eta \neq 0$, by (5.52) for $k = h - 1$. But this would contradict Theorem 12. Hence Lemma 13 is correct.

Let the normalizing procedure of the Appendix (Art. A–3) be applied to carry J_h' into the form J_h^*, with corresponding changes of bases and of the matrices J_{h-1}^*, J_h' in accordance with (D). Normalizing operations on the last γ_{h-1} rows of J_h' are unnecessary, by Lemma 13. Operations on its first $\alpha_h - \gamma_{h-1}$ rows affect only the first $\alpha_h - \gamma_{h-1}$ columns of J_{h-1}^*. Since they contain only zeros, by (5.52) for $k = h - 1$, their elements remain unchanged, only their h-chain labels being affected. The normalizing operations on the columns of J_h' involve a change of base for $\mathfrak{C}_{h+1}$ and a transformation of J_{h+1} into J_{h+1}'. This completes the general step of the proof. The step with $h = m - 1$, in which, of course, there is no J_{h+1} to consider, yields Theorem 13.

(F) Among the numbers τ_i^k, those which exceed 1 are the kth **torsion coefficients** $(\tau_1^k, \ldots, \tau_{\rho_k}^k)$ of K.

(G) Consider a normalized matrix J_k^*, $k > 0$. Let $(A_1^k, \ldots, A_{\gamma_k}^k)$ denote the k-chain labels of its first γ_k rows. Let the last γ_{k-1} rows be labeled $(C_1^k, \ldots, C_{\gamma_{k-1}}^k)$. They consist entirely of zeros, by Lemma 13, hence do not overlap with the first γ_k rows. There may be rows of zeros between row $(A_{\gamma_k}^k)$ and row (C_1^k). If so, let them be labeled $(B_1^k, \ldots, B_{\beta_k}^k)$. As for J_0^*, let its rows be labeled $(A_1^0, \ldots, A_{\gamma_0}^0, B_1^0, \ldots, B_{\beta_0}^0)$. Since the columns of J_{k-1}^* are labeled like the rows of J_k^*, it remains only to assign symbols to the column labels of J_{m-1}^*. Let them be $(B_1^m, \ldots, B_{\beta_m}^m, C_1^m, \ldots, C_{\gamma_{m-1}}^m)$.

This labeling system is displayed as follows for a typical J_k^*. The sets $(A_1^{k+1}, \ldots, A_{\gamma_{k+1}}^{k+1})$ are vacuous if $k = m - 1$; and so are $(C_1^k, \ldots, C_{\gamma_{k-1}}^k)$ if $k = 0$.

The labels at the right and bottom are inserted for reference in Art. 5–9. They are to be ignored for the present.

(5.53)

$$J_k^* = $$ (matrix display)

	$A_1^{k+1} \ldots A_{\gamma_{k+1}}^{k+1}$	$B_1^{k+1} \ldots B_{\beta_{k+1}}^{k+1}$	$C_1^{k+1} \ldots C_{\rho_k}^{k+1}$	$\ldots C_{\gamma_k}^{k+1}$	
A_1^k			$\tau_1^k \quad\quad 0$		X_1^k
$\cdot$	0	0	$\ddots$	0	$\cdot$
$A_{\rho_k}^k$			$0 \quad\quad \tau_{\rho_k}^k$		$X_{\rho_k}^k$
$\cdot$				$1 \quad\quad 0$	$\cdot$
$\cdot$	0	0	0	$\ddots$	$\cdot$
$A_{\gamma_k}^k$				$0 \quad\quad 1$	$X_{\gamma_k}^k$
B_1^k					Y_1^k
$\cdot$	0	0	0	0	$\cdot$
$B_{\beta_k}^k$					$Y_{\beta_k}^k$
C_1^k					Z_1^k
$\cdot$	0	0	0	0	$\cdot$
$C_{\gamma_{k-1}}^k$					$Z_{\gamma_{k-1}}^k$
	$X_1^{k+1} \ldots X_{\gamma_{k+1}}^{k+1}$	$Y_1^{k+1} \ldots Y_{\beta_{k+1}}^{k+1}$	$Z_1^{k+1} \ldots Z_{\rho_k}^{k+1}$	$\ldots Z_{\gamma_k}^{k+1}$	

$$(k = 0, \ldots, m - 1)$$

(H) Since J_k^* has α_k rows and α_{k+1} columns,

(5.54) $\quad \beta_k = \alpha_k - \gamma_k - \gamma_{k-1} \quad\quad (k = 0, 1, \ldots, m; \gamma_{-1} = \gamma_m = 0),$

the values $\gamma_{-1} = \gamma_m = 0$ being conventional, since only $\gamma_0, \ldots, \gamma_{m-1}$

are defined as the ranks of the J_k. From (5.54), it follows that (Exercise 59)

$$(5.55) \qquad N = \sum_{k=0}^{m} (-1)^k \beta_k = \sum_{k=0}^{m} (-1)^k \alpha_k.$$

This number N is the **Euler-Poincaré characteristic** of K. We adopt the notation

$$\{A^k\} = (A_1^k, \ldots, A_{\gamma_k}^k), \quad \{B^k\} = (B_1^k, \ldots, B_{\beta_k}^k), \quad \{C^k\} = (C_1^k, \ldots, C_{\gamma_{k-1}}^k),$$

$$(5.56) \qquad \{A^k, B^k\} = \{A^k\} \cup \{B^k\}, \qquad \{A^k, B^k, C^k\} = \{A^k, B^k\} \cup \{C^k\},$$

$$\{\tau A^k\} = (\tau_1^k A_1^k, \ldots, \tau_{\rho_k}^k A_{\rho_k}^k, A_{\rho_k+1}^k, \ldots, A_{\gamma_k}^k).$$

For any k-chain D^k, $\bar{D}^k$ will denote its homology class. Let

$$(5.57) \qquad \begin{aligned} \{\bar{A}^k\} = \{\bar{A}_1, \ldots, \bar{A}_{\rho_k}\}, \quad \{\bar{B}^k\} = \{\bar{B}_1^k, \ldots, \bar{B}_{\beta_k}\}, \\ \{\bar{A}^k, \bar{B}^k\} = \{\bar{A}^k\} \cup \{\bar{B}^k\}. \end{aligned}$$

Note that the last subscript in the definition of $\{\bar{A}^k\}$ is ρ_k, not γ_k.

THEOREM 14. **The following sets of chains and homology classes are bases* for the indicated groups:**

Group	Base	Description of Group
(a) $\mathfrak{C}_k$	$\{A^k, B^k, C^k\}$	k-chain group
(b) $\mathfrak{Z}_k$	$\{A^k, B^k\}$	k-cycle group
(c) $\mathfrak{D}_k$	$\{A^k\}$	k^{th} boundary divisor§ group
(d) $\mathfrak{F}_k$	$\{\tau A^k\}$	bounding k-cycle group
(e) $\mathfrak{H}_k = \mathfrak{Z}_k/\mathfrak{F}_k$	$\{\bar{A}^k, \bar{B}^k\}$	k^{th} homology† group
(f) $\mathfrak{T}_k$	$\{\bar{A}^k\}$	k^{th} torsion group
(g) $\mathfrak{B}_k$	$\{\bar{B}^k\}$	k^{th} Betti group

§ A boundary divisor cycle is a cycle, some non-zero multiple of which bounds.
† Sometimes, but not here, called the kth Betti group.

Proof. Part (a) follows from the definition of $\{A, B, C\}$. A k-chain $D^k \in \mathfrak{C}_k$ can therefore be uniquely expressed thus:

$$(5.58) \qquad D^k = \sum_{h=1}^{\gamma_k} a_h A_h^k + \sum_{i=1}^{\beta_k} b_i B_i^k + \sum_{j=1}^{\gamma_{k-1}} c_j C_j^k.$$

From the matrix J_k^*, by (5.53) with k replaced by $k-1$,

$$(5.59) \qquad \partial D^k = \sum_{j=1}^{\gamma_{k-1}} c_j \partial C_j^k = \sum_{j=1}^{\gamma_{k-1}} c_j \tau_j^{k-1} A_j^{k-1}$$

where $\tau_j^{k-1} = 1$ for $j > \rho_{k-1}$; so, the A_j^{k-1} being linearly independent,

---

* In the sense of minimal sets of generators.

D^k is a cycle if and only if all the coefficients c_j are zero; hence Part (b). Replacing k by $k + 1$ yields

$$(5.60) \qquad \partial D^{k+1} = \sum_{j=1}^{\gamma_k} c_j \tau_j^k A_j^k \Rightarrow \text{Parts (c) and (d).}$$

Comparing the right side of (5.60) with (5.58), we deduce that

$$(5.61) \quad D^k \sim \emptyset \Leftrightarrow \begin{cases} a_h \equiv 0 \bmod \tau_h^k \quad (h = 1, \dots, \gamma_k) \\ b_i = c_j = 0 \quad (i = 1, \dots, \beta_k; j = 1, \dots, \gamma_{k-1}). \end{cases}$$

Parts (e), (f), and (g) follow with the aid of Art. A–3. See especially Lemma 4 and Theorem 7 of the Appendix (Exercise 60).

COROLLARY 1. **The groups involved in Theorem 14 are related as follows:**

$$(5.62) \qquad \begin{array}{l} \text{(a)} \ \mathfrak{F}_k \subset \mathfrak{D}_k \subset \mathfrak{Z}_k \subset \mathfrak{C}_k \\ \text{(b)} \ \mathfrak{H}_k = \mathfrak{Z}_k / \mathfrak{F}_k \\ \text{(c)} \ \mathfrak{T}_k = \mathfrak{D}_k / \mathfrak{F}_k \\ \text{(d)} \ \mathfrak{B}_k = \mathfrak{H}_k / \mathfrak{T}_k = \mathfrak{Z}_k / \mathfrak{D}_k \end{array}$$

COROLLARY 2. **Two k-cycles $\Sigma_{h=1}^{\gamma_k} a_h A_h^k + \Sigma_{i=1}^{\beta_k} b_i B_i^k$ and $\Sigma_{h=1}^{\gamma_k} a_h' A_h^k + \Sigma_{i=1}^{\beta_k} b_i' B_i^k$ are in the same homology class if and only if $a_h' \equiv a_h \bmod \tau_h^k$ and $b_i' = b_i$.** That is, any k-cycle Z^k satisfies a unique homology of the form

$$(5.63) \qquad Z^k \sim \sum_{h=1}^{\rho_k} \bar{a}_h A_i^k + \sum_{j=1}^{\beta_k} b_j B_j^k \begin{cases} \bar{a}_h \equiv \text{an integer mod } \tau_h^k, \\ b_j = \text{an integer.} \end{cases}$$

The set $(A_1^k, \dots, A_{\rho_k}^k, B_1^k, \dots, B_{\beta_k}^k)$ is called a **homology base of dimension k** or a kth **homology base.** Also, $(A_1^k, \dots, A_{\rho_k}^k)$ is a kth **torsion base** and $(B_1^k, \dots, B_{\beta_k}^k)$ a kth **Betti base.** It is, however, the homology classes of these respective sets of cycles which are bases of the groups $\mathfrak{H}_k$, $\mathfrak{T}_k$, and $\mathfrak{B}_k$.

EXERCISES

50. Show that a 1-complex T which is a tree (Art. 1–3) can have its vertices $(p_1, \dots, p_{\alpha_0})$ and its 1-simplexes $(s_1^1, \dots, s_{\alpha_1}^1)$ so numbered that (a) $s_j^1 = \overrightarrow{p_h\, p_{j+1}}$ for some $h \le j$ $(j = 1, \dots, \alpha_1 = \alpha_0 - 1)$ and (b) the subcomplex $(p_1, \dots, p_{j+1}, s_1^1, \dots, s_j^1)$ is a tree for each $j \in (1, \dots, \alpha_1)$. With such a numbering, what is the form of the incidence matrix J_0?

51. Using a numbering and orientation as described in Exercise 50, let C_i^1 be the sum of the 1-simplexes on the simple broken line from p_1 to p_{i+1} $(i = 1, \dots, \alpha_1)$. Show that the 1-chains C_i^1 and the 0-chains $B_1^0 = p_1$, $A_i^0 = p_{i+1} - p_1$

$(i = 1, \ldots, \alpha_1)$ are bases for the chain groups $\mathfrak{C}_1$ and $\mathfrak{C}_0$ respectively. *Suggestion:* Show that the s_i^1 and the p_i can be uniquely expressed in terms of the C_j^1 and $(A_1^0, \ldots, A_{\alpha_1}^0, B_1^0)$.

52. Write the incidence matrix J_0^* for the bases $(A_1^0, \ldots, A_{\alpha_1}^0, B_1^0)$ and $(C_1^1, \ldots, C_{\alpha_1}^1)$, labeling the rows and columns, respectively, with these chains in the order named.

53. An arbitrary connected 1-complex K^1 can be regarded as a tree T (Art. 1–3, Theorem 2) and a set $(c_1^1, \ldots, c_\mu^1)$ of 1-simplexes, each joining two vertices of T. Let B_j^1 be a 1-cycle which is a sum of c_j and simplexes on T. (a) Show that $(B_1^1, \ldots, B_\mu^1, C_1^1, \ldots, C_{\alpha_0-1}^1)$ is a base for $\mathfrak{C}_1$, where the notation of Exercise 51 defines the C_i^1 relative to $T \subset K$. (b) Write the incidence matrix for the bases $(A_1^0, \ldots, A_{\alpha_1}^0, B_1^0)$ and $(B_1^1, \ldots, B_\mu^1, C_1^1, \ldots, C_{\alpha_0-1}^1)$, labeling the rows and columns with the elements of these bases in the order named.

54. Prove (E) either (a) directly from the fact that each column contains just two non-zero elements, equal to $+1$ and -1 respectively, or (b) with the aid of the result of Exercise 53, noting however that K^1 is no longer assumed to be connected.

55. Let K^3 be the 3-complex consisting of all the faces of $s^3 = p_0p_1p_2p_3$ each positively oriented when its vertices are written in order of increasing subscripts. Write out the incidence matrices of K^3.

56. Reduce to normal form the incidence matrices of K^3 in Exercise 55.

57. Triangulate a polygonal representation CC for a projective plane, orient it, set up its incidence matrices, and give their normal forms.

58. In Exercise 57, specify a first torsion basis for the complex.

59. Deduce (5.55) from (5.54).

60. Complete the establishment of Parts (e), (f), and (g) of Theorem 14.

5–8. Connectivity Groups and Numbers

(A) In this article we outline homology theory mod 2, in which the coefficient group $\mathbf{Z}$ of Arts. 5–1 to 5–7 is replaced by $\mathbf{Z}_2$ (see Art. 5–1(G)). We represent $\mathbf{Z}_2$ by the numbers 0 and 1 with $0 + 0 = 1 + 1 = 0, 0 + 1 = 1 + 0 = 1$.

The incidence matrices mod 2 are

$$(5.64) \qquad \hat{J}_k = (\hat{e}_{ij}^k) \qquad (i = 1, \ldots, \alpha_k; j = 1, \ldots, \alpha_{k+1}; k = 0, \ldots, m-1)$$

with $\hat{e}_{ij}^k = 1$ or 0 according as s_i^k and s_j^{k+1} are incident or not.

(B) The **integral theory**, meaning the theory based on integral coefficients, reduces to the mod 2 theory if two chains $C^k = \Sigma_{i=1}^{\alpha_k} a_i s_i^k$ and $D^k = \Sigma_{i=1}^{\alpha_k} b_i s_i^k$ are identified if and only if $a_i \equiv b_i$ mod 2. Thus C^k is equivalent to the k-chain obtained by changing each even coefficient to 0 and each odd coefficient to 1.

(C) A k-chain $\hat{C}^k$ mod 2 can be interpreted as the set of k-simplexes appearing in it. Then $\hat{C}^k + \hat{D}^k$ consists of the k-simplexes each in $\hat{C}^k$ or $\hat{D}^k$ but not in both. Orientations of simplexes have no significance in the mod 2 theory, since $-1 \equiv +1$ mod 2.

(D) The k-chain group $\hat{\mathfrak{C}}_k$ mod 2 contains exactly 2^{α_k} elements. It is the direct sum of the α_k groups of order 2 generated by $(s_1^k, \ldots, s_{\alpha_k}^k)$.

The mod 2 boundary of a simplex s^k is the sum $\hat{\partial}s^k$ of its $(k-1)$-dimensional faces. In terms of (5.64),

$$(5.65) \qquad \hat{\partial}s_j^{k+1} = \sum_{i=1}^{\alpha_k} \hat{e}_{ij}^k s_i^k$$

and the boundary of a k-chain $\hat{C}^k = \Sigma_{j=1}^{\alpha_k} a_j s_j^k$ is $\hat{\partial}\hat{C}^k = \Sigma_{j=1}^{\alpha_k} a_j \hat{\partial}s_j^k$. In the interpretation of (C), a $(k-1)$-simplex belongs to $\hat{\partial}\hat{C}^k$ if and only if it is incident with an odd number of k-simplexes of $\hat{C}^k$.

As in the case of the operator ∂, $\hat{\partial}$ can be interpreted as a homomorphism (see Art. 5–1(E)) $\hat{\partial} : \hat{\mathfrak{C}}_k \to \hat{\mathfrak{C}}_{k-1}$. Its kernel is the mod 2 k-cycle group $\hat{\mathfrak{Z}}_k$, since a mod 2 k-cycle is by definition a cycle C^k for which $\hat{\partial}C^k = \emptyset$, where $\hat{\partial}C^k$ is ∂C^k reduced mod 2.

(E) The operator $\hat{\partial}$ has the property $\hat{\partial}\hat{\partial}C^{k+1} = \emptyset$, and the mod 2 incidence matrices have the property $\hat{J}_{k-1}\hat{J}_k = O_k$ (see Theorem 12) (Exercise 61).

As in the integral case, the bounding mod 2 cycles form a group $\hat{\mathfrak{F}}_k$. They are said to be **null-homologous mod 2**, symbolized by $Z^k \sim \emptyset$ mod 2. The relation $C_2^k \sim C_1^k$ mod 2 is defined precisely as in Art. 5–2(A) with $\hat{\partial}$ replacing ∂, and mod 2 homology classes are defined by analogy with the integral homology classes of Art. 5–2(B). This leads to the kth **connectivity group**

$$(5.66) \qquad \hat{\mathfrak{H}}_k = \hat{\mathfrak{Z}}_k / \hat{\mathfrak{F}}_k$$

analogous to the kth homology group. For some integer $\hat{\beta}_k$, called the kth **connectivity number** of K, $\hat{H}_k$ is the direct product (or sum) of $\hat{\beta}_k$ groups of order 2. This can be seen by replacing $\mathbf{Z}$ with $\mathbf{Z}_2$ throughout Art. A–3.

(F) For any complex, $\hat{\beta}_0 = \beta_0$ (Exercise 62).

By the procedure of Theorem 11, $\hat{J}_0, \ldots, \hat{J}_{m-1}$ can be normalized into matrices $\hat{J}_0^*, \ldots, \hat{J}_{m-1}^*$ of the form (5.52), with the top right square in (5.52) replaced by a unit matrix of $\hat{\gamma}_k$ rows and columns where $\hat{\gamma}_k =$ the rank of $\hat{J}_k$ (also of $\hat{J}_k^*$).

(G) In the notation of Art. 5–4, especially that used in the proof of Theorem 7, the 2-chain $C^2 = \Sigma_{i=1}^{\alpha_2} s_i^2$ is a 2-cycle mod •2 for the sphere with q crosscaps, since its boundary in the integral theory is $2C_1^*$ (see Lemma 8) which becomes the null cycle in the mod 2 theory. This remark has a bearing on Exercise 64.

The rows and columns of $\hat{J}_k^*$ can be labeled exactly as in (5.53) except that (1) the non-zero elements in the top right square are all

1's, so that there is no ρ_k and (2) each A, B, C, γ, β should be modified by putting $\hat{}$ above it (see Exercise 64 for $\hat{\gamma}$). As in Art. 5–7(H), we find

(5.67)
(a) $\hat{\beta}_k = \alpha_k - \hat{\gamma}_k - \hat{\gamma}_{k-1}$ $(k = 0, \ldots, m; \hat{\gamma}_{-1} = \hat{\gamma}_m = 0)$,

(b) $N = \sum_{k=0}^{m} (-1)^k \hat{\beta}_k = \sum_{k=0}^{m} (-1)^k \alpha_k.$

(H) By analogy with the integral homology theory, $\{\hat{A}^k, \hat{B}^k\} = (\hat{A}_1^k, \ldots, \hat{A}_{\hat{\gamma}_k}^k, \hat{B}_1^k, \ldots, \hat{B}_{\hat{\beta}_k}^k)$ is a base for $\hat{3}_k$, and $\{\hat{A}^k\}$ is a base for $\hat{\mathfrak{F}}_k$. The cycles $(\hat{B}_1^k, \ldots, \hat{B}_{\hat{\beta}_k}^k) = \{\hat{B}^k\}$ are representative of a set of mod 2 homology classes generating $\hat{H}_k$. They are a kth **connectivity base**.

EXERCISES

61. Prove (E).

62. Prove (F).

63. (a) Find the connectivity numbers $\hat{\beta}_0$, $\hat{\beta}_1$, $\hat{\beta}_2$ for a sphere with q crosscaps. (b) Show that, for an orientable surface, $\beta_i = \hat{\beta}_i$ $(i = 0, 1, 2)$. (c) How are β_i and $\hat{\beta}_i$ related for a non-orientable surface?

64. (a) Show that $\hat{\gamma}_k = \gamma_k - e_k$, where e_k is the number of even k^{th} torsion coefficients of K^m. (b) Show that $\hat{\beta}_k = \beta_k + e_k + e_{k-1}$. See ($G$).

65. Show that $\hat{\mathfrak{F}}_k$ is determined by $\mathfrak{F}_{k-1}$ and $\mathfrak{F}_k$.

66. Let the three edges of a triangle, oriented coherently, be identified, creating a space (not a 2-manifold) with the polygonal representation AAA. It can be subdivided into a complex K^2 with the aid of a second barycentric subdivision of the given triangle. What are (a) the Betti numbers and torsion coefficients of K^2? (b) its connectivity numbers?

67. Give the Betti numbers, torsion coefficients, and connectivity numbers of a square with all four edges identified as suggested by the symbol $AAAA$.

5–9. Cohomology Groups

We continue to study a finite oriented simplicial complex $K^m = \{s\} = \bigcup_{k=0}^{m} \{s^k\}$ with oriented k-simplexes $\{s^k\} = (s_1^k, \ldots, s_{\alpha_k}^k)$. We again turn to the theory involving integral chains, although the discussion requires little modification to make it applicable to chains with coefficients in an arbitrary abelian group.

We also continue to use ε_{ij}^k, defined in Art. 5–7(A), for the incidence number of s_i^k and s_j^{k+1}. In cohomology theory, each k-chain C^k has a so-called **coboundary chain** δC^k which is a $(k + 1)$-chain, while the boundary chain ∂C^k is a $(k - 1)$-chain. The **coboundary operator** δ plays a role in cohomology theory analogous to that of ∂ in homology theory. For purposes of comparison, we formulate the boundary and coboundary of the simplest k-chain $C^k = s_i^k$, as follows:

(5.68)
$$\text{(a)} \quad \partial s_i^k = \sum_{j=1}^{\alpha_{k-1}} \varepsilon_{ji}^{k-1} s_j^{k-1} \quad \text{(see (5.46))},$$
$$(i = 1, \dots, \alpha_k).$$
$$\text{(b)} \quad \delta s_i^k = \sum_{h=1}^{\alpha_{k+1}} \varepsilon_{ih}^k s_h^{k+1}$$

Thus ∂s_i^k is the sum of the $(k-1)$-faces of s_i^k, each with the induced orientation, and δs_i^k is the sum of the $(k+1)$-simplexes with k for a face, each with the induced orientation. The **coboundary** of a k-chain $C^k = \Sigma_{i=1}^{\alpha_k} a_i s_i^k$ is the $(k+1)$-chain $\delta C^k = \Sigma_{i=1}^{\alpha_k} a_i \delta s_i^k$.

(A) As in homology theory (see Art. 5–7(A)), but with the roles of rows and columns interchanged, for any bases $\{C^k\}$, $\{C^{k+1}\}$ of $\mathfrak{C}_k, \mathfrak{C}_{k+1}$, the incidence matrix $J_k(\{C^{k+1}\}, \{C^k\})$ has the property that the coboundary of the chain C_i^k labeling a row is the chain $\Sigma_{j=1}^{\alpha_{k+1}} \eta_{ij}^k C_j^{k+1}$ in which the chains labeling the columns appear with the respective elements in the row as coefficients (see Art. 5–7(B)).

A k-**cocycle** is a k-chain C^k for which $\delta C^k = \emptyset$.

THEOREM 15. **Each coboundary chain is a cocycle; that is,** $\delta\delta C^{k-1} = \emptyset$ **(the null $(k+1)$-chain) for any $(k-1)$-chain C^{k-1} (Exercise 72).** (A proof alternative to that of Exercise 72 follows the proof of Theorem 16 below.)

(B) Because δ is a linear operator, it can be interpreted as a homomorphism (Art. A–2) $\delta : \mathfrak{C}_k \to \mathfrak{C}_{k+1}$. The k-cocycles are, as a direct consequence of their definition, the kernel of this homomorphism.

THEOREM 16. **The mappings $\partial : \mathfrak{C}_k \to \mathfrak{C}_{k-1}$ and $\delta : \mathfrak{C}_{k-1} \to \mathfrak{C}_k$ are dual homomorphisms** (Art. A–5).

Proof. Let the chain groups be interpreted as integral modules $\mathfrak{C}_h = [s^h] = [s_1^h, \dots, s_{\alpha_k}^h]$ with $\{s^h\}$ for initial basis $(h = 0, \dots, m)$. Consider two elements

(5.69)
$$C^k = \sum_{i=1}^{\alpha_k} a_i s_i^k \in \mathfrak{C}_k, \qquad C^{k-1} = \sum_{j=1}^{\alpha_{k-1}} b_j s_j^{k-1} \in \mathfrak{C}_{k-1}.$$

Evaluating the two sides of Eq. (A.71) with $f = \partial$, $S = C^k$, $g = \delta$, $W = C^{k-1}$, we find

(5.70)
$$(\partial C^k \cdot C^{k-1}) = \sum_{j=1}^{\alpha_{k-1}} \left(\sum_{i=1}^{\alpha_k} \varepsilon_{ji}^{k-1} a_i \right) b_j,$$
$$(C^k \cdot \delta C^{k-1}) = \sum_{i=1}^{\alpha_k} a_i \sum_{j=1}^{\alpha_{k-1}} \varepsilon_{ji}^{k-1} b_j.$$

Hence

(5.71)
$$(\partial C^k \cdot C^{k-1}) = (C^k \cdot \delta C^{k-1}),$$

which formulates Theorem 16.

We also obtain the following alternative proof of Theorem 15. For any $s_i^{k+1} \in \{s^{k+1}\}$, since the dot product is commutative,

$$(5.72) \qquad (\delta\delta C^{k-1} \cdot s_i^{k+1}) = (\delta C^{k-1} \cdot \partial s_i^{k+1}) = (C^{k-1} \cdot \partial\partial s_i^{k+1}) = 0,$$

which implies that the coefficient of s_i^{k+1} in the expression $\delta\delta C^{k-1} = \Sigma\, a_i s_i^{k+1}$ is zero.

(C) The k-cocycles and the cobounding k-cocycles are subgroups, to be denoted by $\mathfrak{Z}^k$ and $\mathfrak{F}^k$, respectively, of $\mathfrak{C}_k$, and

$$(5.73) \qquad\qquad \mathfrak{F}^k \subset \mathfrak{Z}^k \subset \mathfrak{C}_k \qquad (\mathfrak{F}^0 = \emptyset).$$

Here, and throughout, the groups of cohomology theory will be denoted, as is customary, by the symbols for their analogs in homology theory (see the notation in Theorem 14) with superscripts in place of subscripts. The k-chain group $\mathfrak{C}_k = \mathfrak{C}^k$ plays the same role in both theories. Thus the kth **cohomology group** is denoted by

$$(5.74) \qquad\qquad \mathfrak{H}^k = \mathfrak{Z}^k/\mathfrak{F}^k.$$

We say that two k-chains C_1^k and C_2^k are **cohomologous**, a relation symbolized thus:

$$(5.75) \qquad\qquad C_1^k \smile C_2^k,$$

if there exists a $(k-1)$-chain C^{k-1} such that $\delta C^{k-1} = C_2^k - C_1^k$.

As a consequence of Theorem 15, the relation (5.75) implies $\delta C_1^k = \delta C_2^k$, a condition automatically fulfilled if C_1^k and C_2^k are k-cocycles.

The classes into which $\smile$ separates the k-cocycles are, by (5.74), the elements of $\mathfrak{H}^k$ and are called **cohomology classes**.

(D) The kth cohomology group of a complex K depends only on its $(k+1)$-skeleton. (Compare Theorem 3.)

EXERCISES

68. Write out δp_0 and $\delta(\overrightarrow{p_0 p_1})$ for the complex consisting of all the faces of $s^4 = p_0 p_1 p_2 p_3 p_4$, orienting each simplex according to the order of increasing subscripts on the symbols for its vertices.

69. List all the k-cocycles ($k = 0, 1, 2$) for the complex consisting of all the faces of $s^2 = p_0 p_1 p_2$.

70. By a second direct application of δ, show that $\delta\delta p_0$ and $\delta\delta(\overrightarrow{p_0 p_1})$ are null in Exercise 68.

71. In the complex of Exercise 68, discuss the group $\mathfrak{H}^3$.

72. Prove Theorem 15, by an argument analogous to the proof of Theorem 1.

73. In the notation of this article and Art. 5–7, find, in all dimensions, dual bases $\{A, B, C\}$ and $\{X, Y, Z\}$ for the complex K^2 consisting of the faces of $s^2 = p_0 p_1 p_2$ and of two 1-simplexes $p_0 p_3$ and $p_3 p_1$.

5–10.   Dual Bases

(A) A set $(C_1^k, \ldots, C_r^k)$ of k-cocycles is called **cohomology-independent**, an abbreviation for **linearly independent with respect to cohomology**, if

$$(5.76) \qquad \sum_{i=1}^{r} a_i C_i^k \backsim \emptyset \Rightarrow a_i = 0 \qquad (i = 1, \ldots, r).$$

Consider now the basis $\{A, B, C\} = (A_1^k, \ldots, A_{\gamma_k}^k; \; B_1^k, \ldots, B_{\beta_k}^k; \; C_1^k, \ldots, C_{\gamma_{k-1}}^k)$ of $\mathfrak{C}_k$ mentioned in Theorem 14. Let $\{X, Y, Z\} = (X_1^k, \ldots, X_{\gamma_k}^k; \; Y_1^k, \ldots, Y_{\beta_k}^k; \; Z_1^k, \ldots, Z_{\gamma_{k-1}}^k)$ be the basis of the module $\mathfrak{C}_k = [s^k]$ dual to $\{A, B, C\}$ (see Art. A–5, Theorem 9) with A_h^k dual to X_h^k, B_i^k to Y_i^k, and C_j^k to Z_j^k ($h = 1, \ldots, \gamma_k; \; i = 1, \ldots, \beta_k; \; j = 1, \ldots, \gamma_{k-1}$). The homomorphism $\delta : \mathfrak{C}_k \to \mathfrak{C}_{k+1}$ is determined by

$$(5.77) \qquad \begin{aligned} \delta X_i^k &= \tau_i^k Z_i^{k+1} & (i = 1, \ldots, \rho_k), \\ \delta X_j^k &= Z_j^{k+1} & (j = \rho_k + 1, \ldots, \gamma_k), \\ \delta Y_h^k &= \delta Z_i^k = \emptyset & (h = 1, \ldots, \beta_k; \; i = 1, \ldots, \gamma_{k-1}). \end{aligned}$$

This statement, justified by Lemma 14 below, corresponds to the labeling, in (5.53), of the rows and columns of J_k^* at the right and bottom, in accordance with Art. 5–9(A).

To shed further light on the basis $\{X, Y, Z\}$, consider again the stepwise procedure whereby the incidence matrices $(J_0, J_1, \ldots, J_{m-1})$ were normalized into $J_0^*, J_1^*, \ldots, J_{m-1}^*$. Consider, in particular, the elementary changes of base as described in Art. 5–7(D). The correspondence there described between modifications in the incidence matrices and changes in the labels of columns and rows was determined by Condition (B) of Art. 5–7. The analogous principle from the viewpoint of cohomology is stated in Art. 5–9(A).

LEMMA 14. **Let the incidence matrices be normalized precisely as in Art. 5–7, save that the labels shall be determined in accordance with Art. 5–9(A). Assume at a given stage that the bases for each $\mathfrak{C}^k$ corresponding to ∂ and δ are dual. Then an elementary operation on a matrix results in new bases for each $\mathfrak{C}^k$, for ∂ and δ, which are again dual.**

Proof of Lemma. When changing labels for the sake of ∂ we write them at the top and the left, as in Art. 5–7. When changing labels for the sake of δ, we write them at the bottom and the right. We use J^k in place of J_k for the kth matrix with the rows and columns labeled for the sake of δ. At the start of the process, we have

$$(5.78) \qquad \begin{matrix} (s_j^{k+1}) \\ J_k(\{s\}) = (s_i^k) \| \; \varepsilon_{ij}^k \; \|(s_i^k) = J^k(\{s\}). \\ (s_j^{k+1}) \end{matrix}$$

At a typical later stage, suppose

$$\text{(5.79)} \qquad J_k = U_i^k \, \| \eta_{ij}^k \, \begin{matrix} U_j^{k+1} \\ \\ V_j^{k+1} \end{matrix} \, \| \, V_i^k = J^k.$$

As basis for an induction assume that, at the stage in normalizing represented by (5.79), $\{U^k\} = (U_1^k, \ldots, U_{\alpha_k}^k)$ and $\{V^k\} = (V_1^k, \ldots, V_{\alpha_k}^k)$ are dual bases of $\mathfrak{C}_k$, and $\{U^{k+1}\}$, $\{V^{k+1}\}$ are dual bases of $\mathfrak{C}_{k+1}$. This hypothesis is verified at the initial stage (5.78), since the initial basis $\{s^k\}$ for each module $\mathfrak{C}_k = [s^k]$ $(k = 0, \ldots, m)$ is self-dual (Arts. A–4, 5). For elementary operations of types (1) and (2) in Art. 5–7(D), the conclusion of the lemma is easily verified, and we omit the details. We now reformulate Part (3) of Art. 5–7(D) and combine it with its analog corresponding to Art. 5–9(A) to obtain the following.

(B) Corresponding to the elementary matrix transformation (new col j) = (old col j) + a(col h) in (5.79) are the following changes of basis:

(5.80)
> (a) ∂: Replace U_j^{k+1} by $(U_j^{k+1} + aU_h^{k+1})$,
>
> (b) δ: Replace V_h^{k+1} by $(V_h^{k+1} - aV_j^{k+1})$,

where ∂ and δ indicate the respective changes made, as in Art. 5–7, for the sake of ∂ and, as here, for the sake of δ. Corresponding to the elementary matrix transformation (new row i) = (old row i) + b(row h) are the following changes of basis:

(5.81)
> (a) ∂: Replace U_h^k by $(U_h^k - bU_i^k)$,
>
> (b) δ: Replace V_i^k by $(V_i^k + bV_h^k)$.

The proof is now completed by Exercises 74 and 75.

EXERCISES

74. Establish (B). Note that (5.80a) and (5.81a) are a reformulation of Part 3 of Art. 5–7(D), and that (5.80b) and (5.81b) are analogous statements from the cohomology viewpoint.

75. Complete the proof of Lemma 14, showing that the changes of basis in (5.80) are a dual pair (Art. A–5) and, similarly, so are the changes in (5.81).

5–11. Comments on Cohomology Groups

By (5.77), the chains Y_i^k and Z_j^k are k-cocycles, but the chains X_h^k are not. Let a chain C^k be expressed in terms of the basis $\{X, Y, Z\}$ thus:

$$\text{(5.82)} \qquad C^k = \sum_{h=1}^{\gamma_k} x_h X_h^k + \sum_{i=1}^{\beta_k} y_i Y_i^k + \sum_{j=1}^{\gamma_{k-1}} z_j Z_j^k.$$

Its coboundary is

$$(5.83) \qquad \delta C^k = \sum_{h=1}^{\rho_k} x_h \tau_h^k Z_h^{k+1} + \sum_{h=\rho_k+1}^{\gamma_k} x_h Z_h^{k+1}.$$

Thus C^k is a cocycle if and only if $x_h = 0$ $(h = 1, \ldots, \gamma_k)$. Furthermore, from (5.83) with k replaced by $k - 1$, C^k is a coboundary cocycle if and only if it is a linear combination of $(\tau_1^{k-1} Z_1^k, \ldots, \tau_{\rho_{k-1}}^{k-1} Z_{\rho_{k-1}}^k,$ $Z_{\rho_{k-1}+1}^k, \ldots, Z_{\gamma_{k-1}}^k)$. Hence a cocycle $\Sigma_{i=1}^{\beta_k} y_i Y_i^k + \Sigma_{j=1}^{\gamma_{k-1}} z_j Z_j^k$ cobounds if and only if $y_i = 0$ and $z_j \equiv 0$ (mod $\tau_j^{k-1})$ $(j = 1, \ldots, \rho_{k-1})$.

(A) Hence, (1) $\{X^k, Y^k, Z^k\}$ is a basis for $\mathfrak{C}_k = \mathfrak{C}^k$, (2) $\{Y^k, Z^k\}$ is a basis for $\mathfrak{Z}^k$, (3) $(\tau_1^{k-1} Z_1^k, \ldots, \tau_{\rho_{k-1}}^{k-1} Z_{\rho_{k-1}}^k, Z_{\rho_{k+1}}^k, \ldots, Z_{\gamma_{k-1}}^k)$ is a basis for $\mathfrak{F}^k$, and (4) the cohomology classes of $(Y_1^k, \ldots, Y_{\beta_k}^k, Z_1^k, \ldots, Z_{\rho_{k-1}}^k)$ are a basis for $\mathfrak{H}^k$. The following theorem is a consequence.

THEOREM 17. **The kth cohomology group $\mathfrak{H}^k(K)$ is isomorphic to the direct sum of the $(k-1)^{\text{th}}$ torsion group $\mathfrak{T}_{k-1}$ and the kth Betti group $\mathfrak{B}_k$.**

While the cohomology groups are thus deducible from the homology groups, for finite complexes, they are valuable (1) because their use facilitates the statement and proof of various properties of manifolds, some of which will be established in Chapter 7, and (2) because they have generalizations to spaces other than complexes, where cohomology has led to the discovery of invariants not revealed by homology considerations.

Cohomology theory entered into topology relatively recently, within the past two or three decades, as compared with the homology theory of classical topology. In recent years, cohomology has played an increasingly important role, and an acquaintance with it is of fundamental importance in algebraic topology.

EXERCISES

76. Interpret Theorem 17 for $\mathfrak{H}^k(P^2)$, where P^2 is the projective plane $(k = 0, 1, 2)$.

77. Show that a 0-chain C^0 on K is a cocycle if and only if all the vertices in each component of K enter into C^0 with the same multiplicity.

78. Discuss $\mathfrak{H}^1(K)$ for an arbitrary linear graph.

79. Discuss the 1-cocycles on the 2-complexes shown in Figs. 5–3 and 5–5(b). Find some which are coboundaries and some which are not.

6

Topological Invariance of Homology Properties

A **compact topological polyhedron** was defined as a topological space Π homeomorphic to a finite rectilinear simplicial m-complex in an E^n for some natural numbers (m, n). Given a particular homeomorphism

$$(6.1) \qquad h: |K^m| \to \Pi \qquad K^m \subset E^n$$

and the corresponding triangulation $\Re^m$ of Π, we can apply the considerations of Chapter 5 to K^m and thus arrive at a set $(\beta_k, \tau_1^k, \ldots, \tau_{\rho_k}^k)$ $(k = 0, \ldots, m)$ of Betti numbers and torsion coefficients for $\Re^m$. While these numbers are derived with the aid of a particular triangulation, the following basic result holds.

THEOREM 1. **The Betti numbers and torsion coefficients of a topological polyhedron Π are independent of the triangulation K^m and are topological invariants of Π.**

A proof of Theorem 1 will occupy most of the present chapter. The method consists in giving topologically invariant definitions of so-called **singular simplexes, chains, homology groups**, and so on. It is then shown that the topologically invariant homology, Betti, and torsion groups of the singular theory are, for any homeomorphism (6.1), isomorphic to the corresponding simplicial groups of K^m. The first proof of this fundamental theorem was by J. W. Alexander.* The present improved proof was made possible by Theorem 4 below.

6–1. Singular Simplexes

Let s^k denote a linear k-simplex, and let Σ be an arbitrary topological space.

* "A Proof of the Invariance of Certain Constants in Analysis Situs," *Trans. Am. Math. Soc.* 16 (1915), pp. 148–154.

(A) In our applications, Σ will always be a topological polyhedron. In work beyond the scope of this book, however, singular homology theory like that about to be defined has led to the discovery of important properties of more general spaces.

By a **singular k-simplex** on Σ we mean a pair (γ^k, f) where $f : s^k \to \Sigma$ is a continuous mapping and where

$$(6.2) \qquad\qquad \gamma^k = f(s^k).$$

Although we will use γ^k as a symbol for this singular k-simplex, it is to be understood that the simplex is not merely a subset of Σ but consists of the subset γ^k together with its defining mapping. **Closed singular simplexes** $(\bar{\gamma}^k, f)$ are similarly defined by $f : \bar{s}^k \to \Sigma$.

Examples: (1) A mapping of s^k onto a single point defines a singular k-simplex. (2) If s^1 is mapped onto a Peano curve (Art. 8–1) covering a closed 2-simplex $\bar{s}^2$, then a singular 1-simplex is defined which coincides, as a point set, with $\bar{s}^2$. (3) Let the boundary of a 2-simplex s^2 be mapped onto a point p of a 2-sphere S^2, and let the inner points of s^2 be homeomorphically mapped onto $S^2 - p$. Thus a closed singular 2-simplex covering S^2 is defined.

(B) We say that two singular k-simplexes, $\gamma^k = f(s^k)$ and $\delta^k = g(t^k)$ are **equal**, $\gamma^k = \delta^k$, if there exists a linear homeomorphism λ of s^k onto t^k such that $q = \lambda(p) \Rightarrow f(p) = g(q)$ ($p \in s^k$, $q \in t^k$). Otherwise expressed, $\gamma^k = \delta^k$ if and only if the inverse images, s^k and t^k, correspond under some linear homeomorphism such that corresponding points have identical images on γ^k and δ^k.

If a subset of $\bar{s}^k$ is a linear simplex r^j of arbitrary dimension $j \leq k$, then $f(r^j)$ will be referred to as an f-**linear** (or γ^k-**linear**) j-simplex on the closure of the singular simplex $\gamma^k = f(s^k)$.

(C) Thus the defining mapping f carries the concept of linearity from $\bar{s}^k$ onto $\bar{\gamma}^k$. If $\gamma^k = \delta^k$, then γ^k-linearity agrees with δ^k-linearity, as a direct consequence of (B).

If s^k is an oriented simplex, then $\gamma^k = f(s^k)$ will be called an **oriented singular k-simplex** and a distinction must be made between

$$(6.3) \qquad\qquad +\gamma^k = f(+s^k) \quad \text{and} \quad -\gamma^k = f(-s^k).$$

This is done by changing the definition (B) of **equality**, so as to require that the linear homeomorphism λ map s^k onto t^k so that orientations agree. This implies that, if the condition in Definition (B) holds but orientations are opposite, then $-\gamma^k = \delta^k$.

(D) A singular k-simplex γ^k ($k > 0$) will be described as **degenerate** if $\gamma^k = -\gamma^k$ (Exercise 5); that is, if a linear, orientation-reversing homeomorphism λ of s^k with itself exists, such that if $p = \lambda(q)$, where $p, q \in s^k$, then $f(p) = f(q)$.

EXERCISES

1. Show that (a) a closed singular 1-simplex can be defined which covers an arbitrary compact 2-manifold, M^2, assuming the existence of Peano curves, defined in Art. 8–1 below, and (b) for an arbitrary $k > 0$, a closed singular k-simplex can be defined which covers M^2.

2. Give an example of two continuous mappings of the unit interval $(0 < x < 1)$ onto the unit interval $(0 < y < 1)$ which define unequal 1-simplexes.

3. Given a singular oriented k-simplex $\gamma^k = f(+s^k)$ $(k > 0)$ show that there generally exist $\frac{1}{2}(k + 1)!$ different mappings of s^k which define* γ^k.

4. In the previous example, give a $\gamma^k = f(+s^k)$ $(k > 0)$, such that all mappings of s^k onto the set $f(+s^k)$ define (a simplex equal to) γ^k.

5. Which of the following singular oriented simplexes are degenerate, and why? (a) The 1-simplex $\gamma^1 = f(s^1)$ where $\bar{s}^1$ is the segment $-2 \leq t \leq 2$ on the t-axis and where $f(t) = -t$. (b) The same, where $f(t) = |t|$. (c) The same where $f(t) = |1 + t|$. (d) The singular simplex defined by a linear mapping of s^k onto s^j (see Art. 4–10(B)), where $j < k$.

6. Let $s^2 = abc$ be a rectilinear 2-simplex in the euclidean plane, let m be the midpoint of ab and h the foot of the altitude from c onto ab. Suppose $h \neq m$. Which of the following mappings of s^2 define degenerate simplexes? Justify your answers. (a) The projection of s^2 onto $s^1 = ab$ by lines parallel to ch. (b) The same by lines parallel to cm. (c) The continuous mapping which is the identity on acm and which maps bcm linearly onto acm. (d) The same as (c), but with h in place of m.

7. Show that an arbitrary non-degenerate k-simplex $\gamma^k = f(s^k)$ $(k > 0)$ can coincide, as a point set, with a degenerate k-simplex $\delta^k = g(t^k)$. Give necessary and sufficient conditions on g for $\delta^k = -\delta^k$ in the case $\gamma^k = s^k = t^k$.

6–2.   Singular k-Chains and Groups

A **singular k-chain** on Σ means a finite set $(\gamma_1^k, \ldots, \gamma_\alpha^k)$ of oriented singular k-simplexes where γ_i^k is associated with an integer a_i or, more generally, with an element of an arbitrary given additive (abelian) group. Such a chain is expressed as a linear form

$$(6.4) \qquad C^k = a_1\gamma_1^k + \cdots + a_\alpha\gamma_\alpha^k,$$

which is an appropriate expression in view of the following definitions of **equality** and **addition**.

(A) Two chains are **equal** if they can be reduced to identical forms by a sequence of elementary operations of the following types: (1) replacement of a singular simplex by an equal simplex; (2) omission of a term $a_i\gamma_i^k$ if $a_i = 0$; (3) omission of a term $a_j\gamma_j^k$ if γ_j^k is degenerate; (4) replacement of $a_i\gamma_i^k$ by $(-a_i)(-\gamma_i^k)$; (5) permutation of terms; (6) replacement of $a_i\gamma_i^k + b_i\gamma_i^k$ by $(a_i + b_i)\gamma_i^k$.

---

* Or, more completely, which define simplexes equal to γ^k. However, as here, we will generally not distinguish between equal simplexes.

Consider next a second k-chain

$$(6.5) \qquad D^k = b_1 \delta_1^k + \cdots + b_\beta \delta_\beta^k.$$

The sum $C^k + D^k$ is then defined as

$$(6.6) \qquad C^k + D^k = \sum_{i=1}^{\alpha} a_i \gamma_i^k + \sum_{i=1}^{\beta} b_i \delta_i^k$$

or any chain equal thereto.

LEMMA 1. **The singular k-chains form an additive group $\mathfrak{C}_k^*$** (Exercise 8).

The group is called the k-**chain group of Σ over the coefficient group Z**. The k-chain group of Σ over any additive abelian coefficient group $\mathfrak{G}$ is similarly defined.

Now consider a continuous mapping $f : \bar{s}^k \to \Sigma$ of a closed oriented simplex $\bar{s}^k$ into a topological space. Then $\gamma^k = f(s^k)$ is a singular k-simplex. Its j-**faces** ($j = 0, 1, \ldots, k$) are the singular j-simplexes $\gamma^j = f(s^j)$, where $s^j = $ a j-dimensional face of s^k. If $j < k$, γ^j is a **proper** or **boundary** face and γ^j, γ^k are said to be **incident**. Let the $(k-1)$-dimensional faces of s^k, with the induced orientations, be denoted by s_i^{k-1} ($i = 0, 1, \ldots, k$) so that $\partial s^k = \Sigma_{i=0}^k s_i^{k-1}$, and let $\gamma_i^{k-1} = f(s_i^{k-1})$. Then the **boundary chain** of γ^k is the singular $(k-1)$-chain $\partial \gamma^k = \Sigma_{i=0}^k \gamma_i^{k-1}$.

(B) Since the boundary operator is essential to homology theory, we confine ourselves to singular simplexes whose defining mappings have continuous extensions over the closures of the inverse images. Given a space Σ, let $\mathfrak{C}_k^* = \mathfrak{C}_k^*(\Sigma)$ denote the k-chain group of Σ over a coefficient group $\mathfrak{G}$. We are primarily concerned with integral or mod 2 chains, but the invariance proofs are independent of the coefficient group. The set of all singular k-simplexes which can be defined on Σ generate $\mathfrak{C}_k^*$. The null element $\emptyset$ of $\mathfrak{C}_k^*$ is the chain in which each coefficient is the zero element of $\mathfrak{G}$. The relation

$$(6.7) \qquad \gamma^k = \emptyset \qquad \text{if } \gamma^k \text{ is degenerate}$$

is a group relation.

A singular k-chain $C^k = \Sigma_{i=1}^{\alpha} a_i \gamma_i^k$ is a **cycle** if $\partial C^k = \emptyset$.

As a corollary to Theorem 1 of Art. 5–1, the boundary of each singular $(k+1)$-chain is a singular k-cycle. The relation $C^k \sim 0$ will mean that $C^k = \partial D^{k+1}$, where D^{k+1} is a singular $(k+1)$-chain on Σ. Also, $C_1^k \sim C_2^k$ will mean that $C_1^k - C_2^k \sim 0$.

(C) Just as in the simplicial case, (1) the singular k-cycles constitute a subgroup $\mathfrak{Z}_k^*$ of $\mathfrak{C}_k^*$, (2) the bounding k-chains form a subgroup $\mathfrak{F}_k^*$ of $\mathfrak{Z}_k^*$, and (3) the k-chains having non-zero integral multiples which bound form a subgroup $\mathfrak{D}_k^* \supset \mathfrak{F}_k^*$ of $\mathfrak{Z}_k^*$. **Homology** and **cohomology** are defined and symbolized exactly as in the simplicial case.

The kth **singular homology, torsion,** and **Betti groups** are (see (5.59))

(6.8) $\mathfrak{H}_k^* = \mathfrak{Z}_k^*/\mathfrak{F}_k^*, \qquad \mathfrak{T}_k^* = \mathfrak{D}_k^*/\mathfrak{F}_k^*, \qquad \mathfrak{B}_k^* = \mathfrak{H}_k^*/\mathfrak{T}_k^* = \mathfrak{Z}_k^*/\mathfrak{D}_k^*.$

One also writes, for example, $\mathfrak{H}_k^*(\Sigma)$ and $\mathfrak{H}^*(\Sigma, \mathfrak{G})$, where Σ is the space and $\mathfrak{G}$ is the coefficient group.

THEOREM 2. **A continuous mapping $\varphi : \Sigma_1 \to \Sigma_2$ of a topological space Σ_1 into a topological space Σ_2 induces a homomorphism $\hat{\varphi}_k :$ $\mathfrak{C}_k(\Sigma_1) \to \mathfrak{C}_k(\Sigma_2)$ ($k = 0, 1, \ldots$), with the property $\partial\hat{\varphi}_k = \hat{\varphi}_k\,\partial$.**

Proof. If $\gamma^k = f(s^k)$ is a singular k-simplex on Σ_1, so is $\eta^k = \hat{\varphi}f(s^k)$ on Σ_2 as a result of Theorem 5 in Chapter 3. If γ^k is degenerate, so is η^k. The mapping $\hat{\varphi}_k'$ defined by $\hat{\varphi}_k(\Sigma\, a_i\gamma_i^k) = \Sigma\, a_i\hat{\varphi}_k(\gamma_i^k)$ clearly has the properties $\hat{\varphi}_k(C^k + D^k) = \hat{\varphi}_k(C^k) + \hat{\varphi}_k(D^k)$ and is therefore a homomorphism. It is a direct consequence of the definitions that $\hat{\varphi}_k$ commutes with the boundary operator; that is, for each $C^k \in \mathfrak{C}_k^*$

(6.9) $$\partial\hat{\varphi}_k C^k = \hat{\varphi}_{k-1}\,\partial C^k.$$

COROLLARY. **The mapping $\hat{\varphi}_k$ carries singular k-cycles of Σ_1 into singular k-cycles of Σ_2, bounding cycles into bounding cycles, and homologous cycles into homologous cycles.**

(*D*) Hence $\hat{\varphi}_k$ induces a homomorphism

(6.10) $\varphi_k^* : \mathfrak{H}_k^*(\Sigma_1) \to \mathfrak{H}_k^*(\Sigma_2), \qquad \mathfrak{B}_k^*(\Sigma_1) \to \mathfrak{B}_k^*(\Sigma_2), \qquad \mathfrak{T}_k^*(\Sigma_1) \to \mathfrak{T}_k^*(\Sigma_2).$

THEOREM 3. **The groups $\mathfrak{H}_k^*$, $\mathfrak{B}_k^*$, and $\mathfrak{T}_k^*$ are topologically invariant; that is, $\mathfrak{H}_k^*(\Sigma_1)$ and $\mathfrak{H}_k^*(\Sigma_2)$, for example, are isomorphic if Σ_1 and Σ_2 are homeomorphic.**

Proof. If φ is a homeomorphism, then it and its inverse, φ^{-1}, induce a homomorphism φ^*, as in (6.10), and an inverse homomorphism φ^{*-1} between each of the pairs of groups in question. But a homomorphism with an inverse which is also a homomorphism is easily seen to be an isomorphism.

(*E*) Also, $\mathfrak{C}_k^*$, $\mathfrak{Z}_k^*$, $\mathfrak{D}_k^*$, $\mathfrak{F}_k^*$ are topologically invariant, which implies the theorem, by precisely the same argument; but we must pass to the factor groups ($\mathfrak{H}_k^*, \mathfrak{B}_k^*, \mathfrak{T}_k^*$), to obtain topological invariants.

EXERCISES

8. Establish Lemma 1 by verifying the group axioms for $\mathfrak{C}_k^*$.

9. Show that equal singular k-simplexes have equal boundary chains. Deduce that $\partial\gamma^k = \emptyset$ if γ^k is degenerate.

10. Show that a non-degenerate singular k-simplex can have degenerate boundary faces.

6–3. Sperner's Lemma; Invariance of Dimension

(A) If K is a simplicial subdivision of a topological polyhedron $\Pi = |K|$, then each point p of Π is on a unique simplex of $|K|$, called the **carrier** of p in K. Suppose that K is linear simplicial in E, and let L be a linear simplicial subdivision of K. Let λ_0 be a mapping of the vertices $\{q\}$ of L into the vertices of K such that, for each $q \in \{q\}$, $\lambda_0(q)$ is a vertex of the carrier of q in K. Then λ_0 is easily seen to be a simplicial mapping, in the sense of Art. 4–10, of the abstract complex of L into that of K.

THEOREM* 4. **Given an oriented m-simplex s^m, suppose that $K(s^m)$, the complex consisting of the faces of s^m, is subdivided into a linear simplicial complex K^m whose m-simplexes are oriented like s^m (Art. 5–6). Let f be a mapping of the 0-cells of K^m into those of s^m under which the image of each 0-cell of K^m is a vertex of its carrier in $K(s^m)$. Then the number of m-simplexes of K^m whose vertices are mapped onto all $m + 1$ vertices of s^m with orientation preserved exceeds by one the number whose vertices are mapped onto all $m + 1$ vertices with orientation reversed.**

Proof. We use f also for the induced chain mappings. Using mathematical induction, take $m = 1$ so that $s^m = s^1$ is an oriented 1-cell and let $\partial s^1 = s_1^0 - s_0^0$. Let $\{t_i^1\}$ be the 1-cells of K^1, oriented like s^1. Then $f(\Sigma_i \, \partial t_i^1) = f(s_1^0 - s_0^0) = s_1^0 - s_0^0$. Now suppose that x of the t_i^1 have end points mapped onto s_1^0 and s_0^0 so that orientation of the 1-cell is preserved, that y are mapped with orientation reversed, and z have both end points mapped onto s_1^0 or both onto s_0^0. Then $f(\Sigma_i \, \partial t_i^1) = x(s_1^0 - s_0^0) + y(s_0^0 - s_1^0) + z\emptyset = (x - y)(s_1^0 - s_0^0)$. Hence $s_1^0 - s_0^0 = (x - y)(s_1^0 - s_0^0)$, from which we infer that $x - y = 1$, completing the proof for $m = 1$.

Now assume that the theorem has been proved for $m = 1, 2, \ldots, r$. Let $s_0^r, s_1^r, \ldots, s_{r+1}^r$ be the boundary r-simplexes of s^{r+1}, with the orientations induced by that of s^{r+1}. Let $\{t_i^{r+1}\}$ be the $(r + 1)$-simplexes of K^{r+1} oriented like s^{r+1} and let $\{u_j^r\}$ be the r-simplexes of K^{r+1} which are on $s_0^r, \ldots, s_{r+1}^r$, each oriented like the one of the latter on which it lies.

With the mapping by f of the vertices of each oriented simplex of K^{r+1} we associate in an obvious way a mapping of the oriented simplex itself.

Then $f(\partial \Sigma_i t_i^{r+1}) = f(\Sigma_j u_j^r)$, which, by the theorem for $m = r$, equals $(s_0^r + s_1^r + \cdots + s_{r+1}^r) +$ degenerate r-simplexes. On the other hand, $f(\partial \Sigma_i t_i^{r+1}) = \Sigma_i f(\partial t_i^{r+1})$. Now if the number of distinct 0-cells

---

* Theorem 4, which represents a strengthening of Sperner's lemma (see (B) below), and Lemma 7 below, which is a corollary, are due, together with their present proofs, to Professor Arthur B. Brown (see Preface).

among the images under f of the vertices of t_i^{r+1} is exactly $r + 1$, it is easily verified that $f(\partial t_i^{r+1})$ contains exactly two non-degenerate r-simplexes of opposite orientations, so that $f(\partial t_i^{r+1}) = \emptyset +$ degenerate r-simplexes. If the number is less than $r + 1$, there are no non-degenerate r-simplexes in $f(\partial t_i^{r+1})$. Hence the only cases in which $f(\partial t_i^{r+1}) \neq \emptyset$ when degenerate r-simplexes are dropped are those in which the $r + 2$ vertices of t_i^{r+1} are mapped onto the $r + 2$ vertices of s^{r+1}. Suppose that this happens for x of the t_i^{r+1} with orientation preserved and for y with orientation reversed. Then $\Sigma_i f(\partial t_i^{r+1}) = (x - y)(s_0^r + s_1^r + \cdots + s_{r+1}^r) +$ degenerate r-simplexes and, as in the proof for the case that $m = 1$, we infer that $x - y = 1$. This completes the proof.

(B) It follows from Theorem 4 that an odd number, hence at least one, of the m-simplexes of K^m have their vertices mapped onto, not merely into, the vertices of s^m. This result is **Sperner's lemma.**

THEOREM 5. **If a compact topological polyhedron Π can be triangulated into an m-complex, then Π has Brouwer dimension m.**

Proof. Since Brouwer dimension is topologically invariant, it is sufficient to give the proof for a linear simplicial polyhedron $P = |K^m|$ in a euclidean space E^n.

LEMMA 2. **A closed linear m-simplex $\bar{s}^m = p_0 p_1 \ldots p_m$ in E^n is of Brouwer dimension at least m.**

Proof of Lemma. It is to be shown (Art. 3–8) that, for $\delta > 0$ sufficiently small, a closed finite covering $\{A\}$ of $\bar{s}^m$ is of order $> m$ if diam $A < \delta$ for each $A \in \{A\}$.

(C) Let $\delta > 0$ be so small that (1) no $A \in \{A\}$ intersects all the $(m - 1)$-dimensional faces of s^m and (2) no $A \in \{A\}$ intersects both a vertex p_j of s^m and the closure $\bar{s}_j^{m-1}$ of the opposite face (Exercise 11).

Since $\bar{s}^m \subset \cup \{A\}$ and since (C2) implies that no $A \in \{A\}$ contains two vertices of s^m, it follows that $m + 1$ of the A's can be so numbered that $p_j \in A_j (j = 0, 1, \ldots, m)$. Let $\mathfrak{A}_0$ be the subset of $\{A\}$ consisting of those elements which do not intersect $\bar{s}_0^{m-1}$, and let A_0^* be the union of the sets $\mathfrak{A}_0$. For some $j \in (1, \ldots, m)$ assume $(A_0^*, \ldots, A_{j-1}^*)$ defined, where A_i^* is the union of a subset $\mathfrak{A}_i$ of $\{A\}$ $(i = 0, \ldots, j - 1)$. Let $\mathfrak{A}_j$ be the subset of $\{A\} - \bigcup_{i=0}^{j-1} \mathfrak{A}_i$ consisting of all elements thereof which do not intersect $\bar{s}_j^{m-1}$, and let A_j^* be the union of the sets $\mathfrak{A}_j$.

(D) The recurrent definition just given leads to a partition of $\{A\}$ into subsets $\mathfrak{A}_0, \ldots, \mathfrak{A}_m$ with the property that a closed face $\bar{s}^k = p_{i_0} \ldots p_{i_k}$ of s^m is covered by $\bigcup_{h=0}^{k} \mathfrak{A}_{i_h}$ and is not intersected by $\mathfrak{A}_j$ for $j \notin (i_0, \ldots, i_k)$ (Exercise 13).

Now let $K^m = \{s\}$ be the set of all faces of s^m. Let ν be an integer so large that the mesh of the νth barycentric subdivision K_ν^m of K_0^m is less than the Lebesgue number λ of the covering $A_0^*, \ldots, A_m^*$ (Arts. 4–11(C) and 3–8(H)). Let each vertex q of K_ν^m be mapped onto p_j where j is the smallest number such that $q \in A_j^*$. By (C) and (D), p_j is a vertex of the carrier of q on K_0^m. By Sperner's lemma, there exists an m-simplex $t^m \in K_\nu^m$ whose vertices are mapped onto $(p_0, p_1, \ldots, p_m)$. But $\bar{t}^m$ is a set of diameter less than λ intersecting all the sets $(A_0^*, \ldots, A_m^*)$. Therefore (Chapter 3, Theorem 22) these sets have a non-vacuous intersection; hence, the covering $\{A\}$ is of order at least $m + 1$, proving Lemma 2.

COROLLARY. **If K^m is a finite linear m-complex in E^n, then** dim $|K^m|$ $\geq m$ (Exercise 14).

To complete our proof of Theorem 5, it remains to show that dim $|K^m| \leq m$.

The **star** $St(q)$ of a vertex q of K^m means the union of q and all the simplexes of K^m incident with q.

LEMMA 3. **Let K_1 be the first barycentric subdivision of $K = K^m$, and let $\{q\}$ be the vertices of K. Let $St(q)$ be the star of q on K_1. Then**

$$(6.11) \qquad \{\bar{St}\} = \{\bar{St}(q) \,|\, q \in \{q\}\}$$

is a closed covering of $P = |K|$ of order $m + 1$.

Proof of Lemma. By definition, $St(q)$ is the union of the simplexes of K_1 incident with q. Let $s^k = q_0 q_1 \ldots q_k$ be a k-simplex of K, and let $(u_0, u_1, \ldots, u_k)$ be barycentric coordinates on s^k relative to $(q_0, q_1, \ldots, q_k)$.

(E) The part of s^k covered by $\bar{St}(q_0)$ is defined (Exercise 16) by the inequalities $u_0 \geq u_i$ $(i = 1, \ldots, k)$. Hence, the barycenter of s^k is the only point on $\bar{s}^k$ which belongs to the intersection $\bigcap_{i=0}^{k} \bar{St}(q_i)$. Applying this argument for $k = m$, we find that each barycenter of an m-simplex of K^m belongs to exactly $m + 1$ of the sets $\{\bar{St}\}$, and that these are the only points where $(m + 1)$ of these sets intersect.

COROLLARY. **For an arbitrary $\delta > 0$, there exists a finite covering of $P = |K|$ which is of mesh δ and order $m + 1$.**

For, by Art. 4–11(C), we can choose ν so large that $K_{\nu+1}$ is of mesh $\delta/2$. This implies that each star on $K_{\nu+1}$ is of diameter less than δ. Since $K_{\nu+1}$ is the first barycentric subdivision of K_ν, the lemma implies the corollary. The latter, in turn, implies dim $|K| \leq m$, completing the proof.

(F) **Theorem of the invariance of dimension:** *The dimension number m of an m-complex K^m is a topological invariant of the space $\Pi = |K^m|$.* This follows from Theorem 5 and the topological invariance of Brouwer dimension (Chapter 3, Theorem 20).

This result applies to the case where $\Re$ is infinite, hence Π not compact, if the **Brouwer dimension** of Π is defined as m provided Π contains as a subset some compact topological polyhedron of dimension m but none of dimension $m + 1$.

(G) The dimension number n of euclidean n-space E^n equals its Brouwer dimension.

To establish (G), first subdivide E^n into the infinite complex K consisting of all the faces of all the n-cells of the form $m_i < x_i < m_i + 1$ $(i = 1, \ldots, n)$, where the m's are integers. Even though the polyhedral complex K is infinite, it can be subdivided into a simplicial n-complex by the process used in the proof of Chapter 4, Theorem 8. Statement (G) now follows from Theorem 5.

EXERCISES

11. Show that there exists a number δ which satisfies (C).

12. Draw figures to illustrate the sets A_j^* and A_j in the proof of Lemma 2 for the case where $m = 2$ and $\{A\}$ is a set of overlapping disks.

13. Prove (D).

14. Prove the corollary to Lemma 2 by proving the more general result that $A \subset S \Rightarrow \dim S \geq \dim A$, where A and S are compacta.

15. Draw a diagram to illustrate the covering $\{\overline{St}\}$ in Lemma 3.

16. Prove (E), with the aid of the corollary to Chapter 4, Theorem 6.

6–4.   The Brouwer Fixed-Point Theorem

We include this article here because it involves an application of Sperner's lemma.

A large body of topological theory with important applications in other branches of mathematics is concerned with fixed points of mappings. Let T be a topological space, and let $A \subset T$. Consider a mapping $f : A \to T$ of A onto a subset $f(A)$ of the same topological space T.

(A) A **fixed point** of f is then defined as a point $p \in A$ which coincides with its image; that is

$$(6.12) \qquad p = f(p) \Leftrightarrow p \text{ is a fixed point of } f.$$

Obviously, p must then be in the intersection $A \cap f(A)$.

(B) The **graph** of f is the following subset of $T \times T$:

$$(6.13) \quad F = F(f) = \{(p, q) \in T \times T \mid q = f(p)\} \qquad \text{(see Art. 3–2 (F)).}$$

The graph of the identity mapping i, which maps each $p \in T$ onto itself, $p = i(p)$, is called the **diagonal** D of $T \times T$:

$$(6.14) \qquad D = F(i) = \{(p, p) \mid p \in T\} \subset T \times T.$$

The fixed points of f then correspond to the intersection $F \cap D$, under the projection $T \times T \to T$.

To clarify the foregoing, consider the case where T is the real number system, and let $T \times T$ be interpreted as the (x, y)-plane, so that T is represented by the x-axis X and also by the y-axis Y. A mapping f of $A \subset X = T$ onto $B = f(A) \subset Y = T$ has a fixed point on X corresponding to each point where the graph $F : y = f(x)$ intersects the diagonal, which is the line $D : y = x$ (Fig. 6–1).

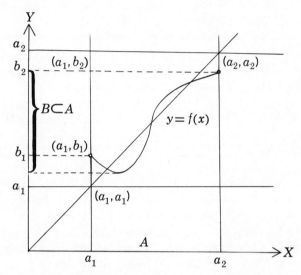

Fig. 6–1. Fixed points for $f : A \to B \subset A$.

THEOREM 6. **Any continuous mapping f of a segment $A : a_1 \leq x \leq a_2$ onto $B \subset A$ possesses at least one fixed point.**

As an aid in proving this theorem, consider Fig. 6–1. Geometrically, the theorem means that the graph F of a continuous mapping cannot cut across the square $A \times A$ from the left side to the right side without intersecting the diagonal (Exercise 17).

THEOREM 7 (BROUWER'S FIXED-POINT THEOREM). **Let D be a space homeomorphic to the solid m-sphere $\Sigma_{i=1}^{m} x_i^2 \leq 1$ in E^m, and $f : D \to D$ a continuous mapping of D into itself. Then f has at least one fixed point.**

Proof. Consider first the case $D = \bar{s}$, where $\bar{s}$ is the closure of a simplex $s = p_0 p_1 \ldots p_m$.

Let $(u) = (u_0, u_1, \ldots, u_m)$ be barycentric coordinates relative to $(p_0, p_1, \ldots, p_m)$, and let $(u_0', \ldots, u_m')$ denote the image under f of a point (u). Let A_j, $j \in (0, 1, \ldots, m)$, be the set of all points (u) for each of which $u'_j \leq u_j$. Suppose $(u) \in p_{i_0} \cdots p_{i_k} = \bar{s}^k$. Then, by definition of barycentric coordinates,

$$(6.15) \qquad u_{i_0} + \cdots + u_{i_k} = u'_0 + \cdots + u'_m = 1.$$

But each u and each u' is non-negative. Hence, $u_{i_h} \geq u'_{i_h}$ for some $h \in (0, 1, \ldots, k)$, for otherwise $u_{i_0} + \cdots + u_{i_k}$ would be less than $u'_{i_0} + \cdots + u'_{i_k} \leq 1$. It follows that each point of $\bar{s}^k = p_{i_0} \cdots p_{i_k}$ belongs to at least one of the sets A_{i_h}. That is,

$$(6.16) \qquad \bar{s}^k = p_{i_0} \cdots p_{i_k} \subset \bigcup_{h=0}^{k} A_{i_h}.$$

Now let $K = \{s\}$ be the set of faces of s^m; and let K_ν be the νth barycentric subdivision of K, where ν is so large that the mesh of K_ν is less than the Lebesgue number λ of the covering $A_0, \ldots, A_m$ of $\bar{s}^m$ (Arts. 3–8 and 4–11). Let $\varphi : K_\nu \to K$ be a simplicial mapping such that, for each vertex q of K_ν, (1) $\varphi(q)$ is a vertex of the carrier of q in K and (2) q and $\varphi(q)$ are common to some set A_j. The possibility of imposing this second condition is assured by (6.16). By Sperner's lemma (Art. 6–3(B)) there exists at least one m-simplex $t^m \in K_\nu$, whose vertices are mapped onto $(p_0, p_1, \ldots, p_m)$. But, by the definition of φ, this implies that $\bar{t}^m$ intersects $(A_0, \ldots, A_m)$. Since diam $\bar{t}^m < \lambda$, the sets $(A_0, \ldots, A_m)$ have a common point p. At p, $0 \leq u'_i \leq u_i$ ($i = 0, 1, \ldots, m$), by definition of A_i, which, with $\Sigma u'_i = \Sigma u_i = 1$, implies $u'_i = u_i$, so that p is a fixed point. By a homeomorphic mapping, this proof can be applied to the general homeomorph D of $\bar{s}$.

EXERCISES

17. (a) Prove Theorem 6, using properties of real continuous functions. (b) Show that Theorem 6 becomes false if A is replaced by an open interval $a_1 < x < a_2$ or a half-open interval $a_1 < x \leq a_2$.

18. Show that a continuous mapping of the circle $x^2 + y^2 = 1$ onto a proper subset of itself has a fixed point.

19. Let f be a homeomorphism of the clockwise oriented circle $x^2 + y^2 = 1$ onto itself, oriented counterclockwise. Show that f has a fixed point.

20. Show that a continuous mapping f of a segment $A : a_1 \leq x \leq a_2$ onto a segment $B : b_1 \leq x \leq b_2$ containing A has a fixed point, but that this is not generally so if $f : A \to B$ is merely into.

21. Show that a continuous mapping of the x-axis onto a bounded subset of itself has a fixed point, but that a continuous mapping of the x-axis onto the subset $x < 1$ need not have a fixed point.

22. Show that the 2-sphere $x^2 + y^2 + z^2 = 1$ can be homeomorphically mapped onto itself by a mapping with exactly one fixed point.

23. Show that the closure $\bar{s}^2$ of a 2-simplex can be homeomorphically mapped onto itself so that the only fixed point is a vertex.

24. Go through the proof of Theorem 7, with figures to show the sets A_j for the case $m = 2$, where $f(u_0, u_1, u_2) = (u_1, u_2, u_0)$.

25. Show that the solid sphere $x^2 + y^2 + z^2 \le 1$ in E^3 can be homeomorphically mapped onto itself (a) so that $(0, 0, 1)$ is the only fixed point, (b) so that $(0, 0, 0)$ is the only fixed point.

6–5. Invariance of Regionality

THEOREM 8. **If h is a homeomorphism which maps the closure $\bar{s}$ of a simplex $s = p_0 p_1 \ldots p_m$ into E^m, then h maps each point of s onto an inner point of $h(\bar{s})$.**

Proof. We commence with a lemma.

LEMMA 4. **Let C be a closed bounded subset of E^m, and let $\{A\} = (A_1, \ldots, A_a)$ be a closed covering of C such that there is just one point $p \in C$ which belongs to $m + 1$ of the sets $\{A\}$. Then, if p is not an inner point of C, there exists, for each $\eta > 0$, a closed covering $\{A'\} = (A_1', \ldots, A_a')$ of order m, where A_i and A_i' coincide outside the spherical η-neighborhood of p.**

Proof of Lemma. Let S be the $(m - 1)$-sphere of radius η about p. Suppose the A's so numbered that $(A_1, \ldots, A_c)$ is the subset of $\{A\}$ consisting of all elements each of which intersects S, and let $A_i^* = A_i \cap S$ $(i = 1, \ldots, c)$. Then $\{A^*\} = (A_1^*, \ldots, A_c^*)$ is a finite closed covering of $C \cap S$ of order at most m. By Lebesgue's lemma (Chapter 3, Theorem 22), there exists a number $\zeta > 0$ so small that the solid sphere $\rho(p, q) \le \zeta$ about a point $q \in S$ intersects at most m elements of $\{A^*\}$.

Since S is of dimension $m - 1$, it admits a closed finite covering $(B_1, \ldots, B_\nu) = \{B\}$ of order m, where diam $B_i < \zeta$ $(i = 1, \ldots, \nu)$. We define a partition $\beta_1, \ldots, \beta_c$ of $\{B\}$ as follows: (1) β_1 is the set of all the sets B_i each of which either intersects A_1^* or else intersects none of the sets $(A_1^*, \ldots, A_c^*)$. (2) Once $(\beta_1, \ldots, \beta_{h-1})$ are defined, for some $h > 1$, β_h is defined as the set of all the sets B_i each of which intersects A_h^* and does not belong to one of the sets $(\beta_1, \ldots, \beta_{h-1})$. This recurrency applies for $h = 2, \ldots, c$.

Now let $A_i^0 = A_i^* \cup \beta_i$ $(i = 1, \ldots, c)$. Then $(A_1^0, \ldots, A_c^0)$ covers S, since $\bigcup_{i=1}^{c} \beta_i = \bigcup_{i=1}^{\nu} B_i$ covers S. If $q \in S$, then the union of the sets B_i containing q is on the spherical ζ-neighborhood of q, which intersects at most m of the sets A_h^*. It follows that q belongs to at most m of the sets A_h^0, since in order to belong to a set A_h^0 it must belong to A_h^* or to a set B_i which intersects A_h^*.

(A) We have just shown that $(A_1^0, \ldots, A_c^0)$ is a covering of S of order $\le m$.

Since p is not an inner point of C, there exists a point p_0 of $E - C$ inside S. Let A_i'' be the union of all the line segments from p_0 to points of A_i^0 $(i = 1, \ldots, c)$. Then $(A_1'', \ldots, A_c'')$ is a closed covering of the solid sphere bounded by S, and p_0 is the only point where more than m of the sets $(A_1'', \ldots, A_c'')$ intersect. Let A_i' be the union of A_i'' with the part of A_i outside S $(i = 1, \ldots, c)$, and let $A_i' = A_i$ $(i = c + 1,$ $\ldots, a)$. Then $(A_i', \ldots, A_a')$ satisfies Lemma 4.

Now suppose that, contrary to Theorem 8, there exists a point $q \in s^m = p_0 p_1 \ldots p_m$ such that $p = h(q)$ is not an inner point of $h(\bar{s}^m)$. Let δ be the complex consisting of the boundary faces of s^m and let δ_1 be its first barycentric subdivision. Let Σ_j be the star of p_j on δ_1 $(j = 0, \ldots, m)$. Then $(\bar{\Sigma}_0, \ldots, \bar{\Sigma}_m)$ is a closed covering of $\bar{s}^m - s^m$ of order m (Lemma 4). Let D_j be the union of all the segments joining q to $\bar{\Sigma}_j$.

(B) Then $(D_0, \ldots, D_m)$ is a closed covering of $\bar{s}^m$, such that p is the only point common to all $m + 1$ of the sets D_j.

(C) There exists a number $\varepsilon > 0$ so small that if (1) $(D_0', \ldots, D_m')$ is a closed covering of $\bar{s}^m$ and (2) the parts of D_j' and D_j outside the ε-sphere about q are identical, then $D_0' \cap \cdots \cap D_m'$ is not vacuous (Exercise 26).

Let $A_j = h(D_j)$ $(j = 0, \ldots, m)$. Then $\{A\} = (A_0, A_1, \ldots, A_m)$ fulfills the hypotheses of Lemma 4 for $C = h(\bar{s}^m)$. Hence, $p = h(q)$ being assumed not to be an inner point of $h(\bar{s}^m)$, there exists, for each $\eta > 0$, a closed covering $A_0', \ldots, A_m'$ such that (1) A_j' and A_j coincide outside the η'-sphere about p and (2) $A_0' \cap \cdots \cap A_m' = \emptyset$.

Now let η be so small that h^{-1} maps the intersection with $h(\bar{s}^m)$ of the spherical η-neighborhood of p into the spherical ε-neighborhood of q, and let $D_j' = h^{-1}(A_j')$ $(j = 0, \ldots, m)$. Then $A_0' \cap \cdots \cap A_m' = \emptyset$ implies $D_0' \cap \cdots \cap D_m' = \emptyset$, contradicting (C) and proving Theorem 8.

COROLLARY 1. **Under the hypotheses of Theorem 8, each point of** $\bar{s}^m - s^m$ **maps onto a non-interior point of** $h(\bar{s}^m)$ (Exercise 27).

COROLLARY 2. **If** h **is a homeomorphism mapping a set** $C \subset E^m$ **onto** $h(C) \subset E_0^m$, **where** E^m **and** E_0^m **are euclidean** m-**spaces, then** h **maps each inner point of** C **onto an inner point of** $h(C)$.

In particular, if C is a region* of E^m, then $h(C)$ consists entirely of inner points. Thus, since $h(C)$ is easily shown to be connected, Theorem 8 implies the topological invariance of the property of being a region.

EXERCISES

26. Prove (C). The material following Art. 6–3 (D) can be used.
27. Establish Corollaries 1 and 2 to Theorem 4.

* That is, a connected subset made up entirely of inner points.

6–6. Singular and Simplicial Groups on a Topological Polyhedron

Consider an arbitrary compact topological m-dimensional polyhedron Π, and let h be a homeomorphism mapping Π onto a simplicial polyhedron $P = |K| \subset E^n$, where $K = \{s\}$ is an oriented simplicial complex. By Chapter 4, Theorems 8 and 9, K is finite and m-dimensional.

(A) Theorem 1 will, by Theorem 3, follow in all its generality if it be shown that the singular homology group $\mathfrak{H}_k^*(P)$ is isomorphic to the simplicial homology group $\mathfrak{H}_k(K)$ as defined in Chapter 5. Symbols for simplicial homology groups and chains are modified by asterisks to obtain symbols for the corresponding singular groups and chains.

The first barycentric subdivision (Art. 4–11) of a complex K will be denoted by $K_1 = \zeta K$, where ζ is the (barycentric) **subdivision operator**. Thus the rth barycentric subdivision of K is

$$(6.17) \qquad K_r = \zeta^r K \qquad (r = 1, 2, \dots), \qquad K_0 = \zeta^0 K = K.$$

(B) We need to define ζ for an oriented complex K. We do so by requiring that all the k-simplexes of $K_1 = \zeta K$ on a k-simplex $s^k \in K$ shall be oriented like s^k (Art. 5–6(A)). The requirement has meaning, since all these k-simplexes are on $\Lambda(s^k)$, which is a euclidean k-dimensional subspace of E^n.

(C) The operator ζ induces a **subdivision operator** $\hat{\zeta}$ for chains, where $\hat{\zeta}s^k$ is the chain of ζs^k (Art. 5–6(F)), and where, if $C^k = \Sigma_{i=1}^{\alpha_k} a_i s_i^k$,

$$(6.18) \qquad \begin{cases} C_1^k = \hat{\zeta} C^k = \Sigma_{i=1}^{\alpha_k} a_i \hat{\zeta} s_i^k, \\ C_r^k = \hat{\zeta}^r C^k = \hat{\zeta}\hat{\zeta}^{r-1} C^k \qquad (r = 2, 3, \dots), \qquad C^k = \hat{\zeta}^0 C^k. \end{cases}$$

LEMMA 5. **The operators ∂ and $\hat{\zeta}$ commute, that is:**

$$(6.19) \qquad \partial \hat{\zeta}^r C^k = \hat{\zeta}^r \partial C^k \qquad (r = 1, 2, \dots).$$

Proof of Lemma. Let the $(k - 1)$-faces of an oriented k-simplex s^k be oriented like s^k, and let the j-faces $(j < k - 1)$ be arbitrarily oriented. Then ∂s^k is the $(k - 1)$-chain of its boundary complex. The faces of the simplexes in ζs^k constitute, by the definitions, a coherently oriented k-pseudomanifold, with the subdivided boundary simplexes of s^k for boundary. Lemma 5 now follows readily from Art. 5–6, Lemma 11 (Exercise 29).

(D) The concept of barycentric subdivisions of simplicial complexes and simplicial chains is carried over to singular complexes and chains in a direct way with the aid of continuous mappings of subcomplexes of K into an arbitrary topological space. Lemma 5 holds for the singular case.

The ideas underlying the present proof of Theorem 1 are as follows. It is to be shown (see (A) above) that $\mathfrak{H}_k^*(P) \approx \mathfrak{H}_k(K)$ where $\approx$ denotes the relationship of being isomorphic. *Simplicial simplexes and chains can be considered as special cases of singular simplexes and chains, where the function f* (Art. 6–1) *maps each point onto itself, and similarly for cycles and boundary cycles.* That is,

$$(6.20) \qquad \mathfrak{C}_k^* \supset \mathfrak{C}_k, \qquad \mathfrak{Z}_k^* \supset \mathfrak{Z}_k, \qquad \mathfrak{D}_k^* \supset \mathfrak{D}_k, \qquad \mathfrak{F}_k^* \supset \mathfrak{F}_k.$$

But the singular groups in (6.20), for $k > 0$, contain vastly more elements than the simplicial.

EXERCISES

28. Verify Lemma 5 directly in the case where $r = 1$, $C^k = +s^2$ and $s^2 = p_0 p_1 p_2$. Illustrate with a diagram.

29. Explain how Lemma 5 follows from Art. 5–6, Lemma 11.

6–7. Simplicial Subsets of Singular Homology Classes

We continue to use the barycentric subdivision operator ζ, subject to Art. 6–6(B). As a consequence of Art. 6–1(C), ζ can operate on singular complexes as well as on linear simplicial complexes, where a **singular complex** is the set of all the faces of a set of singular simplexes. Different simplexes of a singular complex may intersect. They may also have common vertices without having in common the respective boundary faces they determine.

If γ^k is a linear or singular k-simplex, then $\zeta^\nu \gamma^k$ will denote the chain of $\zeta^\nu \gamma^k$ (Art. 5–6(F)). The operator ζ^ν is applied to a singular or simplicial chain as follows:

$$(6.21) \qquad \zeta^\nu \sum a_i \gamma_i^k = \sum a_i \zeta^\nu \gamma_i^k.$$

By the **complex** $K(C_*^k)$ of a singular or simplicial chain $C_*^k = \Sigma_{i=1}^\alpha a_i \gamma_i^k$ we mean the set of all the faces of all the simplexes γ_i^k ($i = 1, \ldots, \alpha$).

Now let K_*^k be a singular k-complex on the linear simplicial complex K. We will say that K_*^k is **star-related** to K^k if the closure $St^*(p)$ of the star on K_*^k of each vertex of K_*^k is on the open star of some vertex of K. That is,

$$(6.22) \qquad St(q) \supset \bar{S}t^*(p) \qquad \text{for some } q \in K.$$

We proceed to obtain a consequence of this relationship.

(A) Extending the definition of **star**, we define the **star** $St(s^h)$ of a simplex s^h of K as the union of all the simplexes of K having s^h for a face. If $p_0, \ldots, p_h$ are the vertices of s^h, then

$$(6.23) \qquad St(s^h) \equiv \bigcap_{i=0}^{h} St(p_i)$$

since the simplexes of K with s^h for a face are precisely the simplexes thereof which have all the points $(p_0, \ldots, p_h)$ among their vertices.

Conversely, if $(p_0, \ldots, p_h)$ is a set of distinct vertices with $\bigcap\limits_{j=0}^{h} St(p_j) \neq \emptyset$, then $(p_0, \ldots, p_h)$ are the vertices of an h-simplex of K (Exercise 30).

Lemma 6. **Let K_*^k be star-related to K, and let $\gamma^k = q_0 q_1 \ldots q_k$ be a simplex of K_*^k. Let p_j be a vertex of K such that $St(p_j) \supset St^*(q_j)$ $(j = 0, 1, \ldots, k)$. Then the distinct vertices in the set $(p_0, \ldots, p_k)$ determine a simplex $s^h \in K$, and $St(s^h) \supset \bar{\gamma}^k$.**

Proof of Lemma. It follows easily from the hypothesis that $\bigcap\limits_{j=0}^{k} St(p_j) \neq \emptyset$; hence, by (A), that $\bigcap\limits_{j=0}^{k} St(p_j) = St(s^h)$ for some $s^h \in K$. Since $\bar{\gamma}^k \subset \overline{St}^*(q_j)$ $(j = 0, \ldots, k)$, we have

$$(6.24) \qquad St(s^h) = \bigcap_{j=0}^{k} St(p_j) \supset \bigcap_{j=0}^{k} \overline{St}^*(q_j) \supset \bar{\gamma}^k$$

as was to be shown.

Now let $\{q\} = (q_0, q_1, \ldots, q_\alpha)$ denote all the vertices of K_*^k, and let g_0 be a mapping of $\{q\}$ into the vertices of K such that $St(g_0(q_j)) \supset \overline{St}^*(q_j)$. As a consequence of Lemma 6 and Art. 4–10, Lemma 7, there is a unique extension $g : |K_*^k| \to |K|$ of g_0 such that $g(\bar{\gamma}^k)$ is a closed simplex of K for each $\gamma^k \subset K_*^k$ and g is linear in terms of singular barycentric coordinates on $\bar{\gamma}^k$ and barycentric coordinates on $g(\bar{\gamma}^k)$.

(B) For each $\gamma^k \in K_*^k$, we will call $s^h = g(\gamma^k)$ the **approximating simplex** to γ^k (**with respect to** g). The set of all such approximating linear simplexes to the singular simplexes of K_*^k will be called the **approximating simplicial complex** $g^*(K_*^k)$ to K_*^k, where g^* is the simplex mapping induced by g.

Theorem 9. **A singular homology class of k-cycles on $|K|$ contains at most one simplicial homology class of k-cycles on K.**

Proof. We will deduce the theorem from the following lemma.

Lemma 7. **If a simplicial k-cycle Z^k is the boundary of a singular $(k + 1)$-chain C_*^{k+1}, it is also the boundary of some simplicial $(k + 1)$-chain D^{k+1}.**

Proof of Lemma. Let ρ be so large that the complex K_*^{k+1} of $\zeta^\rho C_*^{k+1}$ is star-related to K. Let $K^h = g^*(K_*^{k+1})$ be an approximating simplicial complex to K_*^{k+1}, in the notation of (B). We will denote with $\hat{g}$ the chain mapping induced by g^*. As a consequence of Theorem 4, $\hat{g}\zeta^\rho Z^k = Z^k$. But $\hat{g}\zeta^\rho Z^k = \partial\hat{g}\zeta^\rho C_*^{k+1}$, by Theorem 2 and Lemma 5. Hence Z^k is the boundary of the simplicial chain $D^{k+1} = \hat{g}\zeta^\rho C_*^{k+1}$.

Now let Z_1^k and Z_2^k be two simplicial cycles in the same singular homology class, so that $Z_2^k - Z_1^k$ bounds a singular chain. By Lemma 7, $Z_2^k - Z_1^k$ also bounds a simplicial chain. Hence Z_1^k and Z_2^k are in the same simplicial homology class, and Theorem 9 follows.

EXERCISE

30. Prove the last sentence in (A), perhaps by an induction.

6–8. Chains on Prism Complexes

The work of this article is preliminary to a proof that each singular k-cycle on $|K|$ is homologous to some simplicial k-cycle on K (Art. 6–9, Theorem 10).

Let $(x_1, \ldots, x_n, y)$ be a rectangular cartesian coordinate system in an E^{n+1} $(n > 0)$ and let E^n be the subspace $y = 0$. If $p \in E^n$ has coordinates $(x_1, \ldots, x_n, 0)$ then (p, y) will mean the point $(x_1, \ldots, x_n, y)$.

Let $\sigma^k = (\sigma^k, 0)$ be a linear k-simplex in E^n, and let Y be the interval $0 < y < 1$ on the y-axis. The $(k + 1)$-**prism** (or **prism cell**) with **floor** σ^k will mean the convex polyhedral $(k + 1)$-cell (see Fig. 6–2a and Art. 4–12)

$$(6.25) \qquad \pi^{k+1} = \sigma^k \times Y = \{(p, y) \mid p \in \sigma^k, 0 < y < 1\}.$$

The **roof** of π^{k+1} is the k-simplex $r^k = (\sigma^k, 1) = \{(p, 1) \mid p \in \sigma^k\}$.

Now let $F^k = \{\sigma\}$ be a finite linear simplicial complex in E^n with h-simplexes $\{\sigma^h\} = \sigma_1^h, \ldots, \sigma_{\alpha_h}^h$ $(h = 0, \ldots, k)$. Let $\pi_i^{h+1} = \sigma_i^h \times Y$ be the prism cell with σ_i^h for floor, and let r_i^h be the roof of π_i^{h+1}.

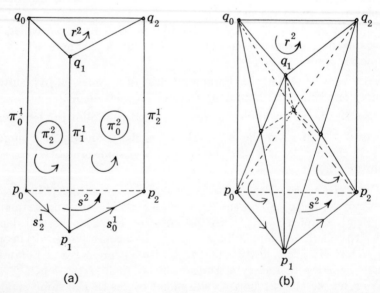

(a)   (b)

Fig. 6–2. A simplicial prism π^3 and its triangulation $\eta_\nu \pi^3$. Lines in interior partially shown. Lines on rear rectangle not shown. (a) π^3; (b) $\eta_0 \pi^3$; (c) $\eta_1 \pi^3$; (d) $\eta_2 \pi^3$.

(A) The set of all the faces of all the prism cells π_i^{h+1} is a special sort of polyhedral $(k+1)$-complex, $\mathfrak{P}^{k+1}$ (Art. 4–12), to be called a **prism complex**. Its cells fall into three categories:

(1) the **floor** simplexes, constituting the **floor complex** $F^k = \{\sigma\}$;

(2) the **roof simplexes**, constituting the **roof complex** $R^k = \{r\} = \{r_i^h \mid h = 0, \ldots, k; \ i = 1, \ldots, \alpha_h\}$;

(3) the **prism cells** or **wall cells** $\{\pi\} = \{\pi_i^{h+1} \mid h = 0, \ldots, k; \ i = 1, \ldots, \alpha_h\}$.

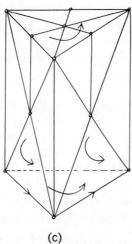

(c)

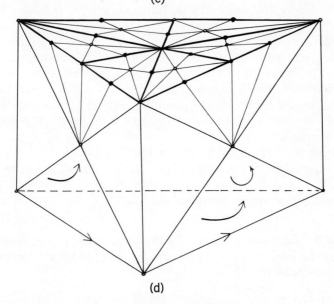

(d)

Fig. 6–2. (cont.)

(B) Since our homology theory has been developed for oriented simplicial complexes, we next define some standard simplicial subdivisions and orientations of $\mathfrak{P}^{k+1}$. We will denote the minimal central subdivision (Art. 4–12(F)) of $\mathfrak{P}^{k+1}$ by $\eta_0\mathfrak{P}^{k+1}$ (Fig. 6–2b). More generally, for $\rho = 0, 1, 2, \ldots$, we will denote by $\eta_\rho\mathfrak{P}^{k+1}$ the triangulation obtained by first replacing R^k by its ρth barycentric subdivision, $\zeta^\rho R^k$ ($\zeta^0 R^k = R^k$), then applying the minimal central subdivision process (Fig. 6–2c, d, where the subdivisions of the interior, and of the rear rectangle, are not shown). Thus $\eta_\rho\mathfrak{P}^{k+1}$ has $\zeta^\rho R^k$ and F^k for subcomplexes. If $h > 0$, it has just one vertex on each π_i^{h+1}, namely the barycenter of π_i^{h+1}, which is the point $(m, \frac{1}{2})$ if m is the barycenter of the floor of π_i^{h+1} (Art. 4–12).

(C) The **standard projection** of $|\mathfrak{P}^{k+1}|$ is the mapping $\varphi : |\mathfrak{P}^{k+1}| \to |F^k|$ defined by $\varphi(p, y) = (p, 0)$ ($p \in |F^k|$). It maps each **element** $p \times Y = \{(p, y) \mid p \in |F^k|, \ 0 \leq y \leq 1\}$ of $|\mathfrak{P}^{k+1}| = |F^k| \times \overline{Y}$ onto its **initial point** $(p, 0)$. For each $\rho \in (0, 1, 2, \ldots)$, φ induces an isomorphism φ_ρ^* between the i-simplexes of $\zeta^\rho R^k$ and those of $\zeta^\rho F^k$ ($i = 0, 1, \ldots, k$).

(D) Let F^k be arbitrarily oriented, and let $\{\sigma\}$ now denote its positive simplexes. Consider a typical h-simplex $\sigma^h = +p_0 p_1 \cdots p_h$. We orient the roof r^h of $\pi^{h+1} = \sigma^h \times Y$ by defining $r^h = +q_0 q_1 \cdots q_h$ where $q_i = (p_i, 1)$ ($i = 0, \ldots, h$). The h-simplexes of $\zeta^\rho r^h$ are, of course, oriented like r^h. *The isomorphism $\varphi_\rho^* : \zeta^\rho R^k \to \zeta^\rho F^k$ is obviously orientation-preserving.*

(E) To orient the $(h + 1)$-simplexes of $\eta_\rho\mathfrak{P}^{k+1}$ ($h > 0$) on the typical $\pi^{h+1} = \sigma^h \times Y$, we first let m denote the barycenter of π^{h+1} and define $\sigma^{h+1} = +m\sigma^h = +mp_0 p_1 \cdots p_h$, thus assigning the orientation induced by σ^h to the incident $(h + 1)$-simplex of $\eta_\rho\mathfrak{P}^{k+1}$ on π^{h+1}. The other $(h + 1)$-simplexes of $\eta_\rho\mathfrak{P}^{k+1}$ on π^{h+1} are to be oriented like σ^{h+1}, which has meaning (Art. 5–6(A)) because they are $(h + 1)$-simplexes on the E^{h+1} containing π^{h+1} (Fig. 6–2). If $h = 0$, with p_i on F^k and q_i the corresponding 0-cell on R^k, the incident wall cell is oriented $+q_i p_i$.

(F) Applying (D) and (E) to all the $\sigma^h \in \{\sigma\}$ ($h = 0, \ldots, k$), a **standard orientation** is induced by the orientation of F^k on the roof complex $\zeta^\rho R^k$ and on each $(h + 1)$-simplex of $\eta_\rho\mathfrak{P}^{k+1}$ on a prism $(h + 1)$-cell. The other simplexes of $\eta_\rho\mathfrak{P}^{k+1}$ can be arbitrarily oriented.

LEMMA 8. **Each roof simplex r_i^h has the opposite of the orientation induced by the incident $(h + 1)$-simplex t^{h+1} of $\eta_0\mathfrak{P}^k$ on π_i^{h+1} under the standard orientation.**

Proof of Lemma. For $h = 0$ the result is obvious from (E). Now suppose $h > 0$. We drop the subscript as in (D) and (F). If σ_0^{h+1} is obtained by translating $\sigma^{h+1} = m\sigma^h$ (see (E)) one unit in the y-direction, then σ_0^{h+1} has r^h for a face with the induced orientation. Furthermore, σ_0^{h+1} is oriented like σ^{h+1}, hence like t^{h+1}, and is adjacent to t^{h+1} with r^h as common face. Hence (Art. 5–6, Lemma 9), t^{h+1} and σ_0^{h+1} induce opposite orientations on r^h, and therefore r^h has orientation opposite to that induced by t^{h+1}, completing the proof.

(G) We adopt the following notation and terms:

(6.26) (a) $\overset{\rho}{\zeta}r_i^h =$ the chain of $\zeta^\rho r_i^h$ (Art. 5–6 (F));

(b) $\hat{\eta}_\rho W_i^{h+1} =$ the chain of the oriented $(h + 1)$-cells of $\eta_\rho \mathfrak{P}^{k+1}$ on π_i^{h+1}.

If $C^h = \Sigma_{i=1}^{\alpha_h} a_i \sigma_i^h$ is an arbitrary h-chain whose oriented cells are cells of F^k, then, letting $D^h = \Sigma_{i=1}^{\alpha_h} a_i r_i^h$, we have

$$\overset{\rho}{\zeta}D^h = \sum_{i=1}^{\alpha_h} a_i \overset{\rho}{\zeta}r_i^h \text{ is the \textbf{corresponding roof chain},}$$

(6.27)

$$\hat{\eta}_\rho W^{h+1} = \sum_{i=1}^{\alpha_h} a_i \hat{\eta}_\rho W_i^{h+1} \text{ is the \textbf{connecting chain},}$$

and we will refer to $(C^h, \hat{\eta}_\rho W^{h+1}, \overset{\rho}{\zeta}D^h)$ as a **triple of related chains**.

LEMMA 9. *Let ε_{ji}^{h-1} be the incidence number of σ_i^h and σ_j^{h-1}, and let $(C^h, \hat{\eta}_\rho W^{h+1}, \overset{\rho}{\zeta}D^h)$ be a triple of related chains, with $h > 0$. Then, in the notation of (G)*

$$(6.28) \qquad \partial \hat{\eta}_\rho W^{h+1} = C^h - \overset{\rho}{\zeta}D^h - \sum_{i=1}^{\alpha_h} \sum_{j=1}^{\alpha_{h-1}} a_i \varepsilon_{ji}^{h-1} \hat{\eta}_\rho W_j^h.$$

Proof of Lemma. The lemma will follow (Exercise 32) in all its generality if we show that

$$(6.29) \qquad \partial \hat{\eta}_\rho W_i^{h+1} \doteq \sigma_i^h - \overset{\rho}{\zeta}r_i^h - \sum_{j=1}^{\alpha_{h-1}} \varepsilon_{ji}^{h-1} \hat{\eta}_\rho W_j^h.$$

Now $\hat{\eta}_\rho W_i^{h+1}$ is the chain of the similarly oriented $(h + 1)$-simplexes of a triangulation of $\bar{\pi}_i^{h+1}$. It is to be shown that the right side of (6.29) represents the chain B_i^h of the coherently oriented boundary h-simplexes on $\bar{\pi}_i^{h+1}$. By (E), σ_i^h appears in B_i^h with coefficient $+1$. By Lemma 8, the simplexes of $\overset{\rho}{\zeta}r_i^h$ appear in B_i^h with coefficient -1. In the chain $\partial\partial\hat{\eta}_\rho W_i^{h+1}$, $\partial\sigma_i^h$ contributes $\varepsilon_{ji}^{h-1}\sigma_j^{h-1}$, which, in (6.29), is canceled, as it should be, by the term in σ_j^{h-1} from the last sum (see (E)). Since any incorrect coefficient in the last sum in (6.29) would clearly give the wrong coefficient of the corresponding σ_j^{h-1} in the boundary of the right-hand side of (6.29), we conclude that all the coefficients in (6.29) are correct, and it is clear that each h-simplex of B_i^h appears on the right side of (6.29).

(H) If C^h is a cycle in Lemma 9, then

$$(6.30) \qquad \partial \hat{\eta}_\rho W^{h+1} = C^h - \overset{\rho}{\zeta}D^h \qquad (\rho = 0, 1, 2, \ldots),$$

so that C^h and $\zeta^\rho D^h$ are homologous cycles on P^{k+1}. For, since C^h is a cycle,

$$\partial C^h = \sum_{i=1}^{\alpha_h} \sum_{j=1}^{\alpha_{h-1}} a_i \varepsilon_{ji}^{h-1} \sigma_j^{h-1} = \emptyset,$$

which implies $\Sigma_{i=1}^{\alpha_h} a_i \varepsilon_{ji}^{h-1} = 0$ $(j = 1, \ldots, \alpha_{k-1})$. Relation (6.30) now follows from (6.28).

LEMMA 10. **In terms of singular homology theory on** $|\mathfrak{P}^{k+1}|$, $C^h \sim \zeta^\rho C^h$ $(\rho = 0, 1, 2, \ldots)$.

Proof of Lemma. Let $\hat{\varphi}$ be the chain mapping induced by the projection φ. It is the identity on the floor chain C^h. By the last statement in (D), $\hat{\varphi}\zeta D^h = \zeta\hat{\varphi}C^h$. Hence, by (H) and Theorem 2, $\hat{\varphi}\,\partial\hat{\eta}_\rho W^{h+1} = \partial\hat{\varphi}\hat{\eta}_\rho W^{h+1} = C^h - \zeta^\rho C^h$, and Lemma 10 follows.

EXERCISES

31. Characterize the "other simplexes" mentioned in (F).
32. Explain how (6.29) implies (6.28).

6–9. Invariance of Homology Properties

LEMMA 11. **Let** Z_*^k **be a singular** k**-cycle on** $P = |K|$**, in the notation of Art. 4–6**(A)**. Then** $Z_*^k \sim \zeta^\rho Z_*^k$.

Proof of Lemma. It is not difficult to show that the complex of Z_*^k can be defined as the image $K_*^k = f(F^k)$ of the floor complex of a prism complex. If $\hat{f}$ is the chain mapping induced by f, then $Z_*^k = \hat{f}C^k$ for some cycle C^k of F^k and $\zeta^\rho Z_*^k = \hat{f}\zeta^\rho C^k$. Lemma 11 now follows from Lemma 10, read with $h = k$.

THEOREM 10. **Let** Z_*^k **be a singular** k**-cycle on** $P = |K|$**. Then there exists a simplicial** k**-cycle** Z^k **homologous to** Z_*^k.

Proof. Case 1. The complex K_*^k of Z_*^k is star-related to K. Let $K_0 = g^*(K_*^k)$ be an approximating simplicial complex to K_*^k, in the notation of Art. 6–7(B). We recall that g^* is the simplex mapping induced by a mapping g which is linear between each closed simplex $\bar{\gamma}^k$ of K_*^k, in terms of γ^k-linearity, and the corresponding linear simplex $\bar{s}^h = g(\bar{\gamma}^k)$.

(A) Let p' be a point on a closed simplex $\bar{\gamma}^k$ of K_*^k, and let $q' = g(p')$. Then, by (6.24), p' is on a simplex s of K with s^h for a face. The line-segment $p'q'$ is therefore on $\bar{s}$, hence on the polyhedron $P = |K|$.

Now let $f : \bar{\sigma}^k \to \bar{\gamma}^k$ be a defining mapping for $\bar{\gamma}^k$, where σ^k is a linear k-simplex in $E^n \subset E^{n+1}$, and let $\bar{\pi}^{k+1} = \bar{\sigma}^k \times \bar{Y}$, with roof r^k and standard projection $\varphi : \bar{\pi}^{k+1} \to \bar{\sigma}^k$ (Art. 6–8(C)). Then the mapping $\psi = gf\varphi : r^k \to s^h$ (Art. 3–1(F)) defines a simplex $\delta^k = \psi(r^k)$ which covers s^h. The linearity of g implies that ψ is a linear mapping of r^k onto s^h.

(B) (1) If $h < k$, then $\delta^k = \psi(r^k)$ is a degenerate (oriented) singular k-simplex*; (2) if $h = k$, then $\delta^k = +s^k$ or $-s^k$.

By f and ψ, the floor and roof of $\bar{\pi}^{k+1}$ are mapped onto $\bar{\gamma}^k$ and its simplicial approximation $g(\bar{\gamma}^k)$ respectively in such a way that if f maps $p \in \bar{\sigma}^k$ onto $p' = f(p) \in \bar{\gamma}^k$ and if $q = (p, 1)$ (equivalent to $p = \varphi(q)$, $q \in \bar{r}^k$) then ψ maps $q \in \bar{r}^k$ onto $q' = \psi(q) = g(p) \in g(\bar{\gamma})$.

Hence, in the terminology of Art. 6–8(C), f and ψ map the respective end points $p = (p, 0)$ and $q = (p, 1)$ of an element of $\bar{\pi}^{k+1}$ onto a pair of points p' and $q' = g(p)$. By (A), the line segment $p'q'$ is on $St(s^h)$.

(C) Let Φ be defined on $\bar{\pi}^{k+1}$ by the requirements (1) $\Phi \mid \bar{\sigma}^k = f$ so that $\Phi(\bar{\sigma}^k) = \bar{\gamma}^k$, (2) $\Phi \mid \bar{r}^k = \psi$ so that $\varphi(\bar{r}^k) = g(\bar{\gamma}^k) = \bar{s}^h$ (though $g(\bar{\gamma}^k) = \varphi(\bar{r}^k)$ will sometimes be interpreted as a closed singular k-simplex $\bar{\delta}^k$ covering $\bar{s}^h$), and (3) Φ maps each element pq of $\bar{\pi}^{k+1}$ linearly onto the segment $p'q'$ on $\overline{St}(\bar{s}^h)$. Then Φ can be shown to be continuous. Hence $\Phi(\bar{\pi}^{k+1})$ can be regarded as a **singular prism** on $St(s^h)$ with linear elements $p'q'$, with $\bar{\gamma}^k$ for floor and its approximating simplex $\bar{s}^h = g(\bar{\gamma}^k)$ for roof (Fig. 6–3).

Let K_*^k be regarded as the image $K_*^k = f(F^k)$ of the floor complex of a prism complex P^{k+1} as in the proof of Lemma 11. The mapping Φ defined in (C) can be extended in an obvious way over all the prisms of P^{k+1}. We are thus led to a **singular prism complex** $\Phi(P^{k+1})$ with $K_*^k = \Phi(F^k)$ for floor, and with the approximating simplicial complex $K_0^k = g*(K_*^k)$ for roof. Each closed **singular prism cell** $\Phi(\bar{\pi}_i^{k+1})$ of $\Phi(P^{k+1})$ is a union of line-segments joining its floor $\Phi(\sigma_i^k)$ to its roof (γ_i^k).

Let $\hat{\Phi}$ be the chain mapping induced on $\eta_0 P^{k+1}$ (Art. 6–8(B)) by Φ. Then, for some cycle C^k on F^k, we have $Z_*^k = \hat{\Phi}(C^k)$. The roof cycle D^k corresponding to C^k maps onto a chain $\hat{\Phi}(D^k)$ which, as a consequence of (B), reduces to a simplicial k-chain Z^k of K when degenerate simplexes are dropped (see (B)). Theorem 10 now follows from Lemma 10, since the homology $C^k \sim D^k = \zeta^0 D^k$ (see Art. 6–8(H)) is carried over by $\hat{\Phi}$ into $\hat{\Phi}(C^k) = Z_*^k \sim Z^k = \Phi(D^k)$.

Case 2. The complex K_*^k of Z_*^k is not star-related to K. Let ρ be so large that $\zeta^\rho K_*^k$ is star-related to K (Exercise 33). By the proof of Case 1, there exists a simplicial chain $Z^k \sim \zeta^\rho Z_*^k$. Theorem 10 follows from Lemma 11 and the transitivity of the homology relation.

(D) *Proof of Theorem 1.* Since simplicial homologies are a special case of singular homologies, the singular homology class $[Z_*^k]$ of a cycle Z_*^k on $P = |K|$ contains the simplicial homology class of a cycle $Z^k \sim Z_*^k$ (see Theorem 10). By Theorem 9, $[Z_*^k]$ therefore contains

---

* Compare Exercise 5d above. This is a simple consequence of the definitions and Art. 4–10(B).

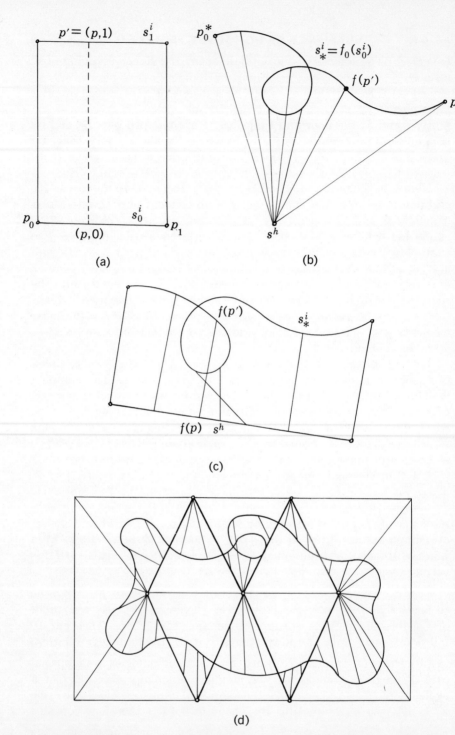

Fig. 6–3. Simplicial approximations to singular complexes. (a) $\bar{\pi}^{i+1}$; (b) $\Phi(\bar{\pi}^{i+1})(h = 0, i = 1)$; (c) $\Phi(\bar{\pi}^{i+1})(h = 1, i = 1)$; (d) $\Phi(P^{k+1})$.

exactly one simplicial homology class. Otherwise expressed, each element of $\mathfrak{H}_k$ is obtained from an element of $\mathfrak{H}_k^*$ merely by dropping from the latter all the non-simplicial k-cycles belonging to it. The mapping which maps each singular homology class onto the simplicial homology class it contains is then clearly an isomorphism. Theorem 1 now follows, by Art. 6–6(A). By Chapter 5, Theorem 17, cohomology groups, as well as homology groups, are invariant.

(E) *A polyhedron* Π *is connected if and only if it has no proper non-vacuous subset which is both open and closed.*

To verify (E), let K be a triangulation of Π. Then (Art. 5–3, Theorem 5), the 0th Betti number, β_0, of K equals the number of its components. The latter are characterized as those connected subsets of the complex K, each of which is both open and closed (see Art. 4–6(E) and (F)). The present statement now follows from Art. 4–6, Lemma 4, and the invariance of β_0.

EXERCISES

33. Show that ρ can be chosen as specified in the proof of Theorem 10, Case 2.

34. Show that if K^j is a subcomplex of K of dimension $j > 0$, then $\zeta^\rho K^j$ is star-related to K if and only if $\rho > 1$.

6–10. Classes of Mappings

Let Σ be a topological space, and consider the product space $\Sigma \times T$ where T is the unit segment $0 \le t \le 1$. Let Ω also be a topological space, and let

$$(6.31) \qquad\qquad f : \Sigma \times T \to \Omega$$

be a continuous mapping of $\Sigma \times T$ into Ω.

The points of $\Sigma \times T$ are representable in the form (p, t), where (1) $p = (p, 0) \in \Sigma$ and (2) $t \in T$. We will denote with

$$(6.32) \qquad\qquad f_t : \Sigma \to \Omega \qquad (t \in T)$$

the mapping of Σ into Ω defined by

$$(6.33) \qquad\qquad f_t(p) = f(p, t) \qquad (p \in \Sigma, t \in T).$$

Then f_t is a continuous one-parameter family of continuous mappings ($0 \le t \le 1$). It will be called a (**homotopic**) **deformation** of f_0 into f_1. It is helpful intuitively, to regard t as the time and to think of the image of a point $p \in \Sigma$ as "moving" from $f_0(p)$ to $f_1(p)$ through the positions $f_t(p)$ as t increases from 0 to 1. Its **deformation path** is a continuous curve, defined by the restriction of f to the segment $p \times T$.

A mapping $g_1 : \Sigma \to \Omega$ is **homotopic** to a mapping $g_0 : \Sigma \to \Omega$ if it is possible to define a deformation of g_0 into g_1. This relation will be symbolized by $g_1 \simeq g_0$.

LEMMA 12. **The relationship $\simeq$ is an equivalence relation.**

Proof of Lemma. It is reflexive, since $f_t = f_0$, $0 \leq t \leq 1$, is a deformation of f_0 into $f_1 = f_0$. It is symmetric, since if f_t is a deformation of f_0 into f_1, then f_{1-t} is a deformation of f_1 into f_0. To prove its transitivity, let f_t be a deformation of f_0 into f_1 and g_t a deformation of $g_0 = f_1$ into g_1.

(*A*) Then F_t, defined for $0 \leq t \leq \frac{1}{2}$ as f_{2t} and for $\frac{1}{2} < t \leq 1$ as g_{2t-1}, is easily seen to be a deformation of f_0 into g_1 (Exercise 35).

(*B*) As a consequence of Lemma 12, the continuous mappings $\Sigma \to \Omega$ fall into **homotopy classes**, generally called merely **classes of mappings**.

(*C*) If $\Sigma = |K|$ where K is a linear simplicial polyhedron, then f_t induces a mapping $f_t^* : K \to \Omega$ defining a family K_t^* $(0 \leq t \leq 1)$ of singular complexes. This leads to the concept of **homotopic singular complexes** and **homotopy classes** of singular complexes on Ω.

Note that $\mathfrak{P}^{k+1} = K \times T$ is a prism complex, and $P_*^{k+1} = f *\mathfrak{P}^{k+1}$ is a singular prism complex with K_0^*, K_1^* for floor and roof, where f^* is the simplex mapping induced by f. This leads to the following result.

LEMMA 13. **Two singular complexes K_0^* and K_1^* are in the same homotopy class if and only if there exists a singular prism complex $\mathfrak{P}_*^{k+1}$ with K_0^* and K_1^* for floor and roof complexes.**

(*D*) The mapping f_t^* induces a chain mapping $\hat{f}_t$ of simplicial chains on K into singular chains on Ω, defining, for each such chain C^k a family C_{*t}^k of singular chains. This leads to the concept of **homotopic singular chains** and **homotopy classes** of singular chains on Ω, where two cycles are homotopic if one can be deformed into the other.

THEOREM 11. **If two cycles are in the same homotopy class, they are in the same homology class.**

This follows from (6.30) applied to singular cycles with $\rho = 0$.

(*E*) The work of this article is applicable if $\Sigma = \Omega$, in which case continuous mappings of a space into itself are involved. A mapping $f : \Sigma \to \Sigma$ is called a **deformation** of Σ if it is in the homotopy class of the identity mapping. As a corollary to Theorem 11 above and Theorem 17 of Chapter 5, *a deformation of Σ induces the identity isomorphism of each homology group, and of each cohomology group, onto itself.*

EXERCISE

35. Prove (*A*).

7

Manifolds

An m-manifold, defined below, is a generalization of a 2-manifold, or surface. Manifolds are of frequent occurrence in analysis and in applications of mathematics. Their topological properties are of fundamental importance. The m-dimensional pseudomanifolds (Art. 5–6) are a broader generalization of surfaces than desired, for they include such geometric objects as the 2-sphere with two points identified.

7–I. Some Homology Properties of Pseudomanifolds

THEOREM 1. **If M is a closed orientable m-pseudomanifold, then**

(7.1) $\mathfrak{H}_0(M) \approx \mathfrak{H}_m(M) \approx \mathfrak{H}^0(M) \approx \mathfrak{H}^m(M) \approx$ **the free cyclic group,**

where $\approx$ denotes the isomorphism relation.

Proof. Part of this result was proved as Theorem 10 of Chapter 5. The rest will be deduced from the following lemma.

LEMMA 1. **Let M be coherently oriented. Then, there exists a linear graph L whose incidence matrix $J_0(L)$ is the transpose of $J_{m-1}(M)$.**

Proof of Lemma. Let s_i^k $(k = m - 1, m;\ i = 1, \ldots, \alpha_k)$ be the k-simplexes of M. The vertices of L will be $(p_1, \ldots, p_{\alpha_m})$. If s_i^{m-1} is incident with (s_j^m, s_k^m) and is oriented like s_k^m, then $s_i^1 = +p_j p_k$ will be a 1-simplex of L and all 1-simplexes of L are thus defined. Then column i of $J_0(L)$ has -1 in row j, $+1$ in row k, and 0's elsewhere; likewise, row i of $J_{m-1}(M)$ has -1 in column j, $+1$ in column k, and 0's elsewhere.

Since a linear graph has no torsion coefficient, it follows from Lemma 1 that M has no $(m - 1)^{\text{th}}$ torsion coefficient. Hence (Art. 5–11, Theorem 17), $\mathfrak{H}^m(M) \approx \mathfrak{B}_m(M) = \mathfrak{H}_m(M)$. The relation $\mathfrak{H}^0(K) = \mathfrak{H}_0(K)$ is valid for all complexes.

(A) As a corollary to Theorem 1, the 0th and m^{th} Betti numbers of an orientable m-pseudomanifold are $\beta_0 = \beta_m = 1$ and there are no $(m - 1)^{\text{th}}$ torsion coefficients.

THEOREM 2. **If M is a closed non-orientable m-pseudomanifold, then its mth Betti number is $\beta_m = 0$ and it has an $(m - 1)^{\text{th}}$ torsion**

coefficient equal to 2. Its mod 2 homology and cohomology groups satisfy

(7.2) $\hat{\mathfrak{H}}_0(M) \approx \hat{\mathfrak{H}}_m(M) \approx \hat{\mathfrak{H}}^0(M) \approx \hat{\mathfrak{H}}^m(M) \approx$ **the group of order 2**

and its 0th and first connectivity numbers are $\hat{\beta}_0 = \hat{\beta}_m = 1$ (Exercise 2).

EXERCISES

1. Draw a diagram showing (a) a triangulation M of a torus; (b) a corresponding linear graph L satisfying Lemma 1.

2. Prove Theorem 2, with the aid of Art. 5–6 and the proof of Theorem 1.

7–2. The m-Sphere

Let E^{m+1} be a euclidean $(m + 1)$-space, with a rectangular cartesian coordinate system $(x) = (x_1, \ldots, x_{m+1})$. The **unit m-sphere** S_0^m in E^{m+1} is defined by

(7.3) $$S_0^m : \sum_{i=1}^{m+1} x_i^2 = 1.$$

A (**topological**) m-sphere means a space S^m homeomorphic to S_0^m.

LEMMA 2. **The boundary** $B^m = \bar{\pi}^{m+1} - \pi^{m+1}$ **of a convex polyhedral** $(m + 1)$-**cell** π^{m+1} **in** E^{m+1} **is an** m-**sphere.**

Proof of Lemma. Choose the system (x) so that its origin O is on π^{m+1}. Each ray from O meets B^m in a single point p and S_0^m in a single point q. The mapping defined by $p \to q$ is easily seen to be a homeomorphism.

COROLLARY. **A triangulation of** B^m **and a homeomorphism** $h : B^m \to S^m$ **define a triangulation of an** m-**sphere** S^m.

(*A*) In particular, the boundary $B^m = \bar{s}^{m+1} - s^{m+1}$ of an $(m + 1)$-simplex s^{m+1} is an m-sphere, and the set of boundary faces of s^{m+1} is a triangulation of B^m.

We will describe a simplicial complex K^n as a **cone complex** or a **closed star** with **center** p_0 if (1) p_0 is a vertex of K^n and (2) each simplex of K^n is a face of a simplex incident with p_0. In other words,* $K^n = \bar{St}(p_0)$, where $St(p_0)$ is the star of p_0 on K^n (Art. 6–3) and $\bar{St}(p_0)$ is the complex consisting of all the faces of simplexes of $St(p_0)$. The subcomplex $B^{n-1} = \bar{St}(p_0) - St(p_0)$ will be called the **outer boundary** of $St(p_0)$ or of K^n (**relative to** p_0). A given complex K^n may be a cone complex with several possible choices of its center. In particular, the set of all faces of a simplex is a cone complex with respect to an arbitrarily selected vertex as center.

* We are here using $St(p_0)$ to denote a set of simplexes, rather than their point-set union.

THEOREM 3. **If K^n is a cone complex, then $\mathfrak{H}_0(K^n)$ is free cyclic, and $\mathfrak{H}_i(K^n)$ reduces to the null element ($i = 1, 2, \ldots$).**

Proof. This follows from Chapter 6, Theorem 11, and the fact that, in a polyhedral representation of K^n, an arbitrary cycle on K^n can be deformed into the center p_0 along segments from p_0.

THEOREM 4. **The 0th and m^{th} homology groups of an m-sphere are free cyclic. Its other homology groups reduce to the null element.**

Proof. By Chapter 6, Theorem 1, it is sufficient to give the proof for the complex B^m consisting of the boundary faces of an $(m + 1)$-simplex $s^{m+1} = p_0 p_1 \cdots p_{m+1}$. The complex K^{m+1} consisting of all the faces of s^{m+1} is a cone complex, with B^m for its m-skeleton. Therefore B^m has the same k^{th} homology groups ($k = 0, \ldots, m - 1$) as K^{m+1}. Since the boundary faces of s^{m+1} are an orientable m-pseudomanifold, Theorem 4 now follows from Theorems 1 and 3. As a corollary,

$$(7.4) \qquad \beta_0(S^m) = \beta_m(S^m) = 1 \qquad \beta_i(S^m) = 0 \qquad (i \neq 0, m).$$

THEOREM 5. **No orientation-reversing self-homeomorphism of an m-sphere is a deformation** (Art. 6–10(E)).

Proof. We continue to represent S^m by B^m. Consider first the linear self-homeomorphism λ of $|B^m|$ which interchanges p_0 and p_1 and leaves p_i fixed ($i > 1$). Let $s_i^m = (-1)^i p_0 \cdots p_{i-1} p_{i+1} \cdots p_{m+1}$ ($i = 0, 1, \ldots, m + 1$) and let $Z^m = \Sigma_{i=0}^{m+1} s_i^m$. The homology class of Z^m generates $\mathfrak{H}_m(S^m)$, and $\mathfrak{H}_m(S^m)$ is the free cyclic group. On the other hand, λ induces a mapping which carries Z^m into $-Z^m$. However, $Z^m \sim -Z^m \Rightarrow 2Z^m \sim \emptyset$, which is impossible, since no cycle kZ^m ($k \neq 0$) can bound on S^m (Exercise 5).

EXERCISES

3. Show that if K^m in a linear simplicial complex in $E^n \subset E^{n+1}$ and $p_0 \in E^{n+1} - E^n$, then p_0 and K^m determine a unique cone complex with p_0 as center and K^m as outer boundary.

4. Show that (a) the only simplicial n-cycle on a cone n-complex K^n is the null n-cycle and (b) at least one simplex of the outer boundary of K^n appears on each simplicial k-cycle on K^n, if $k < n$.

5. Justify the last sentence in the proof of Theorem 5.

7–3. Projective m-Space

Projective m-space P^m is the space of proportionality sets of $m + 1$ real numbers. That is, an ordered set $(x) = (x_1, \ldots, x_{m+1})$ of real numbers, not all zero, represents a point, and the same point is represented by $(y_1, \ldots, y_{m+1}) = (tx_1, tx_2, \ldots, tx_{m+1})$ for each $t \neq 0$. Given (x), (y) can be any point, except the origin O, on the line determined by O and (x) in E^{m+1}.

(A) *Hence P^m can be interpreted as a space whose elements are the lines $\{\lambda\}$ through O in E^{m+1}.* A **neighborhood** of $\lambda = Op$ is the set of all lines Oq with q in a neighborhood of p in E^{m+1}.

(B) Each $\lambda \in \{\lambda\}$ intersects the unit m-sphere $S_0^m \subset E^{m+1}$ in a pair (p, p') of antipodal points; that is, points symmetric to each other in O. *Hence P^m can be interpreted as S_0^m with p and p' identified for each antipodal pair (p, p').*

In a euclidean space E^j with coordinate system $(x_1, \ldots, x_j)$, the **unit j-cell** will mean the spherical region

$$(7.5) \qquad\qquad \sigma_0^j : \sum_{i=1}^{j} x_i^2 < 1.$$

Its boundary is the unit $(j - 1)$-sphere

$$(7.6) \qquad S_0^{j-1} : \sum_{i=1}^{j} x_i^2 = 1, \qquad S_0^{j-1} = \bar{\sigma}_0^j - \sigma_0^j.$$

THEOREM 6. **Projective m-space P^m can be represented topologically as $\bar{\sigma}_0^m$ with antipodal points of S_0^{m-1} identified in pairs.**

Proof. Consider the representation in (B) above. Let S_0^m be analyzed into (1) its **lower hemisphere** Σ_1^m, on which $x_{m+1} < 0$, (2) its **upper hemisphere** Σ_2^m, on which $x_{m+1} > 0$, and (3) its **equatorial $(m-1)$-sphere** S_0^{m-1}, on which $x_{m+1} = 0$. Of a pair of identified antipodal points (p, p') on S_0^m either both are on S_0^{m-1} or one is on Σ_1^m and one on Σ_2^m. Hence, P^m can be represented as $\bar{\Sigma}_2^m$ with antipodal points on $S_0^{m-1} = \bar{\Sigma}_2^m - \Sigma_2^m$ identified. But $\bar{\Sigma}_2^m$ can be defined by

$$(7.7) \qquad \bar{\Sigma}_2^m : x_{m+1} = \sqrt{1 - (x_1^2 + \cdots + x_m^2)}, \qquad (x_1, \ldots, x_m) \in \bar{\sigma}_0^m.$$

Hence, $\bar{\Sigma}_2^m$ is homeomorphically mapped onto $\bar{\sigma}_0^m$ by the projection $(x_1, \ldots, x_m, x_{m+1}) \to (x_1, \ldots, x_m, 0)$, which is the identity on S_0^{m-1}. The theorem now follows easily. (See Exercise 7.)

THEOREM 7. **Projective m-space P^m is orientable if m is odd, nonorientable if m is even.**

Proof. Let T^{m-1} and τ^m be defined, in E^m, as follows:

$$(7.8) \qquad \begin{aligned} & T^{m-1} : \sum_{i=1}^{m} |x_i| = 1, \\ & \qquad\qquad\qquad \text{where } |x| \text{ means absolute value of } x, \\ & \tau^m : \sum_{i=1}^{m} |x_i| < 1. \end{aligned}$$

(C) Then τ^m is a convex polyhedral m-cell inscribed in S_0^{m-1}, with the unit points p_i $(i = 1, \ldots, m)$ on the x_i-axes and the antipodal points p_i' as vertices (Exercise 9).

(D) The $(m - 1)$-dimensional faces of τ^m consist of the $(m - 1)$-simplex $s = p_1 \ldots p_m$, the antipodal simplex $s' = p_1' \ldots p_m'$, and all simplexes of the form $r_1 \ldots r_m$, where $r_i = p_i$ or p_i' ($i = 1, \ldots, m$) (Exercise 10).

(E) Let two points on T^{m-1} be called **antipodal** if they are on a line through the origin. Then $\bar{\tau}^m$ is converted into a projective m-space P^m by the identification of antipodal pairs of points on T^{m-1} (Exercise 11).

The identifications just described identify $s = +p_1 \ldots p_m$ with $s' = +p_1' \ldots p_m'$. Now s has the orientation induced by $t = Op_1 \ldots p_m$ and s' has the orientation induced by $t' = Op_1' \ldots p_m'$, where O is the origin. The linear mapping of E^m onto itself which interchanges p_i and p_i' has jacobian $(-1)^m$. Hence t and t' are oriented alike or oppositely in E^m according as m is even or odd.

(F) In order that P^m be orientable, it is necessary that when t and t' are oriented alike, they induce opposite orientations on s and s' respectively (Exercise 12), in other words that m be odd.

(G) The condition given in (F) is also sufficient (Exercise 13), which completes the proof.

THEOREM 8. **The homology groups of P^m are**

$$\text{(a)} \quad \mathfrak{H}_0(P^m) = \text{the free cyclic group,}$$

(7.9)
$$\text{(b)} \quad \mathfrak{H}_k(P^m) = \begin{cases} \text{the group of order } 2 \text{ (k odd and } <m) \\ \text{the null group (k even and } >0), \end{cases}$$

$$\text{(c)} \quad \mathfrak{H}_m(P^m) = \begin{cases} \text{the free cyclic group (m odd)} \\ \text{the null element alone (m even).} \end{cases}$$

Proof. Part (a) of (7.9) is valid since P^m is connected. Whether P^m is represented as in (B) or as in Theorem 6, the identification of points converts S_0^{m-1} into a projective $(m-1)$-space $P_0^{m-1} \subset P^m$. But S_0^{m-1} can, like S_0^m, be analyzed into its **lower hemisphere** Σ_1^{m-1}, where $x_m < 0$, its **upper hemisphere** Σ_2^{m-1}, where $x_m > 0$, and its **equatorial** $(m-2)$-**sphere** S_0^{m-2}, where $x_m = 0$; and the identifications of antipodal points convert S_0^{m-2} into a $P_0^{m-2} \subset P_0^{m-1} \subset P^m$.

Continuing thus, we are led to

$$\Sigma_1^j : \left(x_{j+2} = \cdots = x_{m+1} = 0, \sum_{i=1}^{j+1} x_i^2 = 1, x_{j+1} < 0 \right),$$

(7.10)
$$\Sigma_2^j : \left(x_{j+2} = \cdots = x_{m+1} = 0, \sum_{i=1}^{j+1} x_i^2 = 1, x_{j+1} > 0 \right),$$

$$S_0^{j-1} : \left(x_{j+1} = x_{j+2} = \cdots = x_{m+1} = 0, \sum_{i=1}^{j} x_i^2 = 1 \right)$$

for each $j = 1, \ldots, m$. In the case $j = 1$, S_0^0 is the pair of points $\Sigma_1^0 : x_1 = -1$ and $\Sigma_2^0 : x_1 = +1$ on the x_1-axis, separating the unit circle of the (x_1, x_2)-plane into the arcs Σ_1^1 and Σ_2^1.

The identification of antipodal points converts each of the spheres S_0^k ($k = 1, \ldots, m - 1$) into a projective k-space P_0^k, and

(7.11) $$P_0^1 \subset P_0^2 \subset \cdots \subset P_0^{m-1} \subset P^m.$$

LEMMA 3. **If Z_*^k is a singular k-cycle on P^m and if $k < m$, then $Z_*^k \sim Y_*^k$ for some singular k-cycle Y_*^k on P_0^{m-1}.**

Proof of Lemma. Let P^m be represented as $\bar{\tau}^m$ with antipodal points of T^{m-1} identified, converting the latter into P_0^{m-1} (see the proof of Theorem 7). Let P^m be triangulated (compare Exercise 12 for example) into simplexes $\{t\}$ which are linear in the representation $\bar{\tau}^m$. Let Z_0^k be a simplicial approximating cycle on $\{t\}$ to Z_*^k and let p_0 be a point on an m-simplex of $\{t\}$. Since Z_0^k is a chain on the k-skeleton of $\{t\}$, its complex $K(Z_0^k)$ does not contain p_0. Each point q on $|K(Z_0^k)|$ but not on T^{m-1} is therefore on a unique ray $p_0 q$ which, since $\bar{\tau}^m$ is convex, intersects P_0^{m-1} in a unique point p, represented by a point on T^{m-1}. If q is on T^{m-1}, there are two such rays, one to each of the two antipodal positions of q, and the two corresponding points p are identified with each other, and with q. The set of all segments qp can be used in defining a deformation of Z_*^k into Y_*^k on P_0^{m-1}, and the lemma follows from Theorem 11 of Chapter 6.

COROLLARY. **The cycle Z_*^k is homologous to some cycle X_*^k on P_0^k.**
This corollary results from successive applications of Lemma 3, with Y_*^k and P_0^{m-1} replacing Z_*^k and P^m, and so on.

Let Σ^k be a triangulation of P_0^k, and let X_0^k be a simplicial approximating cycle on Σ^k to X_*^k. If k is even and positive, then, by (D) and Theorem 2, X_0^k must be the null cycle, since that is the only k-cycle on a non-orientable k-pseudomanifold.

If k is odd, X_0^k is homologous to an integral multiple of the chain V_0^k of Σ^k taken with either possible coherent orientation, and V_0^k is a non-bounding cycle whose double bounds a chain on P_0^{k+1}. Theorem 8 now follows readily.

(H) As a corollary to Theorem 8, the connectivity numbers of P^m are $\hat{\beta}_i = 1$ ($i = 0, \ldots, m$) (Exercise 14).

EXERCISES

6. Draw diagrams to illustrate, in the cases $m = 2$ and $m = 3$, the proofs of Theorems 7 and 8.

7. (a) Show that Theorem 6 leads to the earlier definition of P^2 as the sphere with crosscap. (b) Show that P^1 is a circle.

8. Show that $\sigma_0^m = \sigma_0^m \cup S_0^{m-1}$ is converted into an m-sphere when pairs of points on S_0^{m-1} are identified if and only if they have the same $(x_1, \ldots, x_{m-1})$-coordinates. Their x_m-coordinates will then be $x_m = \pm \sqrt{1 - (x_1^2 + \cdots + x_{m-1}^2)}$. *Suggestions:* (a) Consider first the cases $m = 1, 2$. (b) Let $\bar{\sigma}_1^m$ be the part of $\bar{\sigma}_0$ where $x_m \leq 0$ and $\bar{\sigma}_2^m$ the part where $x_m \geq 0$. Consider the mapping

$\varphi : (x_1, \ldots, x_m) \to (x_1, \ldots, x_{m-1}, y_m, y_{m+1})$, defined as follows, where $k = \sqrt{1 - (x_1^2 + \cdots + x_{m-1}^2)}$:

$$\begin{cases} y_m = -2x_m - k \\ y_{m+1} = -\sqrt{k^2 - y_m^2} \end{cases} \quad (x_1, \ldots, x_m) \in \bar{\sigma}_1^m,$$

$$\begin{cases} y_m = 2x_m - k \\ y_{m+1} = \sqrt{k^2 - y_m^2} \end{cases} \quad (x_1, \ldots, x_m) \in \bar{\sigma}_2^m.$$

9. Prove (C).

10. Prove (D).

11. Prove (E), with the aid of Theorem 6.

12. Prove (F). Note that the faces of the 2^m simplexes $Or_1 \ldots r_m$ (notation as in (D)) are a triangulation of $\bar{\tau}^m$ into an m-pseudomanifold with boundary T^{m-1}. After the identifications in (E), the second barycentric subdivision affords a triangulation of P^m into an m-pseudomanifold, without boundary.

13. Prove (G). *Suggestion:* Consider the effect of orienting positively, relative to E^m, the m-simplexes of the suggested triangulation of P^m.

14. Deduce (H) from Theorem 8.

7–4. Local Homology Groups

Given a topological polyhedron Π and a point $p \in \Pi$, let a neighborhood of p be triangulated so that p is a vertex, and let $St(p)$ be the star of p. The outer boundary B of the closed star $\bar{St}(p)$ (see Art. 7–2 for definitions) is a **surrounding complex** of p, and its kth homology group $\mathfrak{H}_k(B)$ will be called the kth **local homology group** of Π at p, denoted by

$$(7.12) \qquad \mathfrak{H}_k(\Pi, p) = \mathfrak{H}_k(B).$$

THEOREM 9. **The kth local homology group $\mathfrak{H}_k(\Pi, p)$ is a topological invariant.**

Proof. (A) This theorem means that $\mathfrak{H}_k(\Pi, p) \approx \mathfrak{H}_k(\Omega, q)$ if Π and Ω are homeomorphic with p and q corresponding. *This is equivalent to the statement that $\mathfrak{H}_k(B) \approx \mathfrak{H}_k(B^*)$ if B and B^* are two surrounding complexes of p* (Exercise 17).

Let $\bar{St}(p)$ and $\bar{St}^*(p)$ be closed stars with B and B^* for respective outer boundaries. Linearity on the simplexes of $\bar{St}(p)$ and $\bar{St}^*(p)$ (see Art. 6–1(C)) will be called $\bar{St}$-**linearity** and $\bar{St}^*$-**linearity**, respectively. Then $|\bar{St}(p)|$, for example, is the union of the $\bar{St}$-segments pq_0 ($q_0 \in B$).

By the γ-**contraction** γ_r of $|\bar{St}(p)|$ **in the ratio** r, we mean the deformation under which each point q on a segment pq_0 moves toward q along that segment to the point q_r such that $pq_r/pq = r$ ($0 < r < 1$) in terms of $\bar{St}$-linearity. If $\bar{St}(p)$ were in a euclidean space E^n, with origin p and coordinates $(x_1, \ldots, x_n)$, γ_r would move $q_t : (tx_1, \ldots, tx_n)$ from a position $q : (x_1, \ldots, x_n)$ to $q_r(rx_1, \ldots, rx_n)$ as t

decreases from 1 to r. The contraction γ_r of $|\overline{St}(p)|$ deforms $\overline{St}(p)$ into a star $\gamma_r(\overline{St}(p))$ a γ-**contraction** of $\overline{St}(p)$.

Similar considerations in terms of $\overline{St}^*$-linearity lead to the concepts of the γ^*-**contraction of** $|\overline{St}^*(p)|$ **in the ratio** r and of the γ^*-contraction $\gamma_r(\overline{St}^*(p))$.

Given an arbitrary neighborhood N of p on Π, there exists an r so small that N contains the γ_r-contraction of $|\overline{St}(p)|$ and the γ_r^*-contraction of $|\overline{St}^*(p)|$. Hence it is possible to define γ-contractions $\overline{St}_i(p)$ of $\overline{St}(p)$ ($i = 0, 1$) and a γ^*-contraction $\overline{St}_1^*(p)$ of $\overline{St}^*(p)$ so that (1) $|\overline{St}_0(p)| \subset |St^*(p)|$, (2) $|\overline{St}_1^*(p)| \subset |St_0(p)|$, and (3) $|\overline{St}_1(p)| \subset |St_1^*(p)|$ (see Fig. 7–1, where $\overline{St}$-linearity is shown as straight).

Then $B_1^* \subset B_{01} = |\overline{St}_0(p) - St_1(p)|$, where B_{01} shows in Fig. 7–1 as the closed polygonal band between B_0 and B_1.

(*B*) Let $\lambda(pq_0)$ be the $\overline{St}$-segment from p to a point $q_0 \in B_0$. It intersects B_1 in a single point, which will be called the $\overline{St}$-**projection** $\pi_1(q)$ of each point q on $\lambda(pq_0)$. Thus the $\overline{St}$-**projection** π_1 is defined as a continuous mapping $(|\overline{St}_0(p)| - p) \to B_1$. Similarly, by using $\overline{St}^*$-projections, the $\overline{St}^*$-**projection** π_1^* is defined as a mapping $(|\overline{St}^*(p)| - p) \to B_1^*$.

Let ψ be the mapping $B_1^* \to B_1$ defined by $\psi(q) = \pi_1(q)$, $q \in B_1^*$, and let φ be the mapping $B_1 \to B_1^*$ defined by $\varphi(q') = \pi_1^*(q')$, $q' \in B_1$.

LEMMA 4. **The mapping** $g_1 = \varphi\psi : B_1^* \to B_1^*$ **is a deformation of** B_1^* (Art. 6–10).

Proof of Lemma. Let $T = [0, 1]$, the unit segment on a t-axis. First note that the mapping $\psi : B_1^* \to B_1$ is a deformation of B_1^* on $|St_0^*(p)|$. Indeed, if $f_t(B_1^*) = f(B_1^*, t)$ where $f : (B_1^* \times T) \to |St_0(p)|$ maps each segment $q \times T$, $q \in B_1^*$, linearly in terms of $\overline{St}$-linearity on the $\overline{St}$-segment from q to $q' = \psi(q)$, then $f_1 \mid B_1^* = \psi$ and $f_0 \mid B_1^* =$ (the identity). The deformation path of a point $q \in B_1^*$ shows as a line-segment $\lambda(q)$ in Fig. 7–1. Now let $g : (B_1^* \times T) \to B_1^*$ be defined by $g(q, t) = \pi_1^* f(q, t)$, π_1^* being the $\overline{St}^*$-projection into B_1^*. Then $g_0(B_1^*) = g(B_1^*, 0)$ is the identity and $g(B_1^*, 1) = g_1(B_1^*) = \varphi\psi$, so that $g_t(B_1^*) = g(B_1^*, t)$, $0 \leq t \leq 1$, is a deformation of the identity into g_1, establishing the lemma.

Hence (Art. 6–10(*E*)), g_1 induces the identity isomorphism $\mathfrak{H}_k(B_1^*) \to \mathfrak{H}_k(B_1^*)$. But the isomorphism g_1^* induced by g_1 is the product $g_1^* = \varphi^*\psi^*$ of the homomorphism $\psi^* : \mathfrak{H}_k(B_1^*) \to \mathfrak{H}_k(B_1)$ induced by ψ and the homomorphism $\varphi^* : \mathfrak{H}_k(B_1^*) \to \mathfrak{H}_k(B_1)$ induced by φ.

(*C*) Since g_1^* is the identity isomorphism, ψ^* and φ^* are both one-to-one. Hence ψ^* and φ^* are isomorphisms since a one-to-one homomorphism is an isomorphism (Exercise 18).

Theorem 9 now follows, because (1) $\mathfrak{H}_k(\Pi, p) = \mathfrak{H}_k(B)$ is isomorphic

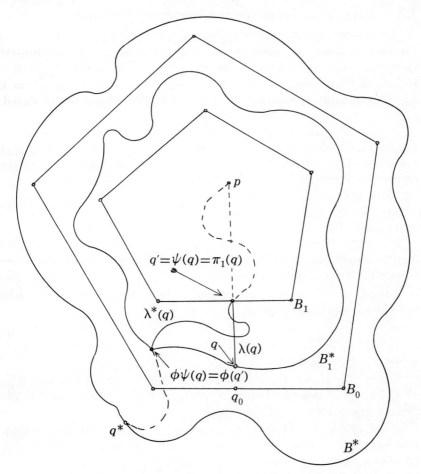

Fig. 7–1. Two nested pairs of star neighborhoods of p on Π.

to $\mathfrak{H}_k(B_1)$, since a γ-contraction of B is a homeomorphism and (2) $\mathfrak{H}_k(\Omega, p) = \mathfrak{H}_k(B_1^*)$ is for similar reasons isomorphic to $\mathfrak{H}_k(B_1^*)$.

EXERCISES

15. Draw a 2-dimensional $St(p)$ whose outer boundary is a closed polygon with p interior to it. Show $\gamma_{\frac{1}{2}}(St(p))$ and $\gamma_{\frac{1}{3}}(St(p))$ on your diagram.

16. Let Σ^2 be the surface of a double cone, vertex at p. What are the local homology groups at p?

17. Prove the italicized part of (A), with the aid of a homeomorphism $\Omega \rightarrow \Pi$.

18. Establish (C).

7–5. Topological Manifolds and Homology Manifolds

A (**closed**) **topological** m-**manifold** Σ^m is a connected compact topological space on which each point has a neighborhood homeomorphic to an m-simplex. For $m < 4$, it is known that Σ^m is a topological polyhedron; in other words, Σ^m can be triangulated. For the general m-manifold, the triangulability question is one of the major unsolved problems of topology.

A (**closed**) **homology*** m-**manifold** $\mathfrak{M}$ is a connected compact topological m-dimensional polyhedron (Art. 4–6(G)) on which the local homology groups $\mathfrak{H}_k(\mathfrak{M}, p)$ at each point are isomorphic to the respective homology groups $\mathfrak{H}_k(S^{m-1})$ of an $(m-1)$-sphere (Theorem 4). This is clearly a topologically invariant definition.

(A) Every triangulable topological m-manifold is a homology m-manifold (Exercise 21).

If $m > 3$, there exist homology m-manifolds which are not topological manifolds; thus homology manifolds are more general than triangulable topological manifolds.

THEOREM 10. **Each triangulation of a homology** m-**manifold** $\mathfrak{M}$ **is a closed** m-**pseudomanifold.**

Proof. It is to be shown that if M is a triangulation of $\mathfrak{M}$ and $s^{m-1} \in M$, then s^{m-1} is incident with exactly two m-simplexes of M. We start with a lemma.

LEMMA 5. **If** ν **is the number of** m-**simplexes of** M **incident with** s^{m-1}, **and** p **is the barycenter of** s^{m-1}, **then** $\mathfrak{H}_{m-1}(\mathfrak{M}, p)$ **is the free abelian group with** $\nu - 1$ **generators.**

Proof of Lemma. Let M be regarded as linear simplicial, which, by Chapter 4, Theorem 2, involves no loss of generality in proving Lemma 5. Let $s^{m-1} = p_0 \ldots p_{m-1}$ and let $s_i^m = q_i s^{m-1}$ ($i = 1, \ldots, \nu$) be the m-simplexes of M, possibly reoriented, incident with s^{m-1}.

The reader should follow this proof, drawing diagrams for $m = 2$.

Let $s_j^{m-2} = (-1)^j p_0 \ldots \hat{p}_j \ldots p_{m-1}$ ($j = 0, \ldots, m-1$) where $\wedge$ denotes omission of p_j. Then $\partial s^{m-1} = \Sigma_{j=0}^{m-1} s_j^{m-2}$. Let $s_{ji}^{m-1} = q_i s_j^{m-2}$ ($i = 1, \ldots, \nu$; $j = 0, \ldots, m-2$).

(B) The faces of the simplexes s_{ji}^{m-1} constitute a surrounding complex B^{m-1} of p on $\mathfrak{M}$ (Exercise 22).

Let $B_i^{m-1} = \Sigma_{j=0}^{m-2} q_i s_j^{m-2}$ ($i = 1, \ldots, \nu$). Then the boundary of $s_h^m - s_i^m$ is (Exercise 23)

(7.13) $\qquad \partial s_h^m - \partial s_i^m = B_i^{m-1} - B_h^{m-1}$ ($h = 1, \ldots, \nu$; $i = 1, \ldots, \hat{h}, \ldots, \nu$).

Hence $B_i^{m-1} - B_h^{m-1}$ is an $(m-1)$-cycle on B^{m-1}.

---

* The term **combinatorial manifold** is thus used in much of the literature. In recent research, however, a **combinatorial manifold** has been defined with the stronger condition that the outer boundary of each star be combinatorially equivalent (Art. 4–12(G)) to the boundary complex of a simplex.

(C) The complex $K(B_i^{m-1})$ of B_i^{m-1} consists of the boundary complex of s_i^m minus the face s^{m-1}, and $K(B_h^{m-1})$ is similarly the boundary complex of s_h^m with s^{m-1} deleted. Hence the complex of $B_i^{m-1} - B_h^{m-1}$ is a closed orientable $(m-1)$-pseudomanifold (Exercise 24).

If Z^{m-1} is a cycle on B^{m-1} and s_{ji}^{m-1} appears in Z^{m-1} with coefficient a_i, then each of the $(m-1)$-simplexes s_{ki}^{m-1} $(k = 0, \ldots, m-1)$ appears in Z^{m-1} with coefficient a_i. Otherwise, some pair of adjacent $(m-1)$-simplexes on $K(B_i^{m-1})$ would appear in Z^{m-1} with unequal coefficients and their common $(m-2)$-face would appear in ∂Z^{m-1}, contradicting its definition as a cycle. Hence each cycle on B^{m-1} is of the form $Z^{m-1} = \Sigma_{i=1}^{\nu} a_i B_i^{m-1}$.

(D) Furthermore, $\Sigma_{i=1}^{\nu} a_i = 0$, since $\partial Z^{m-1} = -(\Sigma_{i=1}^{\nu} a_i) \partial s^{m-1}$ (Exercise 25).

(E) It follows readily that $B_h^{m-1} - B_1^{m-1}$ $(h = 2, \ldots, \nu)$ is a maximal set of linearly independent $(m-1)$-cycles on B^{m-1} (Exercise 26).

Lemma 5 now follows with the aid of Corollary 1 to Theorem 2 of Chapter 5 (Exercise 27).

By definition of **homology m-manifold**, $\mathfrak{H}_{m-1}(\mathfrak{M}, p)$ is the free cyclic group, which is the free abelian group with one generator. Therefore $\nu = 2$, and Lemma 5 implies Theorem 10.

THEOREM 11. *If a topological polyhedron Π can be triangulated into an m-pseudomanifold M, then every triangulation of Π is an m-pseudomanifold.*

Proof. Suppose Π has a triangulation in which some $(m-1)$-simplex s^{m-1} is incident with $\nu \neq 2$ m-simplexes. Then $\mathfrak{H}_{m-1}(\Pi, p) = \emptyset$ if $\nu = 1$, and it has $\nu - 1 > 1$ generators if $\nu > 2$. But, from the triangulation M of Π, $\mathfrak{H}_{m-1}(\Pi, p)$ is free cyclic, which yields a contradiction.

COROLLARY. *If Π can be triangulated into an m-pseudomanifold with boundary B, then every triangulation of Π is an m-pseudomanifold with a boundary which is a triangulation of $|B|$ (Exercise 28).*

(F) Theorem 11 justifies us in referring to Π as a **(topological) m-pseudomanifold** and, in the case of the corollary, as a **(topological) m-pseudomanifold with boundary** $\mathfrak{B} = |B|$.

LEMMA 6. *If $p \in \mathfrak{M}$ and $\mathfrak{M}$ is a topological m-pseudomanifold, then each surrounding complex of p is an orientable $(m-1)$-pseudomanifold.*

Proof of Lemma. In the first place, p is on a face of an m-simplex in each triangulation of a neighborhood of p on $\mathfrak{M}$. Otherwise, the local $(m-1)^{\text{th}}$ homology group would be null. From the fact that each $(m-1)$-simplex s^{m-1} incident with p belongs to exactly two m-simplexes s_1^m and s_2^m of $St(p)$ it follows that the face s^{m-2} of s^{m-1}

opposite p belongs to just two $(m-1)$-simplexes of the outer boundary B^{m-1} of $St(p)$, namely the faces s_1^{m-1} and s_2^{m-1} of s_1^m and s_2^m opposite p. Hence B^{m-1} is an $(m-1)$-pseudomanifold. Its orientability follows from the fact that $\mathfrak{H}_{m-1}(B^{m-1})$ is a free cyclic group.

EXERCISES

19. Let M^2 be the union of two euclidean 2-spheres which intersect in a circle S^1. Find the structure of $\mathfrak{H}_1(M^2, p)$ (a) for $p \in S^1$ and (b) for $p \in M^2 - S^1$.

20. Let M^3 be the union of two euclidean 3-spheres which intersect in a 2-sphere S^2. Find the structure of $\mathfrak{H}_2(M^3, p)$ (a) for $p \in S^2$ and (b) for $p \in M^3 - S^2$.

21. Prove (A).

22. Prove (B). *Suggestion:* First show that the faces of the simplexes ps_{ji}^{m-j} are a subdivision of the closed star of s^{m-1}, which consists of all faces of all m-simplexes of M incident with s^{m-1}.

23. Establish Eq. (7.13).

24. Give details of the argument outlined in (C).

25. Verify (D).

26. Prove (E).

27. Show, in connection with the proof of Lemma 5, that each pair of m-simplexes of M are first and last members of a sequence of m-simplexes, consecutive pairs of which are adjacent. *Suggestion:* Given s^m, let $K(s^m)$ be the subcomplex of M consisting of all faces of all m-simplexes of M, each of which can be joined to s^m by a sequence as described. Assume $M - K(s^m)$ non-vacuous and deduce a contradiction. Note that $|M|$ is connected, which has certain implications for $|K|$ and $|M - K(s^m)|$. The reasoning in the proof of Lemma 6 is relevant.

28. Prove the corollary to Theorem 11.

7–6. Cell Complexes

During the rest of this chapter, we will work with homology manifolds, partly because there is no known set of properties depending only on the incidence numbers which enables us to determine whether a given m-complex $(m > 3)$ is a triangulation of a topological m-manifold. Another reason is that there exist important results depending only on the defining properties of homology manifolds and hence applicable to all triangulable topological manifolds, by Art. 7–5(A).

(A) Let B^m be a finite orientable m-pseudomanifold (Art. 5–6(E)). Then $\mathfrak{B}^m = |B^m|$ is a **homology* m-sphere** if it shares with an m-sphere S^m the properties

(7.14)
$$\mathfrak{H}_m(B^m) \approx \mathfrak{H}_0(B^m) \text{ is free cyclic,}$$
$$\mathfrak{H}_k(B^m) = \emptyset \qquad (k \neq 0, m).$$

---

* Called a **combinatorial m-sphere** in much of the literature, but the latter term has lately been used for a complex combinatorially equivalent (Art. 4–12(G)) to the boundary complex of an $(m+1)$-simplex.

In case $m < 3$, $\mathfrak{B}^m$ is a topological m-sphere, but examples exist showing that this is not necessarily so if $m \geq 3$. A **homology 0-sphere** is a pair of points.

Let B^m, with properties (7.14), be used as outer boundary of a closed star $\overline{St}^{m+1}$, let $\bar{\sigma}^{m+1} = |\overline{St}^{m+1}|$ and let $\sigma^{m+1} = \bar{\sigma}^{m+1} - \mathfrak{B}^m$. Then σ^{m+1} is a **homology $(m + 1)$-cell**, $m \in (0, 1, 2, \ldots)$. A **homology 0-cell** is a point. If $\mathfrak{B}^m$ is a topological sphere, then σ^{m+1} is a topological m-simplex (Art. 4–6), but not otherwise.

LEMMA 7. **If σ^k is a homology k-cell, then $\bar{\sigma}^k$ is an orientable k-pseudomanifold** (Art. 7–5(F)) **with boundary** $\mathfrak{B}^{k-1} = \bar{\sigma}^k - \sigma^k$.

Proof of Lemma. This follows easily with the aid of a triangulation of $\bar{\sigma}^k$ into a closed star with outer boundary B^{k-1}, where B^{k-1} is a $(k - 1)$-manifold and, since $\mathfrak{H}_{k-1}(B^{k-1})$ is free cyclic, is orientable. Compare the proof of Lemma 6.

(B) As a consequence of Lemma 7, the homology k-cell σ^k can be **oriented**, by assigning an arbitrary orientation to its boundary $\mathfrak{B}^{k-1}$ and stipulating that a k-simplex of a triangulation of $\bar{\sigma}^k$ shall be **positive** or **negative** according as it is oriented like or unlike $\mathfrak{B}^{k-1}$. We associate $+\sigma^k$ with the positive orientation and $-\sigma^k$ with the negative. If $+\sigma^{k-1} \subset \mathfrak{B}^{k-1}$ is oriented like $+\sigma^k$, it will be said to have the orientation **induced** by σ^k, otherwise the **opposite** orientation.

(C) A set $\{\sigma\} = \bigcup\limits_{k=0}^{m} \{\sigma^k\}$ of disjoint homology cells will be called a **cell m-complex** Γ^m if (1) the set $\{\sigma^m\}$ of m-cells* is non-vacuous, (2) each boundary $\bar{\sigma}^k - \sigma^k$ of a k-cell $\sigma^k \in \{\sigma\}$ is a union of elements of $\{\sigma\}$, called **boundary faces** of σ^k, and (3) each intersection $\bar{\sigma}_h^j \cap \bar{\sigma}_i^k$ of the closure of two elements of $\{\sigma\}$ is the closure of an element of $\{\sigma\}$. An **oriented** cell complex is such a complex Γ^m with an arbitrary positive orientation assigned to each of its cells.

Let Γ^m be a finite oriented cell m-complex, and let $\{\sigma^k\} = (\sigma_1^k, \ldots, \sigma_{\alpha_k}^k)$ be its positive k-cells. The **incidence number** η_{ij}^k is 0 if σ_i^k is not a face of σ_j^{k+1} and is otherwise $+1$ or -1 according as it is a face with the orientation induced by σ_j^{k+1} or with the opposite orientation.

(D) **Cell chains** $\Sigma_{i=1}^{\alpha_k} a_i \sigma_i^k$ and all the associated concepts of Chapter 5 will be regarded as defined for Γ^m. The **boundary** and **coboundary operators** ∂ and δ are determined for Γ^m by

(7.15)

$$\text{(a)} \quad \partial \sigma_j^{k+1} = \sum_{i=1}^{\alpha_k} \eta_{ij}^k \sigma_i^k,$$

$$\text{(b)} \quad \delta \sigma_i^k = \sum_{j=1}^{\alpha_{k+1}} \eta_{ij}^k \sigma_j^{k+1},$$

respectively. As in Chapter 5, we are led to the concepts of **cycle**

* We generally write **cell** for **homology cell** during the rest of this chapter.

groups $\mathfrak{Z}_k(\Gamma^m)$, **cocycle groups** $\mathfrak{Z}^k(\Gamma^m)$, **bounding cycle groups** $\mathfrak{F}_k(\Gamma^m)$, **cobounding cocycle groups** $\mathfrak{F}^k(\Gamma^m)$, and finally to **homology** and **cohomology groups**

(7.16) $\mathfrak{H}_k(\Gamma^m) = \mathfrak{Z}_k(\Gamma^m)/\mathfrak{F}_k(\Gamma^m)$ $\mathfrak{H}^k(\Gamma^m) = \mathfrak{Z}^k(\Gamma^m)/\mathfrak{F}^k(\Gamma^m)$,

of a cell complex.

LEMMA 8. **A cell m-complex $\Gamma^m = \{\sigma\}$ can be subdivided into a simplicial m-complex $K^m = \{t\}$ such that each $\sigma_i^k \in \{\sigma\}$ is covered by the star T^k of a vertex q_i^k on K^m, where $q_i^k \in \sigma_i^k$.**

Proof of Lemma. (E) The k-skeleton of Γ^m is the cell k-complex $\Gamma^k = \overset{k}{\underset{j=0}{\bigcup}} \{\sigma^j\}$ consisting of the cells of Γ^m of dimensions $\leq k$.

The proof is inductive, commencing with Γ^0, for which $\mathfrak{R}^0 = \Gamma^0$ trivially satisfies the lemma. Assume Γ^{h-1} subdivided into $\mathfrak{R}^{h-1}$ for some positive $h < m$, so that the lemma is satisfied with $h - 1$ replacing m. Then the boundary of each $\sigma_i^h \in \Gamma^h$ is covered by a subcomplex B_i^{h-1} of Γ^{h-1}. It is a simple matter to introduce a vertex q_i^h on σ_i^h and to subdivide σ_i^h into a star T_i^h so that the hypothesis of the recurrency is preserved.

THEOREM 12. **In the notation of Lemma 8,**

(7.17) $\mathfrak{H}_k(\Gamma^m) \approx \mathfrak{H}_k(\mathfrak{R}^m)$ $\mathfrak{H}^k(\Gamma^m) \approx \mathfrak{H}^k(\mathfrak{R}^m)$ $(k = 0, 1, 2, \ldots)$.

Proof. Let the k-simplexes of T_i^k be oriented like σ_i^k, and let $\hat{\sigma}_i^k$ be the chain of T_i^k. Then

(7.18) $\partial \hat{\sigma}_i^{k+1} = \sum\limits_{i=1}^{\alpha_k} \eta_{ij}^k \hat{\sigma}_i^k$ (see (7.15a)).

Let φ be the chain mapping from Γ^m to $\mathfrak{R}^m$ determined by $\varphi(\sigma_i^k) = \hat{\sigma}_i^k$, and let $\{\hat{C}^k\}$ be the image k-chains. Then $\{\hat{C}^k\}$ contains a k-chain $C^k = \Sigma\, b_i t_i^k$ of $\mathfrak{R}^m$ if and only if the terms of C^k can be grouped so as to express C^k in the form $\Sigma_{j=1}^{\alpha_k} a_j \hat{\sigma}_j^k$.

It follows from (7.18) that $\varphi : \Sigma\, a_i \sigma_i^k \to \Sigma\, a_i \hat{\sigma}_i^k$ $(k = 0, 1, 2, \ldots)$ induces a homomorphism $\varphi^* : \mathfrak{H}_k(\Gamma^m) \to \mathfrak{H}_k(K^m)$. We proceed with two lemmas.

LEMMA 9. **Let $C^k = \Sigma\, b_i t_i^k$ be a k-chain on the subcomplex $\mathfrak{R}^k$ of $\mathfrak{R}^m$ covering the k-skeleton Γ^k of Γ^m. If $\partial C^{k-1} \in \{\hat{C}^{k-1}\}$, then $C^k \in \{\hat{C}^k\}$ $(k = 1, 2, \ldots, m)$.**

Proof of Lemma. If $t_i^k \in T_h^k$ appears in C^k with coefficient b_i, then all the k-simplexes on T_h^k appear in C^k with this same coefficient b_i. This follows readily from the facts that (1) $\bar{T}_h^k$ is, by definition, a coherently oriented k-pseudomanifold with boundary and (2) ∂C^{k-1} contains no $(k - 1)$-simplexes incident with the center q_h^k of T_h^k, since $\partial C^{k-1} \in \{\hat{C}^{k-1}\}$.

LEMMA 10. Let $C^k = \Sigma\, b_i t_i^k$ be a k-chain on $\Re^\kappa$ ($\kappa > k$), in the notation of Lemma 9. If ∂C^{k-1} belongs to $\{\hat{C}^{k-1}\}$, then there exists a k-chain D^k on $\Re^{\kappa-1}$ such that $D^k \sim C^k$.

Proof of Lemma. Suppose a k-simplex incident with the center q_h^κ of a star T_h^κ appears in C^k, and let C_h^k be the subchain of C^k consisting of all the terms involving simplexes incident with q_h^κ. Then ∂C_h^k is a $(k-1)$-cycle on the outer boundary $B_h^{\kappa-1}$ of T_h^κ. Since $\mathfrak{H}_{k-1}(B_h^{\kappa-1}) = \emptyset$, there is a chain D_h^k on $B_h^{\kappa-1}$ with boundary ∂C_h^k. But the cycle $C_h^k - D_h^k$ bounds, because $\bar{T}_h^\kappa$ is a cone complex and therefore, by Theorem 3, $\mathfrak{H}_k(\bar{T}_h^\kappa) = \emptyset$. Hence $C^k \sim C^k - (C_h^k - D_h^k)$, and the latter chain involves no k-simplex incident with q_h^κ. By repetitions, we obtain a k-chain homologous to C^k involving no simplex incident with any q_h^κ ($h = 0, \ldots, \alpha_m$), hence lying on $\Re^{\kappa-1}$.

(E) As a corollary to Lemma 10, obtained by repeated applications, there exists a k-chain $\hat{D}^k$ on $\Re^k$ where (1) $\hat{D}^k \sim D^k$ and (2) $\hat{D}^k \in \{\hat{C}^k\}$, as a consequence of Lemma 9.

In the case $\partial C^k = \emptyset$ of Lemma 10, (E) implies that each kth homology class of K^m contains cycles belonging to the set $\{\hat{Z}^k\}$ consisting of the cycles in $\{\hat{C}^k\}$. In other words, each kth homology class $[Z^k]$ of $\Re^m$ contains the image under φ^* of at least one k^{th} homology class of Γ^m. Now if $\hat{Z}_1^k$ and $\hat{Z}_2^k$ are cycles of the set $\{\hat{Z}^k\}$ both in $[Z]$ then, by (E) read with $k + 1$ in place of k, $\hat{Z}_1^k - \hat{Z}_2^k$ bounds a chain $\hat{D}^{k+1} \in \{\hat{C}^{k+1}\}$. Hence $[Z^k]$ contains the image under φ^* of at most one homology class of Γ^m. Therefore φ^* is a one-to-one homomorphism, which is an isomorphism, and Theorem 12 is proved for homology groups. No separate proof is needed for cohomology, because the cohomology groups can be expressed in terms of the homology groups.

EXERCISES

29. Give a subdivision $\Re^m$ satisfying Lemma 8, where Γ^m consists of all the faces, including the interior, of a cube in euclidean 3-space.

30. Use the subdivision of Exercise 29 to illustrate the proof of Theorem 12.

7–7. Cellular Subdivisions of a Homology Manifold

Let $M = \{s\}$ be a coherently oriented triangulation of a compact orientable homology m-manifold $\mathfrak{M}$, and let $M_1 = \{t\}$ be the first barycentric subdivision of M.

(A) Let $s^m = +p_{i_0} p_{i_1} \ldots p_{i_m}$ be a typical m-simplex of M, let $(j_0, \ldots, j_m)$ be a permutation of $(i_0, i_1, \ldots, i_m)$, and let $p_{j_0 \ldots j_k}$ denote the barycenter of the face $p_{j_0} \ldots p_{j_k}$ of s^m. Then, by Art. 4–11(B),

$$(7.19) \qquad t_{j_0 \ldots j_m}^m = \pm p_{j_0} p_{j_0 j_1} \cdots p_{j_0 j_1 \ldots j_m}$$

is a typical m-simplex of M_1. In (7.19), let the sign be $+$ or $-$ according as $(j_0, \ldots, j_m)$ is an even or an odd permutation of $(i_0, \ldots, i_m)$. Then $t^m_{j_0 \ldots j_m}$ is oriented like s^m (Exercise 31).

Another formulation for the simplexes $\{t\}$ is useful. Let $\{s^k\} = (s^k_1, \ldots, s^k_{\alpha_k})$ be the k-simplexes of M $(k = 0, \ldots, m)$, and let p^k_i be the barycenter of s^k_i. A partial ordering of the simplexes $\{s\}$ was defined (Art. 4–5) such that $s^h_i < s^k_j \Leftrightarrow s^h_i$ is a boundary face of s^k_j. Let this ordering be carried over to the barycenters of the simplexes $\{s\}$, so that

$$(7.20) \qquad p^h_i < p^k_j \Leftrightarrow s^h_i < s^k_j \Leftrightarrow (s^h_i \text{ is a boundary face of } s^k_j),$$

and let

$$(7.21) \qquad \{q\} = (q_1, \ldots, q_\alpha) \qquad \left(\alpha = \sum_{k=0}^m \alpha_k\right)$$

be the set of all the points p^k_i, renumbered in the order $(p^0_1, \ldots, p^0_{\alpha_0}; p^1_1, \ldots, p^1_{\alpha_1}; \cdots; p^m_1, \ldots, p^m_{\alpha_m})$.

LEMMA 11. **The unoriented k-simplexes $\{t\}$ of M_1 consist of all simplexes of the form**

$$(7.22) \qquad t^k = q_{h_0} \ldots q_{h_k} \text{ such that } q_{h_0} < \cdots < q_{h_k}.$$

Proof of Lemma. This follows from (A), since the unoriented faces of $t^m_{j_0 \ldots j_m}$ consist of all subsets of the vertices on the right in (7.19), and a typical set of such vertices, in the relative order of their occurrence, is also a typical subset $(q_{h_0}, \ldots, q_{h_k})$ with $q_{h_0} < \cdots < q_{h_k}$.

(B) We remark that each k-simplex of $\{t\}$ which is on a k-simplex of $\{s\}$ takes its orientation from the latter. We will presently specify orientations for the other simplexes of $\{t\}$, which, for the present, we take to be arbitrarily oriented.

(C) We will conventionally write the vertices of a simplex of $\{t\}$ in increasing order, so that

$$(7.23) \qquad t^k = \pm q_{h_0} \ldots q_{h_k} \Rightarrow q_{h_0} < \cdots < q_{h_k}.$$

We refer to q_{h_0} as the **first** vertex of t^k and to q_{h_k} as its **last** vertex.

LEMMA 12. **Let S^k_i be the set of simplexes of $\{t\}$ with p^k_i for last vertex. Then $s^k_i = |S^k_i|$ $(k = 0, \ldots, m; \ i = 1, \ldots, \alpha_k)$ (Exercise 33).**

(D) The subsets S^k_i constitute a partition of the simplexes $\{t\}$ (Art. 3–2(B)). A **dual** partition, which we next study, is afforded by the subsets T^{m-k}_i $(k = 0, \ldots, m; \ i = 1, \ldots, \alpha_k)$, where T^{m-k}_i is the set of simplexes of $\{t\}$ with p^k_i for first, instead of last, vertex.

LEMMA 13. **The set T^m_i is the star of p^0_i on M_1 $(i = 1, \ldots, \alpha_0)$.**

Proof of Lemma. Since its superscript is 0, p^0_i is the first vertex of each simplex of M_1 with which it is incident. Hence the lemma is true.

(E) Let $\tau_i^m = |T_i^m|$. Since $\mathfrak{M}$ is a homology manifold, we see from Arts. 7–5(A), 7–6(A), and Theorem 4 that $\beta_i^{m-1} = \bar{\tau}_i^{m-1} - \tau_i^{m-1}$ is a homology $(m-1)$-sphere, and that τ_i^m is a homology m-cell. The set $\{\tau^m\} = (\tau_1^m, \ldots, \tau_{\alpha_0}^m)$ will be the m-cells of a cell m-complex $\{\tau\}$ covering $\mathfrak{M}$, which we proceed to define.

LEMMA 14. **Each outer boundary** $\beta_i^{m-1} = \bar{\tau}_i^m - \tau_i^m$ **is a homology** $(m-1)$**-manifold.**

Proof of Lemma. The case $m = 1$ being almost trivial (Exercise 34), we assume $m > 1$. Let Σ_1^{m-1} be the star of a point $p \in \beta_i^{m-1}$ under

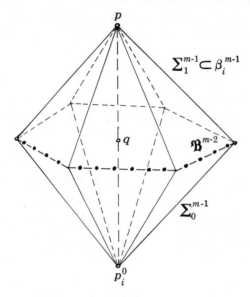

Fig. 7–2. Star neighborhood on β_i^{m-1}.

a triangulation of a neighborhood of p, with p as a vertex. It is to be shown that $\mathfrak{B}^{m-2} = \overline{\Sigma}_1^{m-1} - \Sigma_1^{m-1}$ is a homology $(m-2)$-sphere. Let $\overline{\Sigma}_0^{m-1}$ be the cone complex with center p_i^0 and outer boundary $\mathfrak{B}^{m-2}$.

(F) Then $B^{m-2} = \overline{\Sigma}_0^{m-1} \cap \overline{\Sigma}_1^{m-1}$ is a triangulation of $\mathfrak{B}^{m-2}$ (Fig. 7–2). The union $B_0^{m-1} = \overline{\Sigma}_0^{m-1} \cup \overline{\Sigma}_1^{m-1}$ is a homology $(m-1)$-sphere. For, B_0^{m-1} is the surrounding complex of the midpoint q of $p_i^0 p$ in a certain triangulation Σ^m covering a neighborhood of q on the homology m-manifold M, Σ^m being defined as the cone complex with center q and outer boundary B_0^{m-1}.

Since $\overline{\Sigma}_j^{m-1}$ is a cone complex $(j = 0, 1)$, a k-cycle Z^k on B^{m-2} bounds a chain C_j^{k+1} on $\overline{\Sigma}_j^{m-1}$ (Theorem 3). The difference $Z^{k+1} = C_1^{k+1} - C_0^{k+1}$ is a $(k+1)$-cycle on B_0^{m-1}. Suppose $k < m-2$, so that $\mathfrak{H}_{k+1}(B_0^{m-1}) = \emptyset$ and therefore Z^{k+1} bounds a chain C^{k+2} on B_0^{m-1}. Let

C_1^{k+2} be the subchain of C^{k+2} consisting of all terms of C^{k+2} involving simplexes incident with p, and let $C_0^{k+2} = C^{k+2} - C_1^{k+2}$. Then

$$(7.24) \quad \partial C_1^{k+2} = \partial C^{k+2} - \partial C_0^{k+2} = Z^{k+1} - \partial C_0^{k+2} = C_1^{k+1} - C_0^{k+1} - \partial C_0^{k+2}.$$

Hence the chain $C^{k+1} = C_0^{k+1} + \partial C_0^{k+2}$ is (1) on $\overline{\Sigma}_0^{m-1}$ by definition and (2) on $\overline{\Sigma}_1^{m-1}$ because it equals $C_1^{k+1} - \partial C_1^{k+2}$. It is therefore on $B^{m-2} = \overline{\Sigma}_0^{m-1} \cap \overline{\Sigma}_1^{m-1}$. Now $\partial C^{k+1} = \partial C_0^{k+1} + \partial \partial C_0^{k+2} = \partial C_0^{k+1} = Z^k$. Hence, since $Z^k \sim \emptyset$ was an arbitrary k-cycle on B^{m-2},

$$(7.25) \quad \begin{aligned} \mathfrak{H}_k(B^{m-2}) &= \emptyset \qquad 0 < k < m - 2, \\ \mathfrak{H}_0(B^{m-2}) &\text{ is free cyclic.} \end{aligned}$$

Now suppose $k = m - 2$. Since $H_{m-1}(B^{m-1})$ is free cyclic, $Z^{k+1} = Z^{m-1}$ is a multiple of the chain Z_*^{m-1} of B^{m-1}. But $C_1^{m-1} - C_0^{m-1} = \mu Z_*^{m-1}$ implies that $C_j^{m-1} = \mu D_j^{m-1}$, where D_j^{m-1} is the chain of $\overline{\Sigma}_j^{m-1}$ ($j = 0, 1$). Hence $Z^{m-2} = \partial C_j^{m-1} = \mu \partial D_j^{m-1}$. Thus each $(m - 2)$-cycle Z^{m-2} on B^{m-2} is a multiple of the chain of B^{m-2}, so that $\mathfrak{H}_{m-2}(B^{m-2})$ is free cyclic. This, with (7.25), implies that B^{m-2} is a homology $(m - 2)$-sphere, completing the proof of Lemma 14.

THEOREM 13. **In the notation of (D), let**

$$(7.26) \qquad \tau_i^{m-k} = |T_i^{m-k}| \qquad (k = 0, \ldots, m; \ i = 1, \ldots, \alpha_k).$$

Then (1) τ_i^{m-k} is a homology $(m - k)$-cell, and (2) the set $\{\tau\}$ of all the cells τ_i^{m-k} is a subdivision of $\mathfrak{M}$ into a cell complex.

Proof. If $p_i^h < p_i^k$, then each simplex of T_j^{m-k} is a boundary face of some simplex of T_i^{m-h}.

(G) *Hence* $p_i^h < p_j^k \Rightarrow \tau_j^{m-k} \subset \overline{\tau}_i^{m-h} - \tau_i^{m-h}$. We then say that τ_j^{m-k} is a face of τ_i^{m-h}.

Let t be the carrier in M_1 of a point $p \in \mathfrak{M}$. If p_i^k is the first vertex of t, then $p \in \tau_i^{m-k}$. If p_j^k is any other vertex of M_1, then $p \notin \tau_j^{m-k}$.

(H) *Hence each point of $\mathfrak{M}$ is on exactly one of the elements $\{\tau\}$.*

The elements $\overline{\tau}_i^{m-h}$ and $\overline{\tau}_j^{m-k}$ intersect if and only if there exists a p_e^d such that $p_i^h \leq p_e^d$ and $p_j^k \leq p_e^d$, which is true only if s_i^h and s_j^k are faces of s_e^d. Let s_e^d be the lowest-dimensional simplex with this property.

(I) *Then* $\overline{\tau}_e^d = \overline{\tau}_i^{m-h} \cap \overline{\tau}_j^{m-k}$, *and* τ_e^d *is the highest-dimensional* τ *on* $\overline{\tau}_i \cap \overline{\tau}_j^k$ (Exercise 35).

By (E), each τ_i^m is a homology cell. So is each τ_j^{m-1}, since its outer boundary $\mathfrak{B}_j^{m-2}$ is a homology $(m - 2)$-sphere on some $\beta_j^{m-1} = \overline{\tau}_i^m - \tau_i^m$ (Lemma 14). But β_i^{m-1} is a homology $(m - 1)$-manifold and can play the role of $\mathfrak{M}$ in (E) and Lemma 14, read with $m - 1$ replacing m. This means that each τ_h^{m-2} is a homology cell.

(J) *Continuing thus, inductively, we conclude that each* τ_i^{m-k} *is a homology $(m - k)$-cell* ($k = 0, \ldots, m; \ i = 1, \ldots, \alpha_k$).

Properties (G), (H), (I), and (J) characterize $\{\tau\}$ as a subdivision of $\mathfrak{M}$ into a cell complex.

EXERCISES

31. (a) For the special case $m = 2$ and $s^m = p_0 p_1 p_2$, sketch the six simplexes $t^m_{j_0 j_1 j_2}$ of (7.19), showing their orientations. (b) Show, for the general case, that each $t^m_{j_0 \ldots j_m}$ is oriented like s^m.

32. Illustrate the numbering of the vertices in (7.21) for the special case of Exercise 31.

33. Prove Lemma 12. *Suggestion:* Show that each simplex of $\{t\}$ is a subset of the carrier $s^k \in \{s\}$ of its last vertex.

34. Prove the case $m = 1$ of Lemma 14.

35. Establish Statement (I).

7–8. The Poincaré Duality Theorem

Consider now the triangulation $\{s\} = M$ and the dual cell complex $\{\tau\} = T$ covering the manifold $\mathfrak{M} = |M| = |T|$. We remark that $M_1 = \{t\}$ is a common subdivision of M and T, and that M and T, by Art. 7–7(D) and Theorem 13, are obtainable by partitioning the simplexes $\{t\}$ (1) into the stars S^k_i and letting $s^k_i = |S^k_i|$, then (2) into the stars T^{m-k}_i and letting $\tau^{m-k}_i = |T^{m-k}_i|$ $(k = 0, \ldots, m;\ i = 1, \ldots, \alpha_k)$.

LEMMA 15. **The point p^k_i is the intersection**

$$(7.27) \qquad p^k_i = s^k_i \cap \tau^{m-k}_i \qquad (k = 0, \ldots, m;\ i = 1, \ldots, \alpha_k).$$

Proof of Lemma. By definition, S^k_i is the set of simplexes of M_1 with p^k_i for last vertex and T^{m-k}_i is the set of simplexes of M with p^k_i for first vertex. Hence p^k_i is the only point common to $|S^k_i|$ and $|T^{m-k}_i|$ (see Fig. 7–3).

We next assign special orientations to each cell τ^{m-k}_i, which is possible because T^{m-k}_i is an orientable $(m-k)$-pseudomanifold with boundary. Consider three simplexes

$$
\begin{aligned}
&\text{(a)} \quad t^k_0 = \xi p^0_{i_0} p^1_{i_1} \ldots p^k_{i_k} \in S^k_i \qquad (i = i_k), \\
(7.28) \quad &\text{(b)} \quad t^{m-k}_1 = \eta p^k_{i_k} p^{k+1}_{i_{k+1}} \ldots p^m_{i_m} \in T^{m-k}_i, \\
&\text{(c)} \quad t^m = \zeta p^0_{i_0} \ldots p^m_{i_m} \in M_1,
\end{aligned}
$$

where (1) t^k_0 is an arbitrary k-simplex of S^k_i, with ξ chosen to make the orientation like that of S^k_i, (2) t^{m-k}_1 is an arbitrary $(m-k)$-simplex of T^{m-k}_i, with orientation yet to be specified, and (3) t^m is determined by t^k_0 and t^{m-k}_1, and ζ is chosen to give t^m the positive orientation of $\mathfrak{M}$.

(A) The value η, hence the **positive orientation** of t^{m-k}_1 shall be determined, for each t^{m-k}_1, by the requirement $\xi \eta \zeta = 1$.

LEMMA 16. **(a) The convention (A) specifies a unique orientation for each t^{m-k}_1 on a T^{m-k}_i. (b) These orientations are coherent on each T^{m-k}_i $(k = 0, \ldots, m;\ i = 1, \ldots, \alpha_k)$.**

Proof of Lemma. The vertices in (7.28) are the barycenters of correspondingly indexed simplexes of $\{s\}$ such that

(7.29) $$s_{i_0}^0 < s_{i_1}^1 < \cdots < s_{i_k}^k < \cdots < s_{i_m}^m.$$

All simplexes of S_i^k and of T_i^{m-k} are obtained as $s_i^k = s_{i_k}^k$ is held fixed and the other s's range over all possibilities subject to (7.29). As the

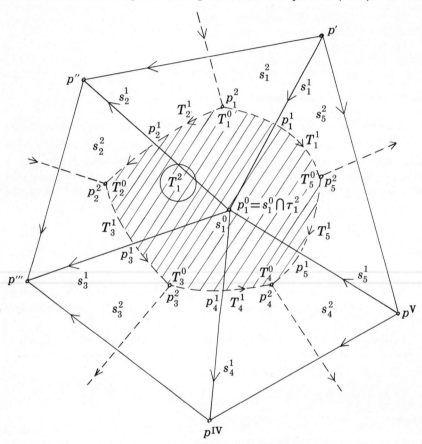

Fig. 7–3. Dual subdivisions of an M^2.

first k of the s's in (7.29) are thus varied, the coherently oriented k-simplexes of S_i^k on s_i^k are obtained. Each such variation entails corresponding changes in the vertices of t_0^k and of t^m, but not in those of t_1^{m-k}. A change which reverses the sign of ξ likewise reverses that of ζ, hence leaves η fixed (Exercise 38). Thus all determinations of η for each t_1^{m-k} are equivalent, proving Lemma 16, Part (a). Now let the first $k + 1$ of the s's be held fixed and the last $m - k$ allowed to vary, subject to (7.29). This keeps s_i^k fixed and yields (1) the set of coherently oriented m-simplexes t^m incident with s_i^k and (2) the set of all $(m - k)$-simplexes t_1^{m-k} of T_i^{m-k}. A variation of the s's which changes the sign of ζ does the same for η. Two selections of the s's yielding adjacent simplexes t^m likewise yield adjacent simplexes t_1^{m-k}, and Part (b) of the lemma is a consequence (Exercise 38).

(B) As a corollary to Lemma 16, the convention (A) specifies a positive orientation for each τ_i^{m-k}, thus orienting the cell complex $T = \{\tau\}$. The m-cells $\{\tau^m\}$ are coherently oriented.

LEMMA 17. *If s_j^{k-1} and s_i^k have incidence number ε_{ji}^{k-1}, then τ_j^{m-k+1} and τ_i^{m-k} have incidence number*

$$(7.30) \qquad\qquad \eta_{ij}^{m-k} = (-1)^k \varepsilon_{ji}^{k-1}.$$

Proof of Lemma. Consider (7.28) for the stars S_i^k and T_i^{m-k} covering s_i^k and τ_i^{m-k}, and suppose the notation such that, for the stars covering s_j^{k-1} and τ_j^{m-k+1},

$$(7.31) \qquad
\begin{aligned}
&\text{(a)} \quad t_0^{k-1} = \xi' p_{i_0}^0 \ldots p_{i_{k-1}}^{k-1} \in S_j^{k-1},\\
&\text{(b)} \quad t_1^{m-k+1} = \eta' p_{i_{k-1}}^{k-1} \ldots p_{i_m}^m \in T_j^{m-k+1},\\
&\text{(c)} \quad t^m = \zeta p_{i_0}^0 \ldots p_{i_m}^m \qquad \text{(identical with (7.28c)).}
\end{aligned}$$

Then the boundary chain ∂t_0^k contains the term $(-1)^k \xi p_{i_0}^0 \ldots p_{i_{k-1}}^{k-1} = (-1)^k \xi \xi' t_0^{k-1}$. Thus the incidence number of t_0^k and t_0^{k-1} is $\varepsilon = (-1)^k \xi \xi' = \varepsilon_{ji}^{k-1}$ (since t_0^{k-1} and t_0^k are oriented like s_j^{k-1} and s_i^k). Similarly, since (1) the incidence numbers of τ_j^{m-k+1} and τ_i^{m-k} are the same as those of t_1^{m-k+1} and t_1^{m-k} and (2) $\partial t_1^{m-k+1} = \eta' p_{i_k}^k \ldots p_{i_m}^m + \cdots = \eta \eta' t_1^{m-k} + \cdots$, we have $\eta_{ij}^{m-k} = \eta \eta'$. But the orientation convention (A) implies $\xi \eta \zeta = \xi' \eta' \zeta$, hence $\xi \xi' = \eta \eta'$ (since each factor is $+1$ or -1), and hence (7.30) holds.

THEOREM 14 (POINCARÉ DUALITY THEOREM). **Let $\mathfrak{M}$ be a compact orientable homology m-manifold. Then**

$$(7.32) \qquad\qquad \mathfrak{H}_k(\mathfrak{M}) \approx \mathfrak{H}^{m-k}(\mathfrak{M}) \qquad (k = 0, 1, \ldots, m),$$

that is, the homology and cohomology groups of $\mathfrak{M}$ in complementary dimensions are isomorphic.

Proof. For the purpose of proving this theorem, we interpret ε_{ji}^{k-1} as the coefficient of s_j^{k-1} in ∂s_i^k and η_{ij}^{m-k} as the coefficient of τ_j^{m-k+1} in $\delta \tau_i^{m-k}$.

(C) Lemma 17 is then equivalent to the statement that s_j^{k-1} has the same coefficient in the boundary chain of $(-1)^k s_i^k$ as τ_j^{m-k+1} has in the coboundary chain of τ_i^{m-k}.

The simplex chain groups of $M = \{s\}$ are the integral modules $\mathfrak{C}_k = [s_1^k, \ldots, s_{\alpha_k}^k]$ (see Art. A–4) and the cell chain groups of $T = \{\tau\}$

are the integral modules $\mathfrak{D}^{m-k} = [\tau_1^{m-k}, \ldots, \tau_{\alpha_k}^{m-k}]$. The correspondence $s_i^k \to \tau_i^{m-k}$ defines an obvious isomorphism between the chain groups $\mathfrak{C}_k$ and $\mathfrak{D}^{m-k}$ of complementary dimensions for each $k = 0, \ldots, m$.

The homomorphisms $\partial : \mathfrak{C}_k \to \mathfrak{C}_{k-1}$ and $\delta : \mathfrak{D}^{m-k} \to \mathfrak{D}^{m-k+1}$ lead in precisely the same way to $\mathfrak{H}_k(M)$ and $\mathfrak{H}^{m-k}(T)$. That is, the kernels of ∂ and δ are the k-cycle group $\mathfrak{Z}_k(M)$ and the $(m - k)$-cocycle group $\mathfrak{Z}^{m-k}(T)$, respectively. The image chains in $\mathfrak{C}_{k-1}$ and $\mathfrak{D}^{m-k+1}$ constitute the bounding k-cycle group $\mathfrak{F}_{k-1}(M)$ and the cobounding cocycle group $\mathfrak{F}^{m-k+1}(T)$. By definition,

(7.33) $\mathfrak{H}_k(M) = \mathfrak{Z}_k(M)/\mathfrak{F}_k(M)$ $\mathfrak{H}^{m-k}(T) = \mathfrak{Z}^{m-k}(T)/\mathfrak{F}^{m-k}(T)$.

Since

(7.34) $\partial s_i^k = \sum_{j=1}^{\alpha_{k-1}} \varepsilon_{ji}^{k-1} s_j^{k-1}$ $\delta \tau_i^{m-k} = (-1)^k \sum_{j=1}^{\alpha_{k-1}} \varepsilon_{ji}^{k-1} \tau_j^{m-k+1}$,

the isomorphism defined by $s_i^j \to \tau_i^{m-j}$ induces an isomorphism between $\mathfrak{H}_k(M)$ and $\mathfrak{H}^{m-k}(T)$. This, with Theorem 12, implies Theorem 14.

COROLLARY 1. **The Betti numbers of $\mathfrak{M}$ satisfy the duality relations $\beta_0 = \beta_m = 1$, $\beta_k = \beta_{m-k}$ $(k = 0, 1, \ldots, m)$, and its kth torsion coefficients are the same as its $(m - k - 1)^{\text{th}}$ torsion coefficients.**

This is the form in which Poincaré duality was generally formulated before cohomology theory was developed. It follows from Chapter 5, Theorem 17, Chapter 6, Theorem 1, and Theorem 14 above (Exercise 39).

COROLLARY 2. **If $\mathfrak{M}$ is a compact homology m-manifold, orientable or not, its connectivity numbers satisfy the duality relations $\hat{\beta}_0 = \hat{\beta}_m = 1$, $\hat{\beta}_k = \hat{\beta}_{m-k}$ $(k = 0, 1, \ldots, m)$.**

This is the result of mod 2 considerations strictly analogous to those leading to Theorem 14.

COROLLARY 3. **The Euler-Poincaré characteristic $N(\mathfrak{M})$ of an odd-dimensional compact homology manifold $\mathfrak{M}$ is zero.**

This follows from $N(M) = \Sigma_{k=0}^m (-1)^k \hat{\beta}_k$ and Corollary 2, since $\hat{\beta}_k$ and $\hat{\beta}_{m-k}$ appear in the summation with opposite signs.

THEOREM 15. **If $\mathfrak{M}$ is a compact 3-manifold, then all its homology groups are determined by $\mathfrak{H}_1(\mathfrak{M})$ and the orientability class of $\mathfrak{M}$.**

Proof. Suppose $\mathfrak{M}$ orientable. Then $\beta_0 = \beta_3 = 1$. Hence $\beta_2 = \beta_1$, since $N(\mathfrak{M}) = \beta_0 - \beta_1 + \beta_2 - \beta_3 = 0$. Since there are no 0th torsion coefficients, there are no second torsion coefficients (Theorem 14, Corollary 1), a fact also known from the orientability. There may be first torsion coefficients. If $\mathfrak{M}$ is non-orientable, then (1) $\beta_0 = 1$, $\beta_3 = 0$, (2) there is a second torsion coefficient equal to 2, and (3) $\beta_0 - \beta_1 + \beta_2 - \beta_3 = 0$. Hence $\beta_2 = \beta_1 - 1$.

COROLLARY. **If $\mathfrak{M}$ is a non-orientable closed 3-manifold, then $\mathfrak{H}_1(\mathfrak{M})$ is infinite.**

For, $\beta_1 = \beta_2 + 1 > 0$.

EXERCISES

36. Work through the proof of Lemma 16 in detail, with illustrative diagrams, in the case where M consists of the boundary faces of a 2-simplex.

37. Continue the special case of Exercise 36 through the proof of Lemma 17.

38. Verify the statements in the proof of Lemma 16. The form $p_{j_0} p_{j_0 j_1} \cdots p_{j_0 \ldots j_m}$ used in Art. 7–7 may prove useful in this connection.

39. Give the details of the proof of Corollary 1 to Theorem 14.

40. Express the first and second Betti numbers of a compact orientable homology 4-manifold in terms of its Euler-Poincaré characteristic.

41. Using methods like those in the proof, find out whether $\mathfrak{H}_1(M)$, $\mathfrak{H}_2(M)$, and the orientability class of $\mathfrak{M}$ determine all its homology groups, if $\mathfrak{M}$ is a compact homology 5-manifold.

42. Express the characteristic $N(M)$ of an even-dimensional compact homology manifold as simply as possible in terms of its connectivity numbers.

43. Show that a connected finite simplicial 3-complex M is a triangulated 3-manifold if and only if the surrounding complex of each of its vertices is a 2-sphere.

44. The 3-dimensional torus T^3 is obtained from the solid cube $|x_i| \leq 1$ ($i = 1, 2, 3$) by identifying pairs of boundary points symmetric to each other in a coordinate plane. (a) Show that T^3 is a 3-manifold and (b) find its homology groups.

7–9. Relative Homology

The theory briefly discussed in this section and the next was developed originally by Solomon Lefschetz. For an account by him of some of its highlights, see $[L_2]$, pp. 195ff.

Relative homology theory is obtained from the **absolute** homology theory already presented in Chapters 5 through 7, by suppressing the simplexes of a subcomplex L of a complex K. Absolute homology is then the case $L = \emptyset$ of relative homology. *We discuss only the case K finite* ($\Leftrightarrow |K|$ compact).

Since K and $L \subset K$ are complexes, they are closed sets of simplexes (Art. 4–6(B)) and $K - L$ is an open set. This implies (Chapter 4, Lemma 4) that $|K|$ and $|L|$ are closed and $|K - L|$ is open.

If C^k is a k-chain on K, then λC^k will denote the chain obtained from C^k by changing to 0 the coefficient of each simplex of L appearing in C^k, a procedure described as **suppressing the simplexes of** L.

LEMMA 18. **The operator** λ **is, for each** $k \in (0, 1, \ldots, m)$, **a homomorphism** $\lambda : \mathfrak{C}_k \rightarrow \mathfrak{C}_k$ (Exercise 47).

Two k-chains C_1^k and C_2^k are **equal** mod L if $\lambda C_1^k = \lambda C_2^k$; that is, if they are the same except for their subchains on L. Symbolically

$$(7.35) \qquad C_1^k = C_2^k \bmod L \Leftrightarrow \lambda(C_2^k - C_1^k) = \emptyset.$$

(A) We refer to $\lambda\mathfrak{C}_k = \mathfrak{C}_k(K, L)$ as the **group of k-chains** mod L or the **k-chain group** mod L. We next define a **boundary operator** ∂_L mod L, a **k-cycle group** mod L, and a **bounding k-cycle group** mod L, as follows:

    (1) $\partial_L = \lambda\partial$ so that the mod L boundary of a k-chain C^k is obtained from ∂C^k by suppressing the simplexes on L.

    (2) C^k is a **k-cycle** mod $L \Leftrightarrow \partial_L C^k = \emptyset$.

    (3) $C^k \sim \emptyset$ mod $L \Leftrightarrow \exists \ C^{k+1}$ such that $\partial_L C^{k+1} = \lambda C^k$.

(B) The mapping $\partial_L : \mathfrak{C}_k(K, L) \to \mathfrak{C}_{k-1}(K, L)$ is a homomorphism (Exercise 48). Its kernel is the **relative k-cycle group** $\mathfrak{Z}_k(K, L)$, or the **k-cycle group** mod L. The image chains under the mapping $\partial_L :$ $\mathfrak{C}_{k+1} \to \mathfrak{C}_k$ constitute the group $\mathfrak{F}_k(K, L)$ of **bounding k-cycles** mod L. The chains with non-zero multiples which bound mod L are the **boundary divisors** mod L, and constitute a group $\mathfrak{D}_k(K, L)$. These groups satisfy the inclusions

$$(7.36) \qquad \mathfrak{F}_k(K, L) \subset \mathfrak{D}_k(K, L) \subset \mathfrak{Z}_k(K, L) \subset \mathfrak{C}_k(K, L).$$

The **relative** (or mod L) **homology groups, torsion groups,** and **Betti groups** are, as in the absolute case (Art. 5–2 and Eq. (5.62)):

$$\mathfrak{H}_k(K, L) = \mathfrak{Z}_k(K, L)/\mathfrak{F}_k(K, L),$$

$$(7.37) \qquad \mathfrak{T}_k(K, L) = \mathfrak{D}_k(K, L)/\mathfrak{F}_k(K, L),$$

$$\mathfrak{B}_k(K, L) = \mathfrak{H}_k(K, L)/\mathfrak{T}_k(K, L) = \mathfrak{Z}_k(K, L)/\mathfrak{D}_k(K, L),$$

and the **relative** (or mod L) **Betti** and **torsion numbers** $\beta_k(K, L)$ and $\tau_i^k(K, L)$ $(i = 1, \ldots, \rho_k)$ are the Betti and torsion numbers of $\mathfrak{H}_k(K, L)$.

(C) The following concepts and results directly generalize the corresponding parts of the absolute homology theory:

    (1) $\beta_0(K, L)$ is the number of components of $|K|$ which do not intersect $|L|$. Hence $\beta_0(K, L) = 0$ for $|K|$ connected and L not vacuous (Exercise 49).

    (2) If K is an m-pseudomanifold with boundary L, then (Exercise 50)
        (a) K orientable $\Rightarrow \beta_m(K, L) = 1$ and $\exists$ no $\tau^{m-1}(K, L)$,
        (b) K non-orientable $\Rightarrow \beta_m(K, L) = 0$ and $\exists$ one $\tau^{m-1}(K, L)$ equal to 2.

(3) The **characteristic of** K **mod** L is

$$(7.38) \qquad N(K, L) = \sum_{k=0}^{m} (-1)^k \alpha_k(K, L) = \sum_{k=0}^{m} (-1)^k \beta_k(K, L),$$

where $\alpha_k(K, L)$ is the number of k-simplexes of $K - L$.

THEOREM 16. **The relative homology group** $\mathfrak{H}_k(K, L)$ **is a topological invariant of** $|K|$ **and** $|L|$.

Outline of proof. A subpolyhedron Λ of a topological polyhedron Π means a subspace $\Lambda \subset \Pi$ such that a subcomplex L of some triangulation K of $\Pi = |K|$ is a triangulation of Λ. The complexes (K, L) are a **covering pair** of (Π, Λ).

(D) The work of Chapter 6 can be adapted (Exercise 53) to the proof of Theorem 16. In the adaptation, singular simplexes are used with the restriction that a simplex intersecting Λ shall be entirely on Λ. *This permits a topologically invariant definition of singular relative homology groups* $\mathfrak{H}_k(\Pi, \Lambda)$. Simplicial approximations and deformations can be used as in Chapter 6, with the restriction that under each deformation no point moves from Λ to $\Pi - \Lambda$, or from $\Pi - \Lambda$ to Λ, to establish that each singular homology class of Π mod Λ contains exactly one simplicial homology class of K mod L.

EXERCISES

45. Let K^2 be the set of boundary faces of a 3-simplex, and let L^1 be the set of boundary faces of one of the 2-simplexes of K^2. Find all the homology groups and the characteristic of K^2 mod L^1.

46. Let M^2 be a triangulation of a 2-manifold with boundary, and let K^1 be the subcomplex of M^2 covering its boundary. Find the homology groups of M^2 mod K^1. The result will be a generalization of Theorem 7 of Chapter 5.

47. Prove Lemma 18.

48. Show that $\partial_L = \lambda \partial$ is a homomorphism for each chain group $\mathfrak{C}_k$ or $\mathfrak{C}_k(K, L)$. Verify the other statements in (B).

49.* Prove Part 1 of (C).

50.* Prove Part 2 of (C).

51.* Establish the second equation in (7.38), the first being a matter of definition.

52. Give an appropriate definition of a **relative** k-**pseudomanifold**; that is, of the statement that K **is a pseudomanifold** mod L.

53.* Develop the details of the outlined proof of Theorem 16.

7-10.　The Lefschetz Duality Theorem

We continue with the notation of Art. 7-9. Our next object is to find a simple expression for the singular homology groups $\mathfrak{H}_k(\Pi - \Lambda)$.

* This problem calls for the writing of a short paper adapting the relevant parts of the absolute theory.

This problem offers some novel features because $\Pi - \Lambda$ is generally not compact, hence cannot be triangulated into a finite (closed) complex.

(*A*) A covering pair (K, L) of (Π, Λ) is called **normal** if each simplex of K with all its vertices on Λ belongs to L (Exercise 54). Given a normal covering pair (K, L), let $St(L)$ be the union of the stars on K of the vertices on L.

The subcomplex (Exercise 55) $M = M(K) = K - St(L)$ is an **approximating complex** to $\Pi - \Lambda$. Let $R = St(L) - L$. Then R is the set of all simplexes of K each with at least one vertex on Λ and at least one on $\Pi - \Lambda$.

Since the structure of the homology groups of a space is the same as for all homeomorphs thereof, we are justified in letting $\Pi = |K|$, where K is a linear simplicial complex in a euclidean space. We do this, as usual, for the sake of having a metric and linearity.

Each k-simplex $\rho^k \in R$ can be written thus:

(7.39) $$\rho^k = p_0 \ldots p_{j-1} q_j \ldots q_k = \lambda^{j-1} \mu^{k-j},$$

where

(7.40)
(a) $\lambda^{j-1} = p_0 \ldots p_{j-1} \in L,$

(b) $\mu^{k-j} = q_j \ldots q_k \in M.$

(*B*) Each point p on ρ^k is on a unique segment $\sigma = ab$, where $a \in \lambda^{j-1}$, $b \in \mu^{k-j}$ (Exercise 56). Let $(u_0, \ldots, u_k)$ be the barycentric coordinates of p relative to $(p_0, \ldots, p_{j-1}, q_j, \ldots, q_k)$. Then $x = u_0 + \cdots + u_{j-1}$ is a parameter, on each $\sigma = ab$, which increases from 0 at b to 1 at a. We will denote the point on σ with parametric value x by $p(\sigma, x)$.

LEMMA 19. **Let $\{\sigma\}$ be the set of all segments ab defined by (B), as ρ^k ranges over all the simplexes of R. Then each point on R is uniquely represented as a point $p(\sigma, x)$, $\sigma \in \{\sigma\}$ and $0 < x < 1$.**

Proof of Lemma. Since (K, L) is a normal covering of (Π, Λ), a point p of Π is on $|L|$ or on $|M|$ or on a simplex with some vertices on L and some on M. In the last case, it is on a unique $\rho^k \in R$ and the lemma follows from (B).

THEOREM 17. **If $M = M(K)$ is an approximating complex to $\Pi - \Lambda$, then**

(7.41) $$\mathfrak{H}_k(\Pi - \Lambda) \approx \mathfrak{H}_k(M) \quad \text{and} \quad \mathfrak{H}^k(\Pi - \Lambda) \approx \mathfrak{H}^k(M).$$

Proof. The mapping f_t defined on $\Pi - \Lambda$ by

(7.42) $$f_t : \begin{cases} q \to q & (q \in |M|) \\ p(\sigma, x) \to p(\sigma, (1 - t)x) & (0 \leq t \leq 1) \end{cases}$$

is a deformation carrying $\Pi - \Lambda$ onto $|M|$. Theorem 17 now follows from Art. 6–10(E).

(C) We refer to Π as a (**relative**) **homology m-manifold** mod Λ if $\Pi - \Lambda$ is connected and the local homology groups at each point of $\Pi - \Lambda$ are isomorphic to those of an $(m - 1)$-sphere.

THEOREM 18 (LEFSCHETZ DUALITY THEOREM). **If Π is a relative orientable homology m-manifold mod Λ, then**

$$(7.43) \qquad \mathfrak{H}_k(\Pi, \Lambda) \approx \mathfrak{H}^{m-k}(\Pi - \Lambda) \qquad (k = 0, 1, \ldots, m).$$

Proof. Note that this generalizes the Poincaré duality theorem, to which it reduces when $\Lambda = \emptyset$.

Let (K, L) be a normal covering pair of (M, Λ). Let (K_1, L_1) be the first barycentric subdivisions of (K, L), and let

$$(7.44) \qquad M_1 = K_1 - St(L_1) \qquad M = K - St(L)$$

be the approximating complexes to $\Pi - \Lambda$ defined by K_1 and K respectively.

(D) We use the notation of Arts. 7–7 and 7–8. The dual cells $\{\tau\}$ are formed only when the first vertex (Art. 7–7(D)) is on $K - L$. The set $T(M)$ of all such dual cells is a closed cellular complex with the approximating complex M_1 for a subdivision (Exercise 58).

It follows from Theorems 12 and 17 that $\mathfrak{H}^{m-k}(\Pi - \Lambda) \approx \mathfrak{H}^{m-k}(T(M))$. The relative homology groups $\mathfrak{H}_k(\Pi, \Lambda)$ are determined by the incidence numbers ε_{ji}^{k-1}, where both s_j^{k-1} and s_i^k are on $K - L$, and these are related to the incidence numbers of $T(M)$ as in Lemma 17. Hence, the arguments used in proving Theorem 14 also establish the present theorem.

COROLLARY. **The relative Betti numbers satisfy the relations**

$$(7.45) \qquad \beta_k(\Pi, \Lambda) = \beta_{m-k}(\Pi - \Lambda) \qquad (k = 0, \ldots, m)$$

and the kth torsion coefficients of Π mod Λ equal the $(m - k - 1)^{\text{th}}$ torsion coefficients of $\Pi - \Lambda$.

EXERCISES

54. (a) Give an example, for a circle Λ on a sphere Π, of a covering pair (K, L) which is not normal. (b) Show, in general, that the first barycentric subdivision of an arbitrary covering pair is a normal covering pair.

55. Show that $M(K)$ is a complex (that is, a closed set of simplexes) in (A).

56. Prove (B). *Suggestion:* Show that a and b are necessarily the points $(v_0, \ldots, v_{j-1}, 0, \ldots, 0)$ and $(0, \ldots, 0, w_j, \ldots, w_k)$, if $v_h = u_h/(u_0 + \cdots + u_{j-1})$ $(h = 0, \ldots, j - 1)$ and $w_i = u_i/(u_j + \cdots + u_k)$ $(i = j, \ldots, k)$.

57. Let T^2 be the torus with the polygonal representation $ABA^{-1}B^{-1}$. For the case $\Pi = T^2$, $\Lambda = A$, find all the homology groups involved in Theorem 18, and verify (7.43).

58. Verify Statement (D).

7–11.   The Alexander Duality Theorem and Consequences

THEOREM 19 (ALEXANDER DUALITY THEOREM). **Let Λ be a topological subpolyhedron of an m-sphere S^m, where $\Lambda \neq \emptyset$ or S^m. If $m = 1$, then**

(7.46) $$\beta_0(\Lambda) = \beta_0(S^1 - \Lambda).$$

If $m > 1$, then

$$(a) \qquad \beta_0(\Lambda) = 1 + \beta_{m-1}(S^m - \Lambda),$$

(7.47) (b) $$\beta_0(S^m - \Lambda) = 1 + \beta_{m-1}(\Lambda),$$

$$(c) \qquad \beta_k(\Lambda) = \beta_{m-k-1}(S^m - \Lambda) \qquad (k = 1, \ldots, m - 2).$$

Proof. Note first the symmetry of these relations in Λ and $S^m - \Lambda$.

Case 1 $(m = 1)$. In this case, S^1 is a circle, Λ is a collection of disjoint closed arcs and isolated points, and (7.46) formulates the obvious fact that the number of components of Λ equals the number of components of $S^1 - \Lambda$.

Case 2 $(m > 1)$. Let C^k be a singular k-cycle of S^m mod Λ, where $1 < k < m - 1$. This implies that $B^{k-1} = \partial C^k$ is a singular cycle on Λ. If $C^k \sim \emptyset$ mod Λ, there exists a $(k + 1)$-chain C^{k+1} such that $\partial C^{k+1} = C^k - D^k$, where D^k is a chain on Λ. But $C^k - D^k$ is a cycle, so $\partial D^k = \partial C^k = B^{k-1}$.

(A) Hence $C^k \sim \emptyset$ mod Λ implies $B^{k-1} = \partial C^k \sim \emptyset$ on Λ. *It follows that the boundary operator ∂ induces a homomorphism ∂^* of $\mathfrak{H}_k(S^m, \Lambda)$ into $\mathfrak{H}_{k-1}(\Lambda)$.* For (1) ∂ maps k-cycles mod Λ on S^m into absolute $(k - 1)$-cycles on Λ; (2) $\partial(C_1^k + C_2^k) = \partial C_1^k + \partial C_2^k$; and (3) if $C_1^k \sim C_2^k$ mod Λ, where C_i^k is a k-cycle mod Λ $(i = 1, 2)$, then $\partial(C_2^k - C_1^k) \sim \emptyset$ on Λ, as we have just seen.

Again let C^k be a k-cycle mod Λ, suppose $B^{k-1} = \partial C^k$ bounds on Λ, and let D^k be a k-chain on Λ with $\partial D^k = B^{k-1}$. Then $C^k - D^k$ is a k-cycle on S^m. Since $k < m$, $C^k - D^k$ bounds some chain C^{k+1} on S^m. Since $\partial_L C^{k+1} = \lambda(C^k - D^k) = \lambda C^k$, it follows that $C^k \sim \emptyset$ mod Λ.

(B) Letting $C^k = C_1^k - C_2^k$, with C_i^k a k-cycle mod Λ $(i = 1, 2)$, we deduce from the preceding paragraph that $\partial C_1^k \sim \partial C_2^k$ on Λ implies $C_1^k \sim C_2^k$ on S^m mod λ. Hence no two different elements of $\mathfrak{H}_k(S^m, \Lambda)$ are mapped by ∂^* onto the same element of $\mathfrak{H}_{k-1}(\Lambda)$; that is, ∂^* is one-to-one.

If B^{k-1} is a cycle on Λ then it bounds on S^m, hence there exists a chain C^k on S^m with $\partial C^k = B^{k-1}$.

(C) It follows that ∂^* is **onto**. But a homomorphism which is one-to-one and onto is an isomorphism. Hence

(7.48) $\mathfrak{H}_k(S^m, \Lambda) \approx \mathfrak{H}_{k-1}(\Lambda) \qquad (k = 2, \ldots, m - 1).$

But, by Theorem 18 for $\Pi = S^m$, this implies

(7.49) $\mathfrak{H}_{k-1}(\Lambda) \approx \mathfrak{H}^{m-k}(S^m - \Lambda).$

Hence, by Chapter 5, Theorem 17, which, as shown by (7.41), applies to $\Pi - \Lambda$ even though the latter is not a complex, (7.47c) follows (Exercise 59).

COROLLARY 1. **The kth torsion coefficients of Λ equal the $(m - k)^{\text{th}}$ torsion coefficients of $S^m - \Lambda$ $(k = 1, 2, \ldots, m - 2)$ (Exercise 60).**

It remains to establish (7.47a,b). Let $Z_1^{m-1}, \ldots, Z_\beta^{m-1}$ be a set of homology-independent $(m - 1)$-cycles on Λ, where $\beta = \beta_{m-1}(\Lambda)$. Since $\beta_{m-1}(S^m) = 0$, there exist chains $C_1^m, \ldots, C_\beta^m$ on S^m with $\partial C_i^m = Z_i^{m-1}$ $(i = 1, \ldots, \beta)$. Since $\mathfrak{H}_m(S^m)$ is free cyclic, there is a cycle Z^m on S^m whose integral multiples are representatives of the respective m^{th} homology classes of S^m.

LEMMA 20. **The chains $\{C^m\} = (C_0^m, \ldots, C_\beta^m)$, where**

(7.50) $C_0^m = Z^m - \sum_{i=1}^{\beta} C_i^m,$

are a maximal set of homology-independent m-cycles of S^m mod Λ.

Proof of Lemma. The $\{C^m\}$ are m-cycles mod Λ, since their boundaries are all on Λ. If $\Sigma_{i=0}^{\beta} a_i C_i^m \sim \emptyset$ mod Λ, there is on S^m an $(m + 1)$-chain C^{m+1} such that $\partial C^{m+1} = D^m - \Sigma_{i=0}^{\beta} a_i C_i^m$ for some D^m on Λ. But, since ∂C^{m+1} is an m-cycle, D^m must have the same boundary as $\Sigma_{i=0}^{\beta} a_i C_i^m$; that is, $\partial D^m = \Sigma_{i=1}^{\beta}(a_i - a_0)Z_i^{m-1}$. Since $(Z_1^{m-1}, \ldots, Z_\beta^{m-1})$ is a homology basis on Λ, this implies $a_i = a_0$ $(i = 1, \ldots, \beta)$, hence $\Sigma_{i=0}^{\beta} a_i C_i^m = a_0 \Sigma_{i=0}^{\beta} C_i^m = a_0 Z^m$. But this is null-homologous only for $a_0 = 0$. Hence $\Sigma_{i=0}^{\beta} a_i C_i^m \sim \emptyset$ mod $\Lambda \Rightarrow a_i = 0$ $(i = 0, \ldots, \beta)$ so that $\{C^m\}$ is a set of homology-independent m-cycles mod Λ. It remains to establish that an arbitrary m-cycle C^m mod Λ is homology-dependent on them. Now $\partial C^m = Z^{m-1}$ is an $(m - 1)$-cycle on Λ. Hence, for some numbers $(a, a_1, \ldots, a_\beta)$, not all zero, $aZ^{m-1} + \Sigma_{i=1}^{\beta} a_i Z_i^{m-1} \sim \emptyset$ on Λ. Hence there is on Λ a chain D^m such that $\partial D^m = aZ^{m-1} + \Sigma_{i=1}^{\beta} a_i Z_i^{m-1} = \partial(aC^m + \Sigma_{i=1}^{\beta} a_i C_i^m)$. It follows that $D^m - (aC^m + \Sigma_{i=1}^{\beta} a_i C_i^m)$ is a cycle, hence that $D^m - (aC^m + \Sigma_{i=1}^{\beta} a_i C_i^m) \sim bZ^m$ for some b. Using (7.50), and noting that D^m is on Λ, we deduce that $aC^m - bC_0^m + \Sigma_{i=1}^{\beta} (a_i - b)C_i^m \sim \emptyset$ mod Λ. Since $(a, a_1, \ldots, a_\beta)$ are not all zero, at least one of the numbers $(a, b, a_i - b)$ $(i = 1, \ldots, \beta)$

must differ from zero. Hence $(C^m, C_0^m, \ldots, C_\beta^m)$ are homology-dependent, and Lemma 20 is proved. Relation (7.47b) now follows from Lemma 20 and (7.45). Relation (7.47a) is suggested as an exercise (Exercise 63).

COROLLARY 2. **The Alexander duality theorem holds with (1)** S^m **replaced by euclidean** m**-space** E^m **and (2) the right sides of (7.46) and (7.47a) diminished by 1. Also, Corollary 1 holds with** E^m **in place of** S^m (Exercise 64).

COROLLARY 3. **The Alexander duality theorem holds with Betti numbers** β **replaced by connectivity numbers** $\hat{\beta}$. **After this replacement,** S^m **can be replaced by** E^m, **with the corresponding other changes listed in Corollary 2.**

For, the connectivity numbers are merely the mod 2 case of the Betti numbers in relative as well as absolute homology theory.

The Alexander duality theorem has been one of the most important bases for the further study of manifolds. We mention one or two of its consequences.

THEOREM 20 (JORDAN-BROUWER THEOREM). **Let** S^{m-1} **be a topological** $(m - 1)$**-sphere in a euclidean** m**-space** E^m **(or on an** m**-sphere** S^m**). Then** S^{m-1} **separates** E^m **(or** S^m**) into exactly two regions.**

For the case where S^{m-1} is a topological subpolyhedron of $R^m = E^m$ or S^m; that is, where S^{m-1} is a subcomplex of some triangulation of R^m, this follows from (7.47b), which becomes

$$(7.51) \qquad \beta_0(R^m - S^{m-1}) = 1 + \beta_{m-1}(S^{m-1}) = 2.$$

We omit the case where S^{m-1} is not assumed to be a subpolyhedron.

COROLLARY (JORDAN THEOREM). **A simple closed curve separates the plane (or the 2-sphere) into exactly two regions.**

This is the case $m = 2$ of Theorem 20.

THEOREM 21. **No topological subpolyhedron of** $R^m = E^m$ **or** S^m **of dimension less than** $m - 1$ **can separate** R^m.

For, dim $\Lambda < m - 1 \Rightarrow \beta_{m-1}(\Lambda) = 0 \Rightarrow \beta_0(R^m - \Lambda) = 1$.

THEOREM 22. **No non-orientable closed** $(m - 1)$**-manifold** M **can be a topological subcomplex of** $R^m = E^m$ **or** S^m.

Proof. For any complex, the 0th Betti number equals the 0th connectivity number. Hence, by Theorem 19 and its Corollary 3, if M is assumed to be a subcomplex of R^m,

$$(7.52) \quad \beta_0(R^m - M) = \hat{\beta}_0(R^m - M) = 1 + \hat{\beta}_{m-1}(M) = 1 + \beta_{m-1}(M).$$

But $\beta_{m-1}(M) = 0$ and $\hat{\beta}_{m-1}(M) = 1$, which contradicts (7.52) and establishes the result.

THEOREM 23. **A connected topological 1-complex L on the plane E^2 or the sphere S^2 separates E^2 or S^2 into $1 + \beta_1(L) = \mu + 1$ parts, where μ is the cyclomatic number.**

Further discussion of duality in E^2 is suggested in Exercise 65.

Consider the Alexander duality theorem in E^3, where $\Lambda = |K|$ and K is a linear simplicial complex of dimension ≤ 3. Let $\Lambda_1, \ldots, \Lambda_{\beta_0}$ be the connected components of Λ. Suppose it possible* to enclose each Λ_i inside a topological 2-sphere S_i^2 which excludes the Λ_j ($j \neq i$). If Z_i^2 is a singular 2-cycle constituting a base for $\mathfrak{H}_2(S_i^2)$, then it can be shown that $(Z_1^2, \ldots, Z_{\beta_0}^2)$ is a homology base for $E^3 - \Lambda$ in dimension 2; that is, each singular 2-cycle Z on $E^3 - \Lambda$ is homologous to a linear combination of the Z_i^2 ($i = 1, \ldots, \beta_0$). This is the meaning, for such a Λ, of the relation (Theorem 19, Corollaries 2 and 3) $\beta_0(\Lambda) = \beta_2(E^3 - \Lambda)$.

Continuing intuitively, if $\Lambda \subset E^3$ is topologically a closed orientable 2-manifold, hence equivalent to a sphere with handles, then $\beta_2(\Lambda) = 1$ and the Alexander duality theorem yields $\beta_0(E^3 - \Lambda) = 2$, meaning that Λ separates E^3 into two regions. If Λ is, for example, topologically the union of $\beta_2(\Lambda)$ disjoint closed orientable 2-manifolds, then Λ separates E^3 into $\beta_0(E^3 - \Lambda) = 1 + \beta_2(\Lambda)$ regions.

We have just commented on the significance of relations (7.47ab) interpreted in E^3. Relations (7.47c) reduce to

$$(7.53) \qquad\qquad \beta_1(\Lambda) = \beta_1(E^3 - \Lambda).$$

Suppose, for example, that Λ is a connected linear 1-complex in E^3, and let $(s_1^1, \ldots, s_{\beta_1}^1)$ be a set of 1-simplexes whose removal will reduce Λ to a tree. Imagine a set $(\Gamma_1^1, \ldots, \Gamma_{\beta_1}^1)$ of small circles, where Γ_i^1 links s_i^1 ($i = 1, \ldots, \beta_1$), in the sense that the plane disk bounded by Γ_i^1 intersects s_i^1 in a single point and does not intersect Λ elsewhere. It can then be shown that cycles $(Z_1^1, \ldots, Z_{\beta_1}^1)$ on $(\Gamma_1^1, \ldots, \Gamma_{\beta_1}^1)$ constitute a first homology basis for $E^3 - \Lambda$, just as a set of cycles $(C_1^1, \ldots, C_{\beta_1}^1)$ on Λ is a first homology basis for Λ if s_i^1 enters into C_i^1, but not into C_j^1 for $j \neq i$. The **dual** first homology bases $(C_1^1, \ldots, C_{\beta_1}^1)$ and $(Z_1^1, \ldots, Z_{\beta_1}^1)$ give a geometric insight into the relation (7.53).

The foregoing intuitive discussion of the geometric significance of duality in the lower dimensions barely touches upon a well-developed duality theory, which is beyond the scope of this book.

EXERCISES

59. Give the details of the last line of the proof of (7.47c).

60. Prove Corollary 1 to Theorem 19.

---

* In some cases, this is impossible; for example, if Λ consists of two linked circles.

61. Follow through the proof of the Alexander duality theorem, using numerical values for the β's, in the special case where $m = 2$ and Λ is homeomorphic to the edges and vertices of a tetrahedron.

62. Let M^2 be a sphere with three handles in E^3. Give the Betti numbers of M^2 (Chapter 5, Theorem 7), than obtain the Betti numbers of $E^3 - M^2$ by duality.

63. Establish Relation (7.47a).

64. Prove Corollary 2. *Suggestion:* Use the fact that E^m is, topologically, the punctured m-sphere; that is, $S^m - q$. Hence $E^m - \Lambda$ is $S^m - \Lambda - q$, topologically, for $q \in S^m - \Lambda$.

65. Discuss the geometric significance of the Alexander duality theorem, where $\Lambda = |K^2|$ and K^2 is a linear simplicial 2-complex in the plane E^2. Illustrate your discussion with examples in which $\beta_0(\Lambda) > 1$ and $\beta_1(\Lambda) > 1$ and in which you indicate homology bases for $E^2 - \Lambda$.

66. Let M^2 be a Moebius strip (Art. 2–2(D)) with a handle in E^3. Find the Betti and connectivity numbers of M^2 (Chapter 5, Theorem 7), then obtain the Betti and connectivity numbers of $E^3 - M^2$ by duality.

8

The Fundamental Group;
Covering Surfaces

In Art. 6–10, **homotopy classes of mappings** were defined, and some basic results stated with regard to corresponding homomorphisms of homology groups. In this chapter, a special category of homotopy classes will be developed, leading to the so-called **fundamental group**, or **Poincaré group**, of a complex, which sometimes enables us to distinguish between some topologically different spaces agreeing in their homology properties.

8–1. Paths and Path Products

In the plane E^2, with a coordinate system (x, y), a **curve** can be parametrically defined in the form $x = f(s)$, $y = g(s)$, subject to suitable restrictions on the functions. In topology, the concept of **curve** is generalized as follows.

Let T be a topological space. A (**continuous**) **curve** or **path** on T is defined by a continuous mapping $f: [a, b] \to T$, where $[a, b]$ is a segment $a \leq s \leq b$ on an s-axis. Although we will refer to the **path** $\pi = f([a, b])$ or $\pi : p = f(s)$, $s \in [a, b]$, a path is not merely an image $f([a, b])$ but consists of such an image together with a defining mapping f. To emphasize this, we sometimes refer to a **path** (π, f). The **initial** and **terminal** points of π are $f(a)$ and $f(b)$. We say that π **joins its initial point to its terminal point**, and we refer to π as a **path from** $f(a)$ **to** $f(b)$.

(*A*) A path (π, f) **equals** a path (π, g), where f has domain $[a, b]$ and g has domain $[c, d]$, if (1) $f(a) = g(c)$, $f(b) = g(d)$, and (2) there exists a homeomorphism $h : [a, b] \to [c, d]$ such that $f = gh$ (see Art. 3–1(*F*)).

Condition (1) means that equal paths have the same initial and terminal points. Two paths can coincide as point sets, agree in initial and terminal points, and still be unequal (Exercise 2).

(*B*) If two paths are equal, we refer to them as the **same** path;

otherwise as **different** paths. *A given path π can be defined by a mapping f with an arbitrary preassigned domain $[a, b]$* (Exercise 5).

Now let (π_1, f_1) and (π_2, f_2) be two paths such that the terminal point of π_1 is the initial point of π_2, and let their defining mappings f_1 and f_2 have domains $[a, b]$ and $[b, c]$, whose union is a segment $[a, c]$. The **product** $\pi_1\pi_2$ is the path defined by

$$(8.1) \qquad \pi_1\pi_2 : f(s) = \begin{cases} f_1(s) & a \leq s \leq b, \\ f_2(s) & b \leq s \leq c. \end{cases}$$

Intuitively, $\pi_1\pi_2$ is π_1 followed by π_2.

(C) Similarly, the **product** $\pi_1\pi_2 \ldots \pi_n$ is defined (Exercise 6) if the terminal point of π_i is the initial point of π_{i+1} $(i = 1, \ldots, n - 1)$.

(D) In particular, the segment $p_0 p_1 = \Gamma(p_0, p_1)$ in E^n as defined in relations (4.4) is a path, and a **broken line** $p_0 p_1 \ldots p_m$ is also a path, namely the product $\pi_1\pi_2 \ldots \pi_m$ where $\pi_i = p_{i-1}p_i$ $(i = 1, \ldots, m)$.

Given a path $\pi \subset T$, the selection of a particular defining mapping $f : [a, b] \to \pi$ constitutes a **parametrization** of π, with s as **parameter**. The parameter is a **coordinate system**, in the sense that a unique point on π is specified by each number $s \in [a, b]$. A point on π has as many parametric values as it has images under f^{-1} (Art. 3–1(H)). A point is **simple** or **multiple**, according as it has one or more parametric values, the number of such values being its **multiplicity**. If each point of π is simple, π is a **simple path**, or an **arc**.

The subset of T covered by a path π may be a single point, or it may, for example, be the closure of an open subset of a euclidean space E^n $(n > 1)$. It is then a **space-filling** or **Peano curve**. One property of a Peano curve π in E^n is that it has an everywhere-dense* set of points, each of multiplicity at least $n + 1$ (Exercise 8). Thus a Peano curve in E^2 has an everywhere-dense set of at least triple points. See $[K_2,$ pp. 101–103$]$ for an example of such a curve covering the interior and boundary of a triangle.

(E) A curve, or path, π is **closed** if its initial and terminal points coincide. If, except for this coincidence, each point of π is simple, then π is a **simple closed curve** or **path**. (See also Exercise 7.)

EXERCISES

1. Show that $x = s$, $y = s$ $(0 \leq s \leq 1)$; $x = 4 + 2s$, $y = 4 + 2s$ $(-2 \leq s \leq -1.5)$; and $x = t^2$, $y = t^2$ $(0 \leq t \leq 1)$ all define equal curves.

2. Show that $x = \cos t$, $y = \sin t$ $(0 \leq t \leq 2\pi)$, and $x = \cos 2t$, $y = \sin 2t$ $(0 \leq t \leq 2\pi)$ define unequal curves, even though they are equal as point sets and have the same initial and terminal points.

* A set of points of π is **everywhere dense** if each point of π is a limit point of the set.

3. Define two unequal curves from $x = 0$ to $x = 1$ on the x-axis, each of which, as a point set, coincides with the segment $[0, 1]$.

4. Show that the broken lines $abcdb$ and $abdcb$ generally represent unequal curves, though they coincide as point sets and agree in their initial and terminal points. Under what conditions are they equal?

5. Prove the italicized part of (B).

6. Write out the definition of $\pi_1 \pi_2 \ldots \pi_n$ in accordance with Statement (C).

7. Define **closed** and **simple closed curves** in terms of mappings of the unit circle $x = \cos 2\pi t$, $y = \sin 2\pi t$ $(0 \le t \le 1)$. Include a definition of **equal** closed curves.

8. With the aid of Brouwer dimension theory, show that a Peano curve covering an n-dimensional space must possess points of multiplicity $n + 1$.

9. Suppose $x = f(t)$, $y = g(t)$ defines a Peano curve in the (x, y)-plane. Show that $x = f(t)$, $y = g(t)$, $z = t$ defines a simple path in (x, y, z)-space.

8–2. The Fundamental Group

A topological space Σ is **arcwise connected** if each two of its points can be joined by a curve on Σ (Exercise 10). Throughout this chapter, Σ denotes an arcwise-connected topological space.

A **singular 1-simplex** (Art. 6–1 with $k = 1$) differs from a **path** in the definitions of **equality** (compare Art. 6–1(B)) (Exercise 11) and also in the algebraic processes applied to them. Singular 1-simplexes were additively combined into 1-chains, including 1-cycles; and homology classes of 1-cycles were used as elements of the first homology group $\mathfrak{H}_1(\Sigma)$. Paths, on the other hand, are combined as products; and homotopy classes of closed paths will be used as elements of the **fundamental group**, which, unlike $\mathfrak{H}_1(\Sigma)$, is generally not commutative.

Except where otherwise stated, each path $\pi = f(t)$ will be defined by a mapping $f : X \to \Sigma$, where $X = [0, 1] : 0 \le x \le 1$.

(A) Let (p, q) be two points, not necessarily distinct, on Σ, and let $\Pi = \Pi(p, q)$ be the set of all paths on Σ from p to q. Two such paths, π_0 and π_1, are **homotopic in** Π, a relation symbolized by

$$(8.2) \qquad \pi_1 \simeq \pi_0 \quad \text{in } \Pi(p, q),$$

if there exists a deformation (Art. 6–10) f_t $(t \in T : 0 \le t \le 1)$ such that f_t defines a path $\pi_t \in \Pi$. As the notation implies, f_0 and f_1 define the given paths. We describe such an f_t as a **deformation in** Π, and we say that it **leaves** (p, q) **fixed.**

Otherwise expressed, Relation (8.2) means that there exists a continuous mapping f of the **unit rectangle**

$$(8.3) \qquad X \times T : (0 \le x \le 1, 0 \le t \le 1)$$

such that

(8.4)

(a) $f(0, t) = p$ and $f(1, t) = q$ $(0 \leq t \leq 1)$,

(b) $\pi_j = f_j(x) = f(x, j)$ $(j = 0, 1)$.

(B) Using the notation of Fig. 8–1, one can describe $f : X \times T \to \Sigma$ as a mapping which maps the edge $a_0 a_1$ onto the point p and $b_0 b_1$

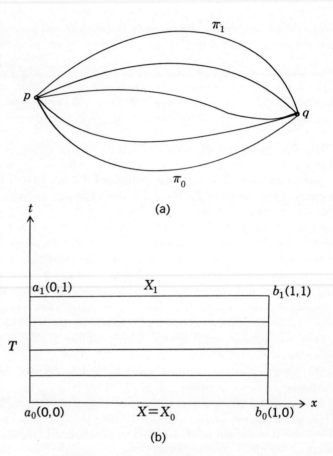

(a)

(b)

Fig. 8–I. The relationship $\pi_1 \simeq \pi_0$.

onto q, so that p and q are the common initial and terminal points of all of the paths π_t $(0 \leq t \leq 1)$, defined by $f_t : X \to \Sigma$ where $f_t(x) = f(x, t)$, $x \in X$.

LEMMA 1. **The relationship of homotopy in Π is an equivalence relationship among elements of Π** (Exercise 12).

(C) Let p_0 be an arbitrary fixed point of Σ, and let $\Pi_0 = \Pi(p_0, p_0)$ be the set of all paths each having p_0 for both initial and terminal point. We will use the symbol $\sim$ to stand for the relationship of homotopy in Π_0; that is,

(8.5) $\gamma_0 \sim \gamma_1$ means $\gamma_0 \simeq \gamma_1$ in Π_0.

The homotopy class (see Exercise 12) of γ_0 in Π_0 will be denoted by

(8.6) $\Gamma_0(\gamma_0) = \{\gamma \mid \gamma \sim \gamma_0\}$.

A deformation in Π_0 is illustrated by a modification of Fig. 8–1 in which $p = q = p_0$.

Attention is temporarily confined to the class Π_0 and the corresponding homotopy relation $\sim$ because the path products $\gamma_1\gamma_2$ and $\gamma_2\gamma_1$ are always defined if γ_1 and γ_2 are in Π_0. Note that a deformation of $\gamma_0 = \gamma_1\gamma_2$ in Π_0 need not leave fixed the terminal point of γ_1, which is the initial point of γ_2, although it must leave fixed the initial point of γ_1 and the terminal point of γ_2, both at p_0, these being the end points of γ_0.

THEOREM 1. **The homotopy classes** $\{\Gamma_0\} = \{\Gamma_0(\gamma_0) \mid \gamma_0 \in \Pi_0\}$ **are the elements of a group** Φ_0 **whose product operation is defined by**

(8.7) $\Gamma_0(\gamma_1)\Gamma_0(\gamma_2) = \Gamma_0(\gamma_1\gamma_2)$.

The unit element of the group is $\Gamma_0(\omega)$ **where** ω **is the singular path defined by** $f : X \to p_0$.

Proof. Note first that $\Gamma_0(\omega)$ consists of those closed curves in Π_0 which can be deformed, in Π_0, into the point p_0.

(*D*) *The product of two homotopy classes, as formulated in* (8.7), *is independent of the representatives* γ_1 *and* γ_2 *used in the formulation.* That is, $\gamma_j' \sim \gamma_j$ $(j = 1, 2)$ implies $\gamma_1'\gamma_2' \sim \gamma_1\gamma_2$ (Exercise 13).

(*E*) For each $\gamma \in \Pi_0$, we have $\Gamma_0(\gamma)\Gamma_0(\omega) = \Gamma_0(\omega)\Gamma_0(\gamma) = \Gamma_0(\gamma)$ (Exercise 14).

(*F*) For each $\gamma \in \Pi_0$, we have $\Gamma_0(\gamma^{-1})\Gamma_0(\gamma) = \Gamma_0(\omega)$ (Exercise 15). The elements of $\Gamma_0(\omega)$ are said to be **null-homotopic**.

(*G*) If $\gamma_j \in \Pi_0$ $(j = 1, 2, 3)$, then $\Gamma_0(\gamma_1)\Gamma_0(\gamma_2\gamma_3) = \Gamma_0(\gamma_1\gamma_2)\Gamma_0(\gamma_3)$. This follows from the fact that multiplication of paths is associative.

The four group axioms (Art. A–1) are verified by Definition (8.7), which is justified by (*D*), together with results (*E*), (*F*), and (*G*).

(*H*) The group Φ_0 will be denoted, more explicitly, by $\Phi(\Sigma, p_0)$ and will be called the **fundamental group of** Σ **with fixed point** p_0.

THEOREM 2. **The groups** $\Phi_j = \Phi(\Sigma, p_j)$ $(j = 0, 1)$ **are isomorphic for each pair of points** (p_0, p_1) **on** Σ.

Proof. Let π be a path from p_0 to p_1. Such paths exist, because Σ is arcwise connected. If $\gamma_1 \in \Pi_1 = \Pi(p_1, p_1)$ (see (*A*)), then $\gamma_0 = \pi\gamma_1\pi^{-1}$ is obviously an element of Π_0.

LEMMA 2. **If γ_1' is homotopic to γ_1 in Π_1, then $\gamma_0' = \pi\gamma_1'\pi^{-1}$ is homotopic to $\gamma_0 = \pi\gamma_1\pi^{-1}$ in Π_0 (Exercise 16).**

It follows that π induces a mapping $\pi^* : \Phi_1 \to \Phi_0$.

LEMMA 3. **The mapping π^* is a homomorphism.**

Proof of Lemma. This means that $\pi^*(\Gamma_1(\gamma_1) \cdot \Gamma_1(\gamma_1')) = \pi^*\Gamma_1(\gamma_1) \cdot \pi^*\Gamma_1(\gamma_1')$, which is equivalent to $\pi^*(\Gamma_1(\gamma_1\gamma_1')) = \Gamma_0(\pi\gamma_1\pi^{-1}) \cdot \Gamma_0(\pi\gamma_1'\pi^{-1})$. But the latter product, by definition of Φ_0, is $\Gamma_0(\pi\gamma_1\pi^{-1}\pi\gamma_1'\pi^{-1}) = \Gamma_0(\pi\gamma_1\gamma_1'\pi^{-1})$, and this equals $\pi^*(\Gamma_1(\gamma_1\gamma_1'))$ by definition of π^*.

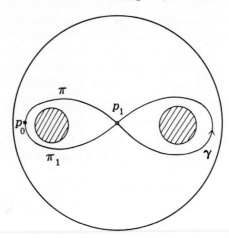

Fig. 8–2. Dependence of π^* on π.

LEMMA 4. **The mapping π^* has an inverse which is a homomorphism** (Exercise 17).

It follows from Lemmas 3 and 4 that π^* is an isomorphism. This and Exercise 17 complete the proof of Theorem 2.

(*I*) In general, the isomorphism π^* depends on the path π which induces it. This can be seen intuitively, in Fig. 8–2, where $\pi\gamma\pi^{-1}$ is not homotopic in Π_0 to $\pi_1\gamma\pi_1^{-1}$.

(*J*) Theorem 2 means that the structure of the fundamental group of Σ with fixed point p_0 is independent of p_0. This justifies the use of the term **fundamental group $\Phi(\Sigma)$ of Σ**, also called its **Poincaré group**, with the understanding that $\Phi(\Sigma)$ is determined up to an isomorphism and is exemplified by $\Phi(\Sigma, p_0)$ for any choice of $p_0 \in \Sigma$.

THEOREM 3. **The fundamental group $\Phi(\Sigma)$ is topologically invariant.**

Proof. We begin with the following lemma.

LEMMA 5. **A continuous mapping of Σ into a space Σ' induces a homomorphism of $\Phi(\Sigma)$ into $\Phi(\Sigma')$ (Exercise 18).**

By Lemma 5, a homeomorphism between Σ and Σ' induces both a homomorphism of $\Phi(\Sigma)$ into $\Phi(\Sigma')$ and an inverse homomorphism of $\Phi(\Sigma')$ into $\Phi(\Sigma)$. But a homomorphism with a homomorphism for inverse is an isomorphism, and Theorem 3 is proved.

THEOREM 4. **In general $\Phi(\Sigma)$ is not abelian.**

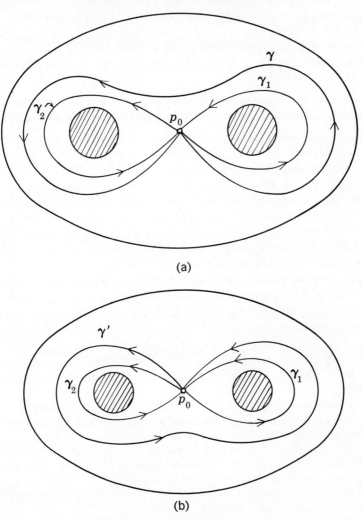

(a)

(b)

Fig. 8–3. The non-abelian nature of Φ.

Proof. This means that, in general, $\gamma_1\gamma_2$ and $\gamma_2\gamma_1$ are not homotopic in Π_0. This fact is illustrated by the two diagrams of Fig. 8–3, where $\gamma_1\gamma_2 \sim \gamma$, $\gamma_2\gamma_1 \sim \gamma'$ but γ and γ' are not homotopic in $\Pi(p_0, p_0)$.

(K) A space Σ is said to be **simply connected** if $\Phi(\Sigma)$ consists of the identity element alone. It is said that a closed curve γ on Σ can be **shrunk to a point** or can be **spanned (by a 2-cell)** on Σ if there exists a continuous mapping $f : \bar{D} \to \Sigma$, where D is the region $x^2 + y^2 < 1$ on an (x, y)-plane, such that γ is defined by the restriction of f to the unit circle $\kappa : x^2 + y^2 = 1$ (see Exercise 7 above).

As a parameter t decreases from 1 to 0, the circle $\kappa_t : x^2 + y^2 = t^2$ shrinks from κ to the origin. The curve γ_t defined by $f \mid \kappa_t$ is correspondingly deformed from $\gamma = f(\kappa)$ into the point $\gamma_0 = f(\kappa_0) = f(0, 0)$, the image of the origin. During the deformation, $\gamma_t = f(\kappa_t)$ sweeps out the topological disk $\bar{\Delta} = f(\bar{D})$, which is the closure of the 2-cell $\Delta = f(D)$.

THEOREM 5. **The space Σ is simply connected if and only if each closed curve on Σ can be shrunk to a point (or can be spanned).**

Proof. Suppose a closed curve γ can be shrunk to a point, and let p_0 be a point on γ. Then γ is null-homotopic (see (F)). This can be seen with the aid of the mapping f of Statement (K), if the circles κ_t are replaced by a family of circles κ_t', where κ_t' is the circle on $\bar{D}$ of radius $t \in [0, 1]$ tangent to κ at a point q such that $f(q) = p_0$ (Exercise 19). This shows that $\Phi(\Sigma, p_0)$ reduces to the identity if each closed curve through p_0 can be spanned. Conversely, suppose that $\Phi(\Sigma, p_0)$ reduces to the identity, and γ is given on Σ. By Theorem 2, we may assume that $\gamma \in \Pi_0$, hence can be deformed in Π_0 into ω (see Theorem 1). This implies the existence of a continuous mapping g of the rectangle in Fig. 8–1, where g maps the three edges $a_0 a_1$, $b_0 b_1$, and $X_0 = a_0 b_0$ onto p_0 and where $g : X_1 \to \Sigma$ defines γ. The proof is easy to complete (Exercise 20).

EXERCISES

10. Show that the property of being arcwise connected is a topological property.

11. Using the above notation, consider a continuous mapping $f : X \to \Sigma$. Show that f and the mapping defined by $p_x = f(x^2)$, $x \in X$, define equal paths on Σ but generally define unequal singular 1-simplexes.

12. Prove Lemma 1. Note that **homotopy in** Π is a restriction of the more general homotopy used to define classes of mappings in Art. 6–10, since the latter has no restriction regarding a particular point p_0.

13. Prove (D). *Suggestion:* Define a deformation in Π_0 of $\gamma_1 \gamma_2$ into $\gamma_1' \gamma_2'$ in terms of deformations of γ_j into γ_j' $(j = 1, 2)$.

14. Prove (E).

15. Prove (F). *Suggestion:* Show that $\gamma \gamma^{-1}$ can be so deformed into p_0 that each deformation path is on γ.

16. Prove Lemma 2. *Suggestion:* From a deformation of γ_1' into γ_1 in Π_1 deduce a corresponding deformation of γ_0' into γ_0 which leaves each point of π and π^{-1} fixed.

17. Prove π^* maps Φ_1 onto Φ_0. Prove π^{-1} induces π^{*-1}, hence Lemma 4.

18. Prove Lemma 5. Note that a similar result was proved for homology groups.

19. In the proof of Theorem 5, complete the demonstration that γ is null-homotopic.

20. Complete the proof of Theorem 5. *Suggestion:* Make use of the mapping g_0 of the rectangle onto a unit disk defined by $x' = t \cos 2\pi x$, $y' = t \sin 2\pi x$ $(0 \leq x \leq 1, 0 \leq t \leq 1)$.

21. Show that a convex subset of euclidean n-space is simply connected.

22. If X is a unit interval, show that $\Phi(\Sigma \times X) \approx \Phi(\Sigma)$.

23. Show that a solid torus (that is, the closure of the region bounded by a torus) has the same fundamental group as a circle.

8–3.   Relation Between $\Phi(\Sigma)$ and $\mathfrak{H}_1(\Sigma)$

To simplify our discussion, we restrict attention to the case where $\Sigma = |K|$ is a topological polyhedron, with oriented triangulation $\mathfrak{K}$. We will work with a rectilinear realization K of $\mathfrak{K}$ in a euclidean space E, and with the polyhedron $P = |K|$, homeomorphic to Σ. The replacement of Σ by P will involve no loss of generality, for present purposes, since $\Phi(P) \approx \Phi(\Sigma)$ by Theorem 3.

Let $\{s\} = \{s_1, \ldots, s_{\alpha_1}\}$ be the 1-simplexes of K, and let s_i be defined as image $s_i = \lambda_i(X_0)$ of a unit segment $X_0 : (0 \leq x \leq 1)$ under a linear homeomorphism $\lambda_i : X_0 \to E$. But λ_i also defines a path e_i, which we will call the path **associated with** s_i. We can write

$$(8.8) \qquad \text{(a) } s_i = \lambda_i(X_0) \qquad \text{(b) } e_i = \lambda_i(X_0) \qquad (i = 1, \ldots, \alpha_1).$$

The distinction between the simplexes s_i and the paths e_i, which we will call **elementary edge paths**, is explained in Art. 8–2 above.

Let $\mu_i : X_0 \to E$ denote the mapping defined by $\mu_i(x) = \lambda_i(1 - x)$, $x \in X_0$. Then μ_i defines the oriented 1-simplex $-s_i$ and the edge path e_i^{-1}, that is,

$$(8.9) \qquad \begin{aligned} &\text{(a) } -s_i = \mu_i(X_0) \\ &\text{(b) } e_i^{-1} = \mu_i(X_0) \end{aligned} \qquad (\mu_i(x) = \lambda_i(1 - x); \ i = 1, \ldots, \alpha_1).$$

(*A*) *Hence, if e_i is the path associated with s_i, then e_i^{-1} is the path associated with $-s_i$.*

An **edge path** in general is a path product

$$(8.10) \qquad \eta = e_{i_1}^{\varepsilon_1} \ldots e_{i_n}^{\varepsilon_n} \qquad (\varepsilon_j = +1 \text{ or } -1 \ \ j = 1, \ldots, n).$$

(*B*) If $n = 3$ and the three factors in (8.10) are the three edges of a 2-simplex $s^2 \in K$, then η is an **elementary boundary path**. Each s^2 has six elementary boundary paths, each determined by the selection of an initial edge and its exponent.

(*C*) Let p and q be the initial and terminal points, respectively, of η in (8.10). (1) If η contains a pair of successive factors of the form ee^{-1}, then $\eta \simeq \eta'$ in $\Pi(p, q)$, where η' is obtained from η by omitting

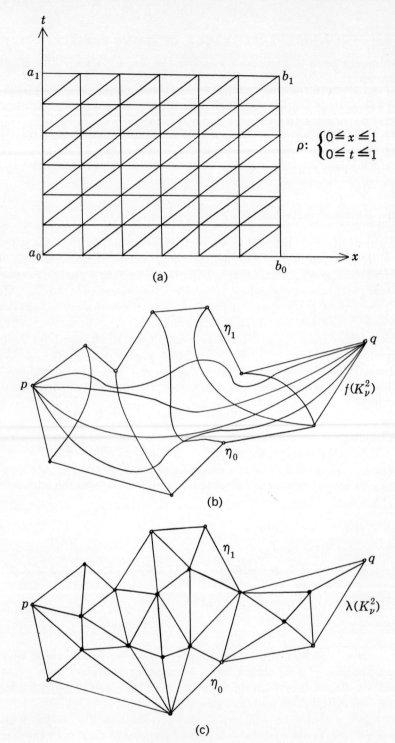

Fig. 8-4. $\eta_1 \simeq \eta_0 \Rightarrow \eta_1 \doteq \eta_0$.

the factor pair ee^{-1} in (8.10) (Exercise 24). (2) If η contains a factor e, and e belongs to some elementary boundary path efg, then $\eta \simeq \eta''$ in $\Pi(p, q)$, where η'' is obtained from η by substituting the factor pair $g^{-1}f^{-1}$ for e in (8.10) (Exercise 25).

(*D*) By an **elementary homotopy operation** we mean (1) the dropping of ee^{-1} as described in Part (1) of (*C*) or (2) the inverse operation of inserting a factor pair ee^{-1} in (8.10) just after a factor f, provided the terminal point of f is the initial point of e or (3) the substitution of $g^{-1}f^{-1}$ for e as described in Part (2) of (*C*).

LEMMA 6. **By elementary homotopy operations, it is possible (a) to replace two consecutive factors ab of an edge path by c^{-1} if abc is an elementary boundary path; (b) to eliminate three successive factors abc from an edge path if abc is an elementary boundary path; (c) to insert three factors abc, constituting a boundary path, immediately after a factor e, provided the terminal point of e is the initial point of a** (Exercise 26).

Given two edge paths, η_1 and η_0, we will say that η_1 is **combinatorially homotopic** on K to η_0, symbolized by

(8.11) $$\eta_1 \overset{*}{\sim} \eta_0,$$

if and only if it is possible to pass from η_1 to η_0 by a sequence of elementary homotopy operations.

The relationship (8.11) implies that η_1 and η_0 have the same initial point and the same terminal point, since none of the elementary combinatorial operations alters either end point of an edge path.

LEMMA 7. **The combinatorial homotopy relation $\overset{*}{\sim}$ is an equivalence relation.**

Proof of Lemma. It is obviously reflexive and transitive. It is symmetric because the inverse of each elementary homotopy operation can be effected by an elementary homotopy operation. This is obvious for the first two operations in (*D*). In the case of (*D*3), it follows from Lemma 6(a).

THEOREM 6. **The relation (8.11) holds if and only if**

(8.12) $$\eta_1 \simeq \eta_0 \text{ in } \Pi(p, q),$$

where p and q are the initial and terminal points of η_0.

Proof. By the definitions and Statement (*C*), (8.11) implies (8.12). To establish the converse, we first recall that (8.12) means that there exists a continuous mapping f of the rectangle $\rho = a_0b_0b_1a_1$ ($0 \leq x \leq 1$, $0 \leq t \leq 1$) (Fig. 8–4) into P such that $\eta_0 = f(a_0b_0)$, $\eta_1 = f(a_1b_1)$, $p = f(a_0a_1)$, $q = f(b_0b_1)$. Since η_j is an edge path ($j = 0, 1$), there exists a subdivision K_j^1 of a_jb_j on whose 1-simplexes f is linear. Let

K^2 be a subdivision of ρ with K_0^1 and K_1^1 as subcomplexes. By the approximation theory in Chapter 6 (see especially Arts. 6–7 and 6–9), there exists, for a sufficiently fine subdivision K_ν^2 of K^2, a mapping $\lambda : \rho \to P$, which (1) is linear on each simplex of K_ν^2, (2) agrees with f on the boundary of ρ, and (3) maps each simplex of K_ν^2 onto a simplex, possibly of lower dimension, of K (see Fig. 8–4bc). It is possible to pass from η_0 to η_1 by a sequence of elementary homotopy operations each involving edges and elementary boundary paths on $\lambda(K_\nu^2)$. The argument can then be completed with the aid of (C) and (D). While the proof is straightforward, its details would involve a somewhat tedious adaptation of methods already used in earlier chapters.

Now let p_0 be a fixed vertex of K and let Π_0^* be the set of all edge paths with p_0 for both initial and terminal point. The **combinatorial homotopy class** of a path η in Π_0^*, defined by $\overset{\star}{\sim}$ (see Lemma 7), will be denoted by $\Gamma_0^*(\eta)$. The vacuous edge-path in Π_0^* will be denoted by ω. Then $\Gamma_0^*(\omega)$ contains ee^{-1}, if e has p_0 for initial point, and also abc, if abc is an elementary boundary path from p_0 to p_0.

THEOREM 7. **The combinatorial homotopy classes** $\{\Gamma_0^*\} = \{\Gamma_0^*(\eta) \mid \eta \in \Pi_0^*\}$ **are the elements of a group** Ψ_0, **whose product operation is defined by**

(8.13) $$\Gamma_0^*(\eta)\Gamma_0^*(\eta') = \Gamma_0^*(\eta\eta').$$

The unit element is $\Gamma_0^*(\omega)$ (Exercise 27).

THEOREM 8. **The group** Ψ_0 **is isomorphic to** $\Phi(P, p_0)$, **hence to** $\Phi(P)$.

Proof. By Theorem 6, it suffices to show that $\Gamma_0(\gamma)$ contains an edge path η. This follows easily, with the aid of the material in Art. 6–9 applied to mappings of the unit circle into P. Figure 6–3 is suggestive.

(E) The **combinatorial fundamental group** Ψ_0 is defined in terms of the edges, finite in number, of a triangulation K of P. This makes it relatively easy to analyze, and its structure is the same as that of the invariantly defined $\Phi(P)$. These groups are related after the fashion of the finitely computable simplicial homology groups and the invariantly defined singular homology groups.

(F) Since Ψ_0 clearly depends only on the 2-skeleton K^2 of K, it follows that $\Phi(\Sigma) \approx \Phi(P) \approx \Phi(|K^2|)$.

Consider a group $\mathfrak{G}$ given by a set of generators $(g_1, \ldots, g_n)$ and defining relations (see Appendix). By $\mathfrak{G}$ **made abelian** we will mean the group $\mathfrak{G}^a$ with generators $(g_1, \ldots, g_n)$ and with the defining relations of $\mathfrak{G}$ supplemented by the commutativity conditions $g_i g_j = g_j g_i$, equivalent to $g_i g_j g_i^{-1} g_j^{-1} = I$ $(i = 1, \ldots, n; \ j = 1, \ldots, n)$.

(G) If $\mathfrak{G}$ is already abelian, then $\mathfrak{G}^a = \mathfrak{G}$. If not, then some elements are equal in $\mathfrak{G}^a$ which are unequal in $\mathfrak{G}$.

THEOREM 9. **The first homology group $\mathfrak{H}_1(P)$ is isomorphic to its fundamental group $\Phi(P)$ made abelian.**

Proof. It is, by Theorem 8 and Art. 6–6, sufficient to show that the simplicial homology group $\mathfrak{H}_1(K)$ is isomorphic to $\Psi_0^a = (\Psi_0$ made abelian).

(*H*) The symbol for an edge path η from p_0 to p_0, modified by a prime, will denote the corresponding chain $\eta' = \varphi(\eta)$. Thus, using $(s_1, \ldots, s_{\alpha_1})$ for the oriented 1-simplexes of K:

$$(8.14) \quad \varphi : \eta = s_{i_1}^{\varepsilon_1} \ldots s_{i_r}^{\varepsilon_r} \to \eta' = \sum_{j=1}^{r} \varepsilon_j s_{i_j} \quad (\varepsilon_j = +1 \text{ or } -1, j = 1, \ldots, r).$$

This defines a mapping φ of edge paths into simplicial 1-chains.

LEMMA 8. **If $\eta_0 \overset{*}{\sim} \eta_1$, then $\eta_0' \sim \eta_1'$. The converse does not hold.**

Proof of Lemma. The elementary operation of deleting a pair of successive factors of the form ss^{-1} in the product form for η does not alter η', nor does the inverse operation. The other elementary operation (*D*3) applied to η corresponds to the addition to η' of the boundary chain of a 2-simplex and therefore yields a cycle homologous to η'. This proves the first part of the lemma. We remark, without proof, that if Σ is a torus with a contour and η is an oriented path around the contour, then $\eta' \sim \emptyset$ but η is not null-homotopic. This illustrates the second sentence of the lemma.

LEMMA 9. **The mapping φ induces a homomorphism $\varphi' : \Psi_0 \to \mathfrak{H}_1(K)$.**

Proof of Lemma. We will denote the homology class of η' by $[\eta']$. By Lemma 8, φ induces a mapping $\varphi' : \Gamma_0^*(\eta) \to [\eta']$. Since $(\eta_0 \eta_1) \to \eta_0' + \eta_1'$, by (8.14) and $\eta \overset{*}{\sim} \eta_0 \eta_1 \Rightarrow \eta' \sim \eta_0' + \eta_1'$, this mapping is a homomorphism.

LEMMA 10. **The homomorphism φ' induces an isomorphism $\varphi^a : \Psi_0^a \to \mathfrak{H}_1(K)$.**

Proof of Lemma. The lemma means that φ' maps two elements $\Gamma_0^*(\eta)$ and $\Gamma_0^*(\zeta)$ of Ψ_0 onto the same element of $\mathfrak{H}_1(K)$ if and only if $\Gamma_0^*(\eta)$ equals $\Gamma_0^*(\zeta)$ in Ψ_0^a.

Since $\varphi'(\Gamma_0^*(\eta_1)\Gamma_0^*(\eta_2)) = [\eta_1 + \eta_2] = [\eta_2 + \eta_1]$, φ' maps equal elements of Ψ_0^a onto the same element of $\mathfrak{H}_1(K)$.

(*I*) To show that $\varphi'(\Gamma_0^*(\eta)) = \varphi'(\Gamma_0^*(\zeta))$ implies $\Gamma_0^*(\eta) = \Gamma_0^*(\zeta)$ in Ψ_0^a, it is sufficient to show that $\varphi'(\Gamma_0^*(\eta)) = \emptyset$ implies $\Gamma_0^*(\eta) = I$ in Ψ_0^a, where $\emptyset$ is the null element of $\mathfrak{H}_1(K)$ (Exercise 29).

(*J*) The condition $\varphi'(\Gamma_0^*(\eta)) = \emptyset$ holds if and only if some path in $\Gamma_0^*(\eta)$ has the property that each edge appears in it equally often with both orientations. Thus the proof reduces to the following lemma.

LEMMA 11. **If η is a path in whose expression of the form (8.14) each edge appears as often with exponent $+1$ as with exponent -1, then η is in the identity element of Ψ_0^a.**

Proof of Lemma. To simplify the notation, let $e_j = s_{i_j}^{\varepsilon_i}$ $(j = 1, \ldots, r)$, so that

$$(8.15) \qquad \pi = e_1 \ldots e_r = s_{i_1}^{\varepsilon_1} \ldots s_{i_r}^{\varepsilon_r}.$$

Let G be the linear graph composed of the edges appearing in π, and their vertices. If G is a tree (Art. 1–3), let e be the first edge in π whose terminal vertex is a terminal vertex of G (Art. 1–3(B)). Then e^{-1} immediately follows e in π, and ee^{-1} can be eliminated to obtain $\pi' \overset{*}{\sim} \pi$ where π' has two fewer edges than π. Now $G(\pi')$, if not vacuous, is a tree. By repetitions, we deduce that π is in the unit element of Ψ_0, hence of Ψ_0^a.

If G is not a tree, let e be the first edge of π on a circuit of G. Then, by hypothesis, e^{-1} is an edge s of π and we can write

$$(8.16) \qquad \pi = \pi_1 e \pi_2 e^{-1} \pi_3.$$

Since e is on a circuit of G, $G - s$ is connected. Hence there exists a path π_0 on $G - s$ from the terminal point of e to the initial point of e. Then, by (C) and (D),

$$(8.17) \qquad \pi \overset{*}{\sim} (\pi_1 e \pi_0)(\pi_0^{-1} \pi_2 \pi_0)(\pi_0^{-1} e^{-1} \pi_3).$$

The transposition of the last two parentheses yields the path

$$(8.18) \qquad (\pi_1 e \pi_0)(\pi_0^{-1} e^{-1} \pi_3)(\pi_0^{-1} \pi_2 \pi_0) \overset{*}{\sim} (\pi_1 \pi_3 \pi_0^{-1} \pi_2 \pi_0) = \pi',$$

where π' contains the elements e and e^{-1} each once less than π. Also π' and π are in the same element of Ψ_0^a, though not necessarily in the same element of Ψ_0. Now $G(\pi') = G(\pi)$ or $G(\pi') = G(\pi) - s$ according as e appears or does not appear in π'. In the former case, we repeat the process until we arrive at a π'' in the same element of Ψ_0^a as π for which $G(\pi'') = G(\pi) - s$. Continuing thus, we finally arrive at a π''' for which $G(\pi''')$ is a tree, and the lemma is proved.

EXERCISES

24. Prove Part (1) of (C) by showing that η can be deformed into η' in $\Pi(p, q)$ (see Art. 8–2(A)) by a deformation affecting only the factor pair ee^{-1} and reducing ee^{-1} to a point.

25. Prove Part (2) of (C).

26. Prove Lemma 6.

27. Prove Theorem 7, following the pattern of the proof of Theorem 1.

28. Which of the following surfaces are simply connected? Justify your answers. (a) The curved surface of a double cone. (b) Euclidean n-space. (c) An annulus.

29. Deduce (I) from the fact that φ' is a homomorphism.

8–4.   The Fundamental Groups of E^n and of a Circle

(A) It is a simple matter to show (Exercises 21 and 28b above) that euclidean n-space E^n is simply connected, using deformations along line-segments (Exercise 30).

THEOREM 10. **The fundamental group of a simple closed curve κ is a free cyclic group.**

Proof. We will establish Theorem 10 by a method intended to lay a foundation for more general procedure.

(B) Let $U = [0, 1] : (0 \le u \le 1)$ be the unit segment on a u-axis. Let $g : U \to \Sigma$ define a path $\alpha = g(U)$ on Σ, and let $\varphi : \Sigma \to \Sigma'$ be a continuous mapping. As a ready consequence of the definitions, $\varphi g : U \to \Sigma'$ defines a path $\beta = \varphi g(U)$ on Σ'. *We will also write $\beta = \varphi(\alpha)$ to symbolize this manner of defining a curve β on Σ' by a mapping φ from another space Σ containing α.*

We will make use of (B) in proving Theorem 10, with $\Sigma' = \kappa$ and $\Sigma = E^1$, the motive being to capitalize on the simplicity of the deformation properties of E^1.

As a consequence of Theorem 3 and Exercise 7 above, our proof will lose no generality in being given for the case where κ is the unit circle $x^2 + y^2 = 1$ in an (x, y)-plane E^2. Let E^1 be interpreted as a t-axis, and let $\varphi : E^1 \to E^2$ be defined by

$$(8.19) \qquad \varphi(t) = (x, y) \text{ where } x = \cos 2\pi t, y = \sin 2\pi t.$$

LEMMA 12. **An arbitrary path $\beta = g(U)$ on κ can be expressed in the form $\beta = \varphi(\alpha)$, where α is a path on E^1.**

Proof of Lemma. The mapping φ is of period 1 in t. It is a **local homeomorphism** in the following sense. (1) If $\tau \subset E^1$ is a segment of length $\lambda < 1$, then the restriction $\varphi_\tau = \varphi \mid \tau$ is a homeomorphism of τ onto an arc $\gamma = \varphi_\tau(\tau) = \varphi(\tau)$, of arc length $2\pi\lambda$. (2) Given an arc $\gamma \subset \kappa$ of length $2\pi\lambda < 2\pi$, the inverse set $\varphi^{-1}(\gamma)$ consists of a set of disjoint arcs $\{\tau\} = \varphi^{-1}(\gamma)$, and $\{\tau\}$ is mapped onto itself by a translation $t' = t + m$ (m an integer). If $\tau \in \{\tau\} = \varphi^{-1}(\gamma)$ then φ_τ^{-1} is a homeomorphism and is a **local inverse** to φ.

Case 1. β is on an arc $\gamma \subset \kappa$ of arc length $<2\pi$. Let $\tau \in \varphi^{-1}(\gamma)$, and let $\alpha = \varphi_\tau^{-1}(\beta) = \varphi_\tau^{-1}g(U)$. Then $\beta = \varphi(\alpha) = \varphi\varphi_\tau^{-1}g(U)$, since $\varphi\varphi^{-1}$ is the identity on τ.

Case 2. The general case. By the uniform continuity of g on U, we can express β as a product $\beta = \beta_1 \ldots \beta_\nu$ where $\beta_i = g(U_i)$ ($i = 1, \ldots, \nu$) is on an arc $\gamma_i \subset \kappa$ of length $< 2\pi$. Then Case 1 applies to each individual β_i.

Hypothesis. For some $j \in 2, \ldots, \nu$ the product $\beta^{j-1} = \beta_1 \ldots \beta_{j-1}$ can be expressed in the form $\beta^{j-1} = \varphi(\alpha^{j-1})$ where α^{j-1} is a path on E^1.

Applying Case 1, let $\beta_1 = \varphi(\alpha^1)$, fulfilling the hypothesis for $j = 2$. Let q_{j-1} be the terminal point of α^{j-1}. Among the inverse images $\varphi^{-1}(\gamma_j)$ let τ_j be the one containing q_j. Let $\alpha_j = \varphi_{\tau_j}^{-1}(\beta_j)$. Then $\beta_j = \varphi(\alpha_j)$. Since the initial point of α_j is the terminal point of α^{j-1}, the product $\alpha^{j-1}\alpha_j = \alpha^j$ is defined. Since continuous mappings commute with the path product operation, $\varphi(\alpha^j) = \beta_1 \ldots \beta_j$ and the inductive argument establishing Lemma 12 is complete.

COROLLARY. **If $q_0 \in \varphi^{-1}(p_0)$, where p_0 is the initial point of β, then there is a unique $\alpha = \alpha(q_0)$ satisfying Lemma 12 and having q_0 as initial point.**

(C) Theorem 10 will follow (see Theorems 2 and 3) if $\Phi_0(\kappa, p_0)$ is shown to be free cyclic (where $p_0 = \varphi(0) = (1, 0)$). Let $\Pi_0 = \Pi(p_0, p_0)$ on κ (Art. 8–2(A)).

LEMMA 13. **Let α be a path on E^1 from $t = 0$ to $t = m$ (an integer). Then $\varphi(\alpha) \in \Pi_0$. Conversely, if $\beta \in \Pi_0$, then $\beta = \varphi(\alpha)$ for some α on E^1 from $t = 0$ to $t = m$, where m is an integer uniquely determined by β.**

This follows easily from Lemma 12 and corollary.

LEMMA 14. **Let f_u be a deformation of β in Π_0 and let $\beta_u = f_u(\beta)$. Let $g_u(\alpha)$ be the path on E^1 from $t = 0$ such that $\beta_u = \varphi g_u(\alpha)$. Then g_u is a deformation of α with fixed end points.**

It is a routine procedure to verify that g_u is a deformation with the initial point of α fixed at $t = 0$. Initially, the terminal point of α is fixed, by Lemma 13, at some integral point $t = m$. Since the terminal point varies continuously with u and is always an integral point, it must remain fixed.

If ζ is a closed path, the path $\zeta \zeta \ldots \zeta$ (m factors) is denoted by ζ^m.

LEMMA 15. **Let $\tau_m = [0, m] : 0 \leq t \leq m$, and let $\gamma_m = \varphi(\tau_m)$. Then (1) $\gamma_m = \gamma_1^m$ and (2) each $\beta \in \Pi_0$ is homotopic in Π_0 to γ_m for a unique integer m.**

Proof of Lemma. Part (1) holds because φ is of period 1 in t. Part (2) follows from Lemma 14 and the fact that an arbitrary path on E^1 from $t = 0$ to $t = m$ can be deformed into τ_m on E^1 with fixed end points.

With Lemma 15, the proof of Theorem 10 is complete.

EXERCISES

30. Let $f_j : X \to E^n$ $(j = 0, 1)$ define two paths π_j $(j = 0, 1)$, where $X = [0, 1] : 0 \le x \le 1$, and where $f_1(0) = f_2(0) = f_1(1) = f_2(1)$. Formulate a deformation f_t of π_0 into π_1 along line segments $(0 \le t \le 1)$.

31. Show that β can be expressed as $\beta_1 \ldots \beta_\nu$ as asserted in Case 2 under Lemma 12.

32. Prove Lemma 13, with special attention to the uniqueness of m.

33. Write up the proof of Lemma 15 in greater detail.

8–5. The Fundamental Group of a Surface

THEOREM 11. **The fundamental group of a torus is free abelian with two generators.**

Proof. We use the same type of argument as in the case of Theorem 10.

Let E^2 be the euclidean plane of a coordinate system (x, y) and let E^3 be euclidean 3-space with a cylindrical coordinate system (r, θ, z). We lose no generality in proving the theorem for the special torus

(8.20)
$$T^2 : \begin{cases} \theta = 2\pi x, \\ r = 2 + \cos 2\pi y, \\ z = \sin 2\pi y. \end{cases}$$

Let φ be the mapping of E^2 into E^3 defined by $\varphi(x, y) = (r, \theta, z)$, where (r, θ, z) are given by (8.20). Then $T^2 = \varphi(E^2)$.

The reader would do well to draw diagrams, showing E^2, $T^2 \subset E^3$, the coordinate systems, and the various geometric objects in the following proof.

LEMMA 16. **Let α be a path on E^2. Then $\gamma = \varphi(\alpha)$ is a path on T^2. Each path γ on T^2 can be thus defined.**

Proof of Lemma. The lemma and its proof are strictly analogous to Lemma 12 and proof. We comment on some major points (Exercise 35).

(A) The mapping φ has period 1 in x and in y. Its restriction to a square region $(x_0 < x < x_0 + \lambda, y_0 < y < y_0 + \lambda)$, where $0 < \lambda < 1$, is a homeomorphism. Hence so is its restriction to a circular region of diameter <1.

(B) There exists a number $d > 0$ so small that each subset of T^2 of diameter $<d$ is on the image under φ of some circular region on E^2 of diameter <1.

In the inductive argument analogous to that for Lemma 12, the role of the β_j is played by sub-arcs γ_j of γ of diameter $<d$, and the role of the τ_j is played by circular regions of diameter <1.

COROLLARY. **Given a path γ on T^2 with initial point p_0, let $(x_0, y_0) \in \varphi^{-1}(p_0)$. Then there is a unique path α_0 on E^2 with (x_0, y_0) for initial point, such that $\gamma = \varphi(\alpha_0)$. A translation of α_0 by a vector with integral components (m, n) takes α_0 into the path α with initial point $(x_0 + m, y_0 + n)$ such that $\gamma = \varphi(\alpha)$.**

We prove Theorem 11 by showing that $\Phi_0(T^2, p_0)$ has the specified structure where $p_0 = \varphi(0, 0)$, the point with cylindric coordinates $(r_0, \theta_0, z_0) = (3, 0, 0)$. Let Π_0 be the class of closed paths on T^2 from p_0 to p_0.

LEMMA 17. **A path γ on T^2 belongs to Π_0 if and only if there exists a path α on E^2 such that**

$$(8.21) \quad \gamma = \varphi(\alpha) \quad \begin{cases} \text{initial point of } \alpha \text{ is } (0, 0), \\ \text{terminal point of } \alpha \text{ is } (m, n) \text{ where } (m, n) \text{ are integers.} \end{cases}$$

The path α is unique, given β (Exercise 36).

LEMMA 18. **Let f_t be a homotopic deformation of γ in Π_0 and let $g_t(\alpha)$ be the path in E^2 from $(0, 0)$ such that $f_t(\beta) = \varphi(g_t(\alpha))$. Then g_t is a homotopic deformation of α with both end points fixed (Exercise 37).**

LEMMA 19. **Let α_m be the linear path along the x-axis from $(0, 0)$ to $(m, 0)$ and let β_n be the linear path along the y-axis from $(0, 0)$ to $(0, n)$. Let $a = \varphi(\alpha_1)$, $b = \varphi(\beta_1)$. Then (1)**

$$(8.22) \quad\quad\quad a^m = \varphi(\alpha_m), \quad\quad b^n = \varphi(\beta_n)$$

and (2) each path $\gamma \in \Pi_0$ is homotopic in Π_0 to $a^m b^n$ for a unique pair of integers (m, n).

Proof of Lemma. Part (1) follows from the fact that φ is of period 1 in x and in y. Part (2) follows from Lemma 17, an obvious deformation in E^2, and the fact that φ maps a deformation on E^2 into a deformation on T^2. If $m = 0$, α^m is a null path, and similarly for β^n, a^m, b^n.

Theorem 11 now follows.

(C) Intuitively, the fact that $\gamma \simeq a^m b^n$ in Π_0 means that γ runs around T^2 m times in the sense of a, while it twists around it n times in the sense of b before returning to its starting point (Fig. 8–5). These are the net numbers of times that γ thus runs and twists around T^2. Thus, $m = 3$ if γ makes five circuits in the positive sense of a, then doubles back and makes two circuits in the negative sense of a.

THEOREM 12. **Let M^2 be a compact surface, represented (see Chapter 2) by one of the following polygonal symbols:**

$$(8.23)$$

    (a) $M^2 = AA^{-1}$ (M^2 **is a topological sphere**);

    (b) $M^2 = A_1 B_1 A_1^{-1} B_1^{-1} \dots A_h B_h A_h^{-1} B_h^{-1} K_1 D_1 K_1^{-1} \dots K_r D_r K_r^{-1}$
         (sphere with h handles and r contours, $h + r > 0$);

    (c) $M^2 = C_1 C_1 \dots C_q C_q K_1 D_1 K_1^{-1} \dots K_r D_r K_r^{-1}$ **(sphere with $q > 0$ crosscaps and $r \geq 0$ contours).**

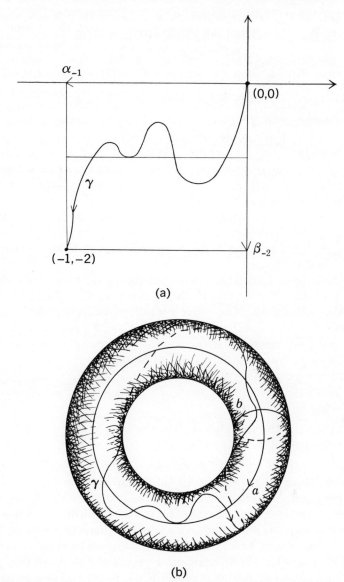

(a)

(b)

Fig. 8–5. The relation $\gamma \simeq a^m b^n$ where $\gamma = \varphi(\alpha)$ and $m = -1$, $n = -2$.

Then, in Case (a) and in Case (b) with $h = 0$, $r = 1$, M^2 is simply connected. In Case (b) with $h > 0$ or with $h = 0$, $r > 1$, $\Phi(M^2)$ is isomorphic to a group with $2h + r$ generators $(\alpha_i, \beta_i, \delta_j)$ $(i = 1, \ldots, h;$ $j = 1, \ldots, r)$ and the single group relation

(8.24) $\qquad \alpha_1 \beta_1 \alpha_1^{-1} \beta_1^{-1} \ldots \alpha_h \beta_h \alpha_h^{-1} \beta_h^{-1} \delta_1 \delta_2 \ldots \delta_r = I.$

In Case (c), $\Phi(M^2)$ is isomorphic to a group with $q + r$ generators $(\gamma_1, \ldots, \gamma_q, \delta_1, \ldots, \delta_r)$ **and the single group relation**

(8.25) $$\gamma_1^2 \gamma_2^2 \ldots \gamma_q^2 \delta_1 \ldots \delta_r = I.$$

Outline of Proof. The cases where M^2 is simply connected offer no difficulty.

Let M^2 be triangulated into a complex so that the edges of a polygonal representation P^2 in the form (8.23) are covered by a subcomplex, and let the complex K^2 be represented as a triangulation of P^2 with boundary simplexes suitably identified. Let p_0 be the common initial and terminal point of the A's and B's in Case (b), where it is also initial point of each K_i. In Case (c), let p_0 be similarly defined for the C's and the K's.

It suffices to show that the combinatorial fundamental group $\Psi(K^2, p_0)$ has the specified structure. An edge path on M^2 belongs to $\Pi_0 = \Pi_0(p_0, p_0)$ if and only if its representation on K^2 has copies of p_0 for initial and terminal point.

(*D*) Each homotopy class in Π_0 contains an edge path on the boundary of P_2. For, any path in Π_0 can first be deformed into an edge path γ (Art. 8–3). Then, any part of γ joining a point q_1 on the boundary of P^2 to another such point q_2 and composed of edges interior to P^2 can clearly be deformed into either of the two parts into which q_1 and q_2 separate the polygonal boundary.

(*E*) Each edge path on the boundary of P^2 from one copy of p_0 to another is a path product made up of factors each of which is one of the following or its inverse:

  (1) in Case (8.23b), the edge path α_i along A_i or the path β_i along B_i or the path δ_j first along K_j, then D_j, then K_j^{-1};

  (2) in Case (8.23c), the path γ_i along C_i or the path δ_j just described.

This yields Theorem 12, except for the group relationships.

The only null-homotopic paths on the boundary of P^2 are those which begin and end at the same copy of p_0. From this fact it is easy to deduce that (8.24) and (8.25) are group relations on which all group relations depend, in Cases (8.23b) and (8.23c) respectively.

(*F*) For example, the fundamental group of the projective plane has just two elements, and that of the Klein bottle has two generators (Γ_1, Γ_2) with the defining relation $\Gamma_1^2 \Gamma_2^2 = I$.

EXERCISES

34. Show that if Σ is the square region $0 < x < 1$, $0 < y < 1$ and (x, y) is restricted to $\overline{\Sigma}$, then Eqs. (8.20) are a formulation of a definition of T^2 as $\overline{\Sigma}$ with opposite edges identified.

35. Write out the proof of Lemma 16 and corollary as summarized.

36. Prove Lemma 17, which is analogous to Lemma 13.

37. Prove Lemma 18, analogous to Lemma 14.

38. With the aid of the representation suggested in Exercise 34 above, show that $aba^{-1}b^{-1}$ is null-homotopic.

39. Show (a) that the Betti numbers and torsion coefficients of a closed 3-manifold are determined by its fundamental group, (b) that the fundamental group of a non-orientable closed 3-manifold is infinite.

40. Illustrate Exercise 39a for projective 3-space.

8–6. Covering Complexes

(A) Let $g : \tilde{\Pi} \to \Pi$ be a continuous mapping of a connected topological polyhedron $\tilde{\Pi}$ onto a connected topological polyhedron Π. The pair $(\tilde{\Pi}, g)$ is a **covering space** of Π if (1) for each $p \in \Pi$, the set $\{\tilde{p}\} = g^{-1}(p)$ of its inverse images, called its **covering set**, is denumerable; and (2) letting

$$(8.26) \qquad \{\tilde{p}\} = (\tilde{p}_1, \tilde{p}_2, \ldots),$$

there exists a neighborhood N of p and neighborhoods $\tilde{N}_i$ of $\tilde{p}_i$ ($i = 1, 2, \ldots$) such that (a) g maps $\tilde{N}_i$ homeomorphically onto N and (b) each inverse image of a point on N is on one of the neighborhoods $\{\tilde{N}\} = (\tilde{N}_1, \tilde{N}_2, \ldots)$. We call $\tilde{\Pi}$ a **covering space** and g its **projection**. Property (a) is a local homeomorphism property (Art. 8–4).

(B) Each $\tilde{p}_i \in \{\tilde{p}\}$ is said to **cover** or to be **above** p, which is called its **base point**, and $\tilde{N}_i$ is said to **cover** or **be above** N ($i = 1, 2, \ldots$). If $\{\tilde{p}\}$ contains the same finite number k of points for each $p \in \Pi$, then $(\tilde{\Pi}, g)$ is a **k-fold covering** of Π. If $\{\tilde{p}\}$ is infinite for each $p \in \Pi$, then $(\tilde{\Pi}, g)$ is an **infinite covering** of Π.

(C) As a first trivial example, an arbitrary Π is covered by itself, $\tilde{\Pi} = \Pi$, with an arbitrary self-homeomorphism (the identity for example) as projection.

(D) The unit circle κ has an infinite covering (E^1, φ), defined by (8.19). The covering set of a point $p : (x, y)$ on κ is of the form $\{\tilde{p}\} = (t, t \pm 1, t \pm 2, \ldots)$, since φ is of period 1 in t. We can use for $\tilde{N}(t + m)$ an open interval of length $\frac{1}{2}$, center at $(t + m)$.

(E) The torus T^2 has an infinite covering (E^2, φ), with φ defined by (8.20). If $\tilde{p}_1(x, y)$ is a point on E^2 above p on T^2, then $\{\tilde{p}\}$ consists of all the points $(x + m, y + n)$ as m, n range over the integers. Circular regions of radius $d < 1$ about each of these points can be used for $\{\tilde{N}\}$, since φ is of period 1 in x and in y.

(F) Let κ be the unit circle of (8.19) and let $\tilde{\kappa}$ be another circle defined by

$$(8.27) \qquad \tilde{\kappa} = \tilde{\varphi}(E^1) : \begin{cases} x = \cos \dfrac{2\pi t}{k} \\[2mm] y = \sin \dfrac{2\pi t}{k} \end{cases} \qquad (k \in 2, 3, 4, \ldots)$$

and let $g : \tilde{\kappa} \to \kappa$ be defined by the condition $g(\tilde{\varphi}(t)) = \varphi(t)$. Then $(\tilde{\kappa}, g)$ is a k-fold covering of κ (Exercise 41).

(G) Coverings of the torus analogous to the covering of the circle in (F) are obtained as follows: Let T^2 be defined as in (8.20), let $\tilde{T}^2$ be defined by $\tilde{T}^2 = \tilde{\varphi}(E^2)$, where $\tilde{\varphi}(x, y) = (r, \theta, z)$ is defined by

$$(8.28) \qquad \tilde{T}^2 = \tilde{\varphi}(E^2) : \begin{cases} \theta = \dfrac{2\pi x}{m} & m \in (1, 2, \ldots) \\[2mm] r = 2 + \cos \dfrac{2\pi y}{n} \\[2mm] z = \sin \dfrac{2\pi y}{n} & n \in (1, 2, \ldots) \end{cases}$$

and let $g : \tilde{T}^2 \to T^2$ be defined by $g(\tilde{\varphi}(x, y)) = \varphi(x, y)$. Then $(\tilde{T}^2, g)$ is an mn-fold covering of T^2 (Exercise 42).

As another example, consider a manifold M in the form of a sphere with three handles. Let M be covered with five layers of identical manifolds $M_1, M_2, \ldots, M_5$, like layers of skin, so that the result could be regarded as a laminated surface made up of six juxtaposed membranes $(M, M_1, \ldots, M_5)$ which, for the sake of being specific, we number from the inside layer outward. The juxtaposition of the layers affords a natural homeomorphism among them. If p is any point on M, then $\tilde{p}_i$ will denote the corresponding point on M_i $(i = 1, \ldots, 5)$. The mapping $g : \tilde{p} \to p$ will be called the **projection** of the union $M_0^* = \bigcup\limits_{i=1}^{5} M_i$ of the M_i onto M. Now (M_0^*, g) fails to satisfy the definition of a **covering space** in that M_0^* is not connected. To correct this, first let three closed cuts be made, as suggested by a, b, and c in Fig. 8–6, through all five surfaces M_i. Allowing surfaces to penetrate one another, let the edges be matched as suggested in the figure to obtain a covering $(\tilde{M}, g)$. Thus, along b, the two edges of M_1 are rejoined, and so are those of M_2, while M_3 is joined to M_5, M_4 to M_3, and M_5 to M_4 in the direction of the arrow cutting across b in the figure.

(H) The surface $\tilde{M}$, with the projection g, is a 5-fold covering space of M.

Consider a closed path π on M from p_1 to p_1, where no point on a cut is above p_1, and let $\tilde{\pi}$ be the path on $\tilde{M}$ obtained by lifting† π into $\tilde{M}$ so that $\tilde{p}_1$ on M_1 is the initial point of $\tilde{\pi}$. Then $\tilde{\pi}$ stays on M_1 unless it crosses a, in which case it shifts to M_2. Hence, $\tilde{\pi}$ goes from $\tilde{p}_1$ to $\tilde{p}_2$ or else from $\tilde{p}_1$ to $\tilde{p}_1$, according as it crosses a an odd or an even number of times.

THEOREM 13. **Given a topological polyhedron Π and a covering space $\tilde{\Pi}$, there exist triangulations K and $\tilde{K}$ of Π and $\tilde{\Pi}$ such that the**

---

† That is, finding $\tilde{\pi}$ so that $\pi = g(\tilde{\pi})$ (Exercise 43).

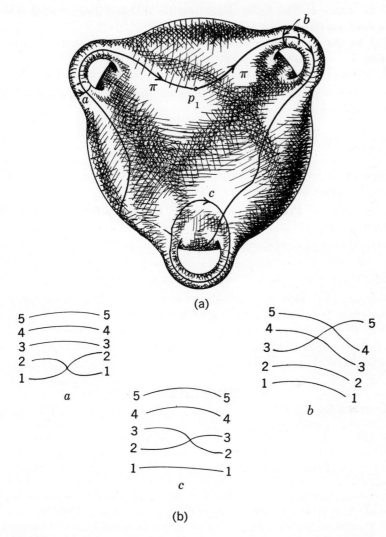

(a)

(b)

Fig. 8–6. A 5-fold covering space of the sphere with three handles.

mapping g induces a mapping of the j-simplexes of $\tilde{K}$ onto the j-simplexes of K $(j = 0, 1, \ldots, m)$.

Outline of Proof. Let K be so fine a triangulation of Π that each of its simplexes is on a neighborhood N of the sort entering into Definition (A). Then the inverses of the mappings $g \mid \tilde{N}_i$ define a triangulation $\tilde{K}$ of $\tilde{\Pi}$ satisfying the theorem.

COROLLARY 1. **If $\tilde{\Pi}$ is a k-fold [infinite] covering space of Π, then g maps exactly k [infinitely many] simplexes of $\tilde{K}$ onto each simplex of K.**

COROLLARY 2. **The Euler characteristic of $\widetilde{\Pi}$ is k times that of Π if $\widetilde{\Pi}$ is a k-fold covering space of Π.**

For, in the notation of Theorem 13, if α_j is the number of j-cells of K, then $\tilde{\alpha}_j = k\alpha_j$ is the number of j-cells of $\tilde{K}$.

From the fact that the characteristic of a closed 2-manifold M is

(8.29) $N(M) = \alpha_0 - \alpha_1 + \alpha_2 = \begin{cases} 2 - 2h \text{ for a sphere with } h \text{ handles,} \\ 2 - q \text{ for a sphere with } q \text{ crosscaps,} \end{cases}$

we deduce the following result.

COROLLARY 3. **A k-fold covering space of a sphere with h handles is a sphere with $kh - k + 1$ handles. A k-fold covering of a torus is a torus** (Exercise 45b).

THEOREM 14. **Projective m-space P^m can be doubly covered by the m-sphere S^m.**

Proof. One can represent P^m as S^m with antipodal pairs of points (p, p') identified. The mapping g which maps each point p of S^m onto the identified pair (p, p') yields a double covering space (S^m, g).

COROLLARY. **The only k-fold covering space $(k > 1)$ of the projective plane is a double covering by the sphere.**

For, P^2 has characteristic $+1$. A k-fold covering space of P^2 is a closed 2-manifold of characteristic k. The 2-sphere is the only closed 2-manifold of characteristic $k > 1$.

EXERCISES

41. Give a proof of (F).

42. Give a proof of (G).

43. Discuss the lifting of a curve into a covering complex. This involves writing a short paper, using methods analogous to those used in connection with Lemma 12 and corollary, also Lemma 16 and corollary. Include a proof of Theorem 15 below.

44. Given the closed path π of Fig. 8–6, discuss all paths obtainable by lifting π into $\tilde{M}$. If π^k is lifted onto $\tilde{\pi}^k$ on M, under what conditions will $\tilde{\pi}^k$ be closed?

45. (a) Prove that a covering space of a closed orientable m-pseudomanifold is a closed orientable m-pseudomanifold. (b) Establish Corollary 3 to Theorem 13.

46. Show that a k-fold covering space $(k > 1)$ of a sphere M with $h > 1$ handles is not homeomorphic to M.

47. Show that a 2-sphere can have no k-fold covering $(k > 1)$. Compare the proof of the corollary to Theorem 14.

8–7. Fundamental Groups and Coverings

Let $(\widetilde{\Pi}, g)$ be a covering of a topological polyhedron Π, and let $f : X \to \widetilde{\Pi}$ define a path

(8.30) $\tilde{\pi} = f(X) \qquad X = [0, 1], \quad 0 \le x \le 1.$

Then $\tilde{\pi}$ **covers**, or is a **covering path** of,

$$(8.31) \qquad \pi = g(\tilde{\pi}) = gf(X) \qquad \text{(see Lemma 12)},$$

which is the **base path**, or the **projection**, of π.

THEOREM 15. **If π is a path on Π and $\tilde{p}$ on $\widetilde{\Pi}$ covers the initial point p of π, then there is a unique covering path of π with initial point $\tilde{p}$.**
The proof is left to the reader (Exercise 43 above).

LEMMA 20. **Let $(\tilde{p}) = \tilde{p}_1, \tilde{p}_2, \ldots$ be the covering set of p on $\widetilde{\Pi}$ and let $\tilde{\pi}_i$ be the path above π with initial point $\tilde{p}_i$ $(i = 1, 2, \ldots)$. Let $\tilde{q}_i$ be the terminal point of $\tilde{\pi}_i$. Then $\tilde{q}_i \neq \tilde{q}_j$ if $i \neq j$.**

Proof of Lemma. As a consequence of Theorem 15, $\tilde{\pi}_i^{-1}$ is the only path above π_i^{-1} with $\tilde{q}_i$ for initial point. Hence $\tilde{q}_i = \tilde{q}_j$ would imply $\tilde{p}_i = \tilde{p}_j$.

COROLLARY. **A covering $(\widetilde{\Pi}, g)$ is either k-fold for some k or is an infinite covering.**
For, the paths $\tilde{\pi}_i$ $(i = 1, 2, \ldots)$ and $\tilde{\pi}_i^{-1}$ establish a one-to-one correspondence between the covering sets of p and q if π goes from p to q.

THEOREM 16. **If, on $\widetilde{\Pi}$, $\tilde{\pi}_1 \simeq \tilde{\pi}_2$ with fixed end points, then the projections $\pi_i = g(\tilde{\pi}_i)$ $(i = 1, 2)$ are also homotopic with fixed end points.**
This follows easily, since a deformation rectangle $f(X \times T)$ for a homotopy of $\tilde{\pi}_1$ into $\tilde{\pi}_2$ with fixed end points projects into such a rectangle $gf(X \times T)$ for π_1 and π_2.

THEOREM 17. **If, on Π, $\pi_1 \simeq \pi_2$ with fixed end points, and $(\tilde{\pi}_1, \tilde{\pi}_2)$ are paths above (π_1, π_2) with a common initial point $\tilde{p}$, then $\tilde{\pi}_1 \simeq \tilde{\pi}_2$ with fixed end points.**

Outline of Proof. This theorem is analogous to Lemmas 14 and 18, but the argument must be modified, unless we introduce metrics on Π and $\widetilde{\Pi}$. Let a deformation rectangle on Π for a deformation $\pi_0 \to \pi_1$ be triangulated into a singular complex K^2 so fine that each of its simplexes is on a neighborhood N satisfying Art. 8–6(A). Then there is a unique singular complex $\widetilde{K}^2$ such that $g(\widetilde{K}^2) = K^2$ and $|\widetilde{K}^2|$ is a deformation rectangle for a deformation of $\tilde{\pi}_1$ into $\tilde{\pi}_2$ with fixed end points (Exercise 48).

THEOREM 18. **Let $\Phi(\widetilde{\Pi}, \tilde{p})$ be the fundamental group of $\widetilde{\Pi}$ with a fixed point $\tilde{p}$. The projection $g : \widetilde{\Pi} \to \Pi$ induces a homomorphism $g^* : \Phi(\widetilde{\Pi}, \tilde{p}) \to \Phi(\Pi, p)$, where $p = g(\tilde{p})$.**

Proof. In the first place, Theorem 16 implies that g takes homotopy classes into homotopy classes. Secondly, g commutes with the path product operation, since $g(\tilde{\pi}\tilde{\pi}') = g(\tilde{\pi})g(\tilde{\pi}')$ provided $\tilde{\pi}\tilde{\pi}'$ is defined.

THEOREM 19. **The homomorphism g^* is an isomorphism between $\Phi(\widetilde{\Pi}, \tilde{p})$ and the image subgroup $g^*\Phi(\widetilde{\Pi}, \tilde{p}) \subset \Phi(\Pi, p)$.**

Proof. This follows from Theorems 16 and 17. The latter implies that no two different homotopy elements of $\Phi(\widetilde{\Pi}, \tilde{p})$ can map onto the same element of $\Phi(\Pi, p)$.

(A) For example, in the case of the 3-fold covering $\tilde{\kappa}$ of κ in Art. 8–6(F) with $k = 3$, g^* maps the free cyclic group $\Phi(\tilde{\kappa}, \tilde{p})$ onto the elements Γ^{3m} of $\Phi(\kappa, p)$ where Γ is a generator of $\Phi(\kappa, p)$ and $m = 0$, $\pm 1, \pm 2, \ldots$.

(B) In the case of the coverings (E^1, φ) of κ and (E^2, φ) of T^2 (Art. 8–6(F)(G)), the fundamental group of the covering space consists of the unit element alone and g^* maps it onto the unit element of the base space.

For another example, see Exercise 49.

A general analysis of relations between the fundamental group of a topological polyhedron Π and the possible covering spaces of Π would lead us into group-theoretic considerations beyond the scope of this book. It turns out that there is a one-to-one correspondence between classes of possible covering spaces and classes of so-called **conjugate subgroups** of $\Phi(\Pi)$. The problem of determining all k-fold covering spaces of Π is thereby reducible to the group-theoretic problem of finding all classes of conjugate subgroups with a so-called **index** k in $\Phi(\Pi)$.

(C) In particular, it can be shown that each connected topological polyhedron Π admits a **universal covering complex**, $\hat{\Pi}$, characterized by the property of being simply connected. We found the universal covering of (1) the circle κ by E^1, (2) the torus by E^2, (3) the projective plane P^2 by S^2. With suitably defined projections, one can show that the universal covering $\hat{\Pi}$ is a covering of each covering $\widetilde{\Pi}$ of Π, and that a covering space of all coverings of Π must be its universal covering. Further details are to be found in [S–T], for example.

EXERCISES

48. Write out the outlined proof of Theorem 17. This involves writing a short paper.

49. Consider the 6-fold covering of T^2 in Art. 8–6(G) with $m = 3$, $n = 2$. If $[a], [b]$ are the generating homotopy classes of a, b for T^2, show that g^* maps $\Phi(\widetilde{T}^2, \tilde{p}_0)$ onto the subgroup of $\Phi(T^2, p_0)$ generated by $[a^3], [b^2]$.

Bibliography

The following list makes no claim to completeness. Additional references can be found in the works here listed. The symbols in brackets are used in this book for reference purposes.

ALEKSANDROV, P. S. *Combinatorial Topology.* Vols. 1, 2, 3. Albany: Graylock Press, 1956, 1957, 1960.

ALEXANDROFF, PAUL. *Einfachste Grundbegriffe der Topologie.* Berlin: Julius Springer, 1932.

ALEXANDROFF, PAUL, and HOPF, HEINZ. *Topologie I.* Berlin: Julius Springer, 1935.

COURANT, RICHARD, and ROBBINS, H. E. *What is Mathematics?* New York: Oxford University Press, 1948. Chap. 5.

HILBERT, DAVID, and COHN-VOSSEN, S. *Geometry and the Imagination.* New York: Chelsea Publishing Co., 1952. Chap. 6.

[K₁] KELLEY, JOHN L. *General Topology.* New York: D. Van Nostrand & Co., Inc., 1955.

[K₂] KERÉKJÁRTÓ, B. v. *Vorlesungen über Topologie I.* Berlin: Julius Springer, 1923.

[L₁] LANDAU, EDMUND. *The Foundations of Analysis.* New York: Chelsea Publishing Co., 1951.

[L₂] LEFSCHETZ, SOLOMON. *Introduction to Topology.* Princeton: Princeton University Press, 1949.

PONTRYAGIN, L. S. *Foundations of Combinatorial Topology.* Albany: Graylock Press, 1952.

[S–S] SCHREIER, O., and SPERNER, E. *Introduction to Modern Algebra and Matrix Theory.* New York: Chelsea Publishing Co., 1951.

[S–T] SEIFERT, H., and THRELFALL, W. *Lehrbuch der Topologie.* New York: Chelsea Publishing Co., 1957. Original ed.: Leipzig: Teubner, 1934.

[T] THURSTON, H. A. *The Number-System.* London: Blackie & Son, 1956.

[V] VEBLEN, OSWALD. *Analysis Situs.* 2d ed. Vol. V, part II. American Mathematical Society Colloquium Publication, 1931.

APPENDIX

Group-Theoretic Background

The purpose of this appendix is to set forth the concepts and results of group theory used in this book. We confine ourselves largely to descriptive statements, omitting many important logical considerations. A good modern approach to the subject for its own sake would be quite different from the present assemblage of facts for reference purposes. A few exercises are included.

A–I. Basic Terminology

A (**multiplicative**) **group** $\mathfrak{G}$ is a set of elements $\{g\}$ and a **product operation**, called (**group**) **multiplication**, as follows: Given $g_1 \in \mathfrak{G}$ and $g_2 \in \mathfrak{G}$, there exists a product $g_1 g_2$, subject to the following **group axioms**:

I. $g_1 g_2$ is an element of $\mathfrak{G}$.

II. If $g_i \in \mathfrak{G}$ ($i = 1, 2, 3$), then $g_1(g_2 g_3) = (g_1 g_2)g_3$. That is, multiplication is associative.

III. There exists an element $1 \in \{g\}$, called the **unit** element, such that $g1 = 1g = g$ for each $g \in \mathfrak{G}$.

IV. For each $g \in \mathfrak{G}$, there exists an element $g^{-1} \in \mathfrak{G}$, the **inverse** of g, such that $gg^{-1} = g^{-1}g = 1$.

Added conditions define special groups or classes of groups. In particular, the important class of **commutative** (or **abelian**) groups is defined by adding the following **axiom of commutativity**:

V. If $g_1 \in \mathfrak{G}$ and $g_2 \in \mathfrak{G}$, then $g_1 g_2 = g_2 g_1$.

(A) The "product" operation for a commutative group is frequently written in the form of a "sum," and the following definition is used. An (**abelian**) **additive group** $\mathfrak{A}$ is a set of elements $\{a\}$ and a **sum operation** called (**group**) **addition**, as follows: Given $a_1 \in \mathfrak{A}$, $a_2 \in \mathfrak{A}$, there exists a sum, $a_1 + a_2$, subject to the following **axioms for abelian additive groups**:

I. $a_1 + a_2 \in \mathfrak{A}$.

II. $a_1 + (a_2 + a_3) = (a_1 + a_2) + a_3$ (Associativity).

III. There exists an element $0 \in \mathfrak{A}$, called the **zero** or **null element** such that $a + 0 = a$ for each $a \in \mathfrak{A}$.

IV. For each $a \in \mathfrak{A}$, there exists an element $-a \in \mathfrak{A}$, the **negative** of a, such that $a + (-a) = 0$. This relation is generally expressed in the form $a - a = 0$.

V. $a_1 + a_2 = a_2 + a_1$.

Axioms II justify such notation as

(A.1)
$$g_1 g_2 g_3 = g_1(g_2 g_3) = (g_1 g_2)g_3,$$
$$a_1 + a_2 + a_3 = a_1 + (a_2 + a_3) = (a_1 + a_2) + a_3.$$

By a recurrent definition, a meaning is attached to

(A.2)
$$\prod_{i=1}^{m} g_i = g_1 g_2 \cdots g_m,$$
$$\sum_{i=1}^{m} a_i = a_1 + a_2 + \cdots + a_m.$$

In the special case of (A.2) where the elements g_i, or the elements a_i, are all equal, one writes

(A.3)

$g^m = gg \cdots g$ (*m* factors)

$g^{-m} = g^{-1}g^{-1} \cdots g^{-1} = (g^m)^{-1}$ (*m* factors)

$ma = a + a + \cdots + a$ (*m* terms)

$-ma = (-a) + (-a) + \cdots + (-a) = -a - a \cdots - a$ (*m* terms)

(*B*) *Examples which the reader may wish to verify:* (1) the integers **Z**, with addition, but not with multiplication; (2) the integers mod *m*, **Z**$_m$ (see (*H*) below), with addition, but not with multiplication, where *m* is a positive integer; (3) the rational numbers **Q** or the reals **R**, with addition, but not with multiplication; (4) the non-zero rational or real numbers, with multiplication, but not with addition; (5) square matrices of equal size whose elements belong to **Z** or to **Z**$_m$ or to **Q** or to **R**, with matrix addition; (6) square matrices of equal size having non-zero determinants, with rational or with real elements, and with matrix multiplication. This is the only one of the six examples which is not commutative. The symbols **Z** and **R** are frequently used below.

Permutations on a given finite set of objects, with the **product** $P_1 P_2$ of two permutations defined as the permutation resulting from P_1 followed by P_2, constitute a group. The reader may verify the group axioms and decide whether the group is commutative.

A **set of generators** of a multiplicative [additive] group 𝔊 is a set $\{\gamma\} \subset$ 𝔊 of elements of 𝔊 such that each element of 𝔊 is expressible as a product [sum] of the elements $\{\gamma\}$ and their inverses [negatives].

(*C*) *We confine attention, save where the contrary is explicitly stated, to groups admitting a finite number of generators.* Such groups are described as **finitely generated**.

Let $\mathfrak{G}$ be a multiplicative group with generators $(g_1, \ldots, g_n)$. Then, by definition, each element $g \in \mathfrak{G}$ can be expressed in the form

$$(A.4) \quad g = g_{i_1}^{\varepsilon_1} \ldots g_{i_r}^{\varepsilon_r} \qquad (\varepsilon_j = +1 \text{ or } -1; \; i_j \in 1, \ldots, n; \; j = 1, \ldots, r).$$

In a product like that on the right of (A.4), one can eliminate factors equal to the identity, and one can combine consecutive factors with equal subscripts, using (A.3) and the easily proved relation $g^m g^n = g^{m+n}$ $(m, n \in \mathbf{Z})$ to reduce (A.4) to the form

$$(A.5) \quad \begin{aligned} & g = g_{j_1}^{m_1} \ldots g_{j_k}^{m_k} \text{ or } 1, \text{ where} \\ & j_h \neq j_{h-1}, \qquad m_h \in \mathbf{Z}, \qquad g_{j_h} \neq 1 \qquad (h = 1, \ldots, k). \end{aligned}$$

We refer to (A.5) as the **reduced form** of (A.4), **relative to** $(g_1, \ldots, g_n)$. Thus $g = g_3 g_3 g_3^{-1} g_4 g_4 g_3^{-1}$ reduces to $g = g_3 g_4^2 g_3^{-1}$.

The inverse of (A.5) is easily seen to be

$$(A.6) \quad g^{-1} = g_{j_k}^{-m_k} \ldots g_{j_1}^{-m_1}.$$

(*D*) In the case of an abelian additive group $\mathfrak{G}$ with n generators $(g_1, \ldots, g_n)$, an arbitrary element $g = \Sigma_{j=1}^r \varepsilon_j g_{i_j}$ similarly reduces, with the aid of permutations of terms and the property $mg + ng = (m + n)g$, to a unique **reduced form relative to** $(g_1, \ldots, g_n)$, namely

$$(A.7) \quad g = \sum_{i=1}^n m_i g_i \qquad (m_i \in \mathbf{Z}).$$

(*E*) The **free multiplicative group with n generators** $(g_1, \ldots, g_n)$ is the group consisting of all elements expressible in the form (A.4), two elements being **equal** if and only if they have identical reduced forms (A.5) relative to $(g_1, \ldots, g_n)$. The **free abelian additive group with n generators** is defined in the same way, save that (A.4) is put in additive form and its reduced form is (A.7) instead of (A.5).

A group $\mathfrak{G}$ (multiplicative or additive) with generators $(g_1, \ldots, g_n)$ can be specified by supplementing the axioms by a set of **group relations**, each of which asserts the equality of two elements g and h whose reduced forms are not identical, thus:

$$(A.8) \quad g_{i_1}^{m_1} \ldots g_{i_k}^{m_k} = g_{j_1}^{n_1} \ldots g_{j_k}^{n_k} \text{ (subscripts from the set } (1, \ldots, n)).$$

This relation can be written as

$$(A.9) \quad g_{i_1}^{m_1} \ldots g_{i_k}^{m_k} g_{j_k}^{-n_k} \ldots g_{j_1}^{-n_1} = 1$$

where the reduced form of the left side is not 1.

(F) *Thus the set of all group relations is equivalent to the set of all representations of the unit element 1 or, in the additive case, of the zero element 0.* A set of group relations

$$\text{(a)} \quad \prod_{h=1}^{r_j} (g_{i_{jh}})^{m_{i_{jh}}} = 1 \qquad (j = 1, 2, \ldots, k) \qquad \text{(multiplicative case), or}$$

(A.10)

$$\text{(b)} \quad \sum_{h=1}^{r_j} m_{i_{jh}} g_{i_{jh}} = 0 \qquad (j = 1, \ldots, k) \qquad \text{(additive case),}$$

is **independent** if no one of them is a consequence of the others. If one of them is a consequence of the others, it will be said to **depend on** them.

For example, in the following set of relations, for an abelian additive group,

$$\text{(a)} \qquad 2g_1 + 3g_2 - 2g_3 = 0,$$

(A.11) $$\text{(b)} \quad g_1 - 4g_2 + 3g_3 + g_4 = 0,$$

$$\text{(c)} \qquad 8g_1 + g_2 + 2g_4 = 0,$$

each pair is independent, but (c) follows from (a) and (b).

(G) A set of group relations on which all other group relations for $\mathfrak{G}$ depend is a set of **defining relations** of $\mathfrak{G}$. *A group is determined by a set of generators and defining relations.*

A group with just one generator g is described as **cyclic.** It is necessarily abelian. If there are no group relations, its elements are

(A.12)
$$1, g^{\pm 1}, g^{\pm 2}, \ldots \qquad \text{(multiplicative)}$$

$$0, \pm g, \pm 2g, \ldots \qquad \text{(additive)}$$

and the group is called the **free** cyclic group. If there exist group relations, then all such relations are easily seen to depend on a single relation $g^m = 1$ or $mg = 0$.

The elements are then

(A.13) $$1, g, g^2, g^3, \ldots, g^{m-1} \text{ or } 0, g, 2g, \ldots, (m-1)g,$$

and the group is described as **cyclic** of **order** m (Exercise 1).

Given a positive integer m, x is said to be **congruent** to y **modulo** m (abbreviated mod m), where x and y are integers, if and only if

(A.14) $$x - y = km \text{ for some integer } k.$$

This relationship is symbolized thus:

(A.15) $$x \equiv y \text{ mod } m.$$

A **residue class** mod m consists of all integers congruent mod m to a given integer. Let the residue class mod m containing a number j be denoted by $\bar{j}$.

(H) There exist exactly m different residue classes mod $m : \bar{0}, \bar{1},$ $\bar{2}, \ldots, \overline{m-1}$. They constitute an abelian group with $\bar{j} + \bar{k} = \overline{j+k}$ as the group operation. This group is denoted by $\mathbf{Z}_m$ and called the group of integers mod m. It is cyclic of order m (Exercise 2). The additive group $\mathbf{Z}$ of the integers is free cyclic.

The statements in *(H)* illustrate that an element of a group may be an entire equivalence class of objects. Such is the case in most topological applications.

EXERCISES

1. Show that, if m is a positive integer, then

(A.16) $$A = e^{\frac{2\pi i}{m}} = \cos \frac{2\pi}{m} + i \sin \frac{2\pi}{m} \qquad (i^2 = -1)$$

generates a cyclic group of order m, with multiplication of complex numbers as the group operation.

2. Establish the three statements in *(H)*.

A–2. Homomorphisms and Isomorphisms

Just as we consider mappings of a set into or onto a set (Art. 3–1), so we consider mappings of a group $\mathfrak{G}$ into [onto] a group $\overline{\mathfrak{G}}$, restricted by the requirement that the product or sum of two elements of the first group shall map onto the product or sum of their images. Let $\bar{g} \in \overline{\mathfrak{G}}$ denote the image of $g \in \mathfrak{G}$. The requirement just stated can then be symbolized thus:

(A.17) $\qquad \bar{g}_3 = \bar{g}_1 \bar{g}_2$ if $g_3 = g_1 g_2$ or $\bar{g}_3 = \bar{g}_1 + \bar{g}_2$ if $g_3 = g_1 + g_2$.

A mapping of $\mathfrak{G}$ into $\overline{\mathfrak{G}}$ satisfying this condition is called a **homomorphism** of $\mathfrak{G}$ into $\overline{\mathfrak{G}}$. A homomorphism is called an **isomorphism** if it is onto (Chapter 3) and one-to-one. An isomorphism can be described as a homomorphism with an inverse which is also a homomorphism. A group $\mathfrak{G}$ is **isomorphic** to a group $\overline{\mathfrak{G}}$ if it is possible to establish an isomorphism of $\mathfrak{G}$ onto $\overline{\mathfrak{G}}$. The relation of being isomorphic is an equivalence relation. A **group invariant** is a property which, if possessed by a group $\mathfrak{G}$, is possessed by each group isomorphic to $\mathfrak{G}$. To say that two groups **have the same structure** is to say that they are isomorphic.

A set of properties will be said to **characterize** a group $\mathfrak{G}$ or to **determine its structure** if each group sharing all these properties with $\mathfrak{G}$ is isomorphic to $\mathfrak{G}$.

A **subgroup** of a group $\mathfrak{G}$ is a group $\mathfrak{G}_0$ whose elements all belong to $\mathfrak{G}$ and whose group operation is the same as that of $\mathfrak{G}$. We symbolize this relation by $\mathfrak{G}_0 \subset \mathfrak{G}$. If the elements of $\mathfrak{G}_0$ are a proper subset* of those of $\mathfrak{G}$, then $\mathfrak{G}_0$ is a **proper subgroup** of $\mathfrak{G}$.

Let $\mathfrak{G}$ be an additive group and $\mathfrak{N}$ a subgroup of $\mathfrak{G}$. Then $B_2 \in \mathfrak{G}$ is **congruent** mod $\mathfrak{N}$ to $B_1 \in \mathfrak{G}$, symbolized by

(A.18) $$B_2 \equiv B_1 \bmod \mathfrak{N},$$

if $B_2 - B_1$, hence also $B_1 - B_2$, is an element of $\mathfrak{N}$.

(A) The relation (A.18) is an equivalence relation. The set of all elements congruent mod $\mathfrak{N}$ to $B \in \mathfrak{G}$ will be denoted by $\bar{B}$ and is the **coset** of $\mathfrak{N}$ containing B. Thus $\bar{0}$ is the set of elements of $\mathfrak{N}$.

THEOREM 1. **Let B_1, B_2 be two elements of an abelian additive group $\mathfrak{G}$ with subgroup $\mathfrak{N}$. If $C_1 \in \bar{B}_1$ and $C_2 \in \bar{B}_2$, then $C_1 + C_2 \in \overline{B_1 + B_2}$. The cosets of $\mathfrak{G}$ mod $\mathfrak{N}$ form an abelian group, with addition defined by $\bar{B}_1 + \bar{B}_2 = \overline{B_1 + B_2}$.**

Proof. The relation $C_i \in \bar{B}_i$ $(i = 1, 2)$ means that there exist elements $A_i \in \mathfrak{N}$ such that $C_i = B_i + A_i$. Hence $C_1 + C_2 = B_1 + B_2 + A_1 + A_2 \in \overline{B_1 + B_2}$, since $A_1 + A_2 \in \mathfrak{N}$. This proves the first part of the theorem and verifies Axiom I. The rest of the proof is left to the reader (Exercise 7).

(B) The group defined in Theorem 1 is the **factor group** or **quotient group**

(A.19) $$\bar{\mathfrak{G}} = \mathfrak{G}/\mathfrak{N}.$$

It is sometimes called the **difference group** and denoted by $\mathfrak{G} - \mathfrak{N}$.

(C) Let $\mathfrak{G}$ and $\mathfrak{G}^1$ be abelian additive groups and let $h : \mathfrak{G} \to \mathfrak{G}^1$ be a homomorphism. The set $\mathfrak{N}$ of all elements of $\mathfrak{G}$ which map onto the unit element of $\mathfrak{G}^1$ is a subgroup of $\mathfrak{G}$, called the **kernel** of h. The homomorphism h can be interpreted as an isomorphism between $\mathfrak{G}/\mathfrak{N}$ and $h(\mathfrak{C})$ (Exercise 8).

Suppose that $\mathfrak{G}$ is defined by a set of generators $(A_1, \ldots, A_m)$ and a set of relations

(A.20) $$\varphi_i(A_1, \ldots, A_m) = 0 \qquad (i = 1, \ldots, r)$$

where $\varphi_i(A_1, \ldots, A_m)$ is a sum of multiples $k_i A_i$ $(k_i \in \mathbf{Z})$ of the generators A_i. Let $\mathfrak{N}$ be the subgroup of $\mathfrak{G}$ generated by a given set of elements $(X_1, \ldots, X_n)$, and let the X's be expressed in the form

(A.21) $$X_i = \theta_i(A_1, \ldots, A_m) \qquad (i = 1, \ldots, n),$$

which is possible, since the A's generate $\mathfrak{G}$.

THEOREM 2. **The factor group $\bar{\mathfrak{G}} = \mathfrak{G}/\mathfrak{N}$ is isomorphic to the additive group defined by generators $(A_1, \ldots, A_m)$ with relations (A.20) and**

(A.22) $$\theta_i(A_1, \ldots, A_m) = 0 \qquad (i = 1, \ldots, n).$$

* That is, if there exists an element in $\mathfrak{G}$ which is not in $\mathfrak{G}_0$.

Proof. In the first place, if $Y \in \mathfrak{N}$, then Y is expressible in terms of the X's, and if $Y \notin \mathfrak{N}$, then Y is not expressible in terms of the X's (Exercise 9). The proof can now be completed with the aid of (C) (Exercise 10).

THEOREM 3. **The adjunction to a set of defining relations (A.20) for an abelian group $\mathfrak{G}$ of a set of relations (A.22) yields a set of defining relations for a group isomorphic to $\mathfrak{G}/\mathfrak{N}$, where $\mathfrak{N}$ is the subgroup of $\mathfrak{G}$ generated by the elements $X_i = \theta_i(A_1, \ldots, A_m)$ $(i = 1, \ldots, n)$** (Exercise 11).

EXERCISES

3. (a) Show that the mapping $\mathbf{Z} \to \mathbf{Z}_m$ defined by $j \to \bar{j}$ is a homomorphism (see Art. A–1(H) for notation). (b) Define an isomorphism between $\mathbf{Z}_m$ and the group defined in Exercise 1.

4. Show that

$$b = e^{\frac{ki}{m}} \qquad (k, m \text{ are integers}; \ i^2 = -1),$$

with multiplication as operation, generates a group isomorphic to $\mathbf{Z}_m$ if and only if k and m are relatively prime.

5. Show that the multiples of an integer m constitute a subgroup of $\mathbf{Z}$, with addition, but that the odd numbers do not. Determine whether the odd numbers, with multiplication, are a group.

6. Prove the first and last sentences in (A).

7. Complete the proof of Theorem 1 by verifying Additive Group Axioms II–V.

8. Establish Statement (C).

9. Establish the first statement in the proof of Theorem 2.

10. Carry out the suggested completion of the proof of Theorem 2.

11. Prove Theorem 3.

A–3. The Structure of Finitely Generated Abelian Groups

(A) An abelian additive group $\mathfrak{F}$ is the (**internal direct**) **product***

$$(\text{A.23}) \qquad \mathfrak{F} = \mathfrak{F}_1 \times \mathfrak{F}_2 \times \cdots \times \mathfrak{F}_n$$

of the additive groups $\mathfrak{F}_1, \ldots, \mathfrak{F}_n$ if (1) $\mathfrak{F}_i \subset \mathfrak{F}$ $(i = 1, \ldots, n)$ and (2) each element of $\mathfrak{F}$ except 0 can be expressed in one and only one way in the form $A_{i_1} + A_{i_2} + \cdots + A_{i_n}$ where $A_{i_j} \in \mathfrak{F}_j$ $(j = 1, \ldots, n)$. The product of a given set of abelian additive groups $\mathfrak{F}_i$ $(i = 1, \ldots, n)$ is generated by the aggregate of the generators of the groups $\mathfrak{F}_i$ and has for a set of defining relations the aggregate of a collection of defining relations for the respective groups $\mathfrak{F}_i$.

---

* Sometimes called the **sum** $\mathfrak{F} = \mathfrak{F}_1 + \mathfrak{F}_2 + \cdots + \mathfrak{F}_n$.

(B) The factor group $\mathfrak{F}/\mathfrak{F}_i$ is isomorphic to $\mathfrak{F}_1 \times \cdots \times \mathfrak{F}_{i-1} \times \mathfrak{F}_{i+1} \times \cdots \times \mathfrak{F}_n$ (Exercise 12).

Let $\mathfrak{F}$ be an abelian additive group with a finite set $(A_1, \ldots, A_n)$ of generators. A general form for an element of $\mathfrak{F}$ is then

$$(A.24) \qquad\qquad A = \sum_{i=1}^{n} x_i A_i \qquad (x_i \text{ an integer}).$$

A group relation can be expressed thus:

$$(A.25) \qquad\qquad \sum_{i=1}^{n} y_i A_i = 0 \qquad (y_i \neq 0 \text{ for some } i).$$

(C) The free abelian group $\mathfrak{F}$ with n generators $(A_1, \ldots, A_n)$ is isomorphic to the additive group of integral vectors* in E^n (see also Exercise 13). A **basis** for $\mathfrak{F}$ is a subset of its elements in terms of which each of its elements is uniquely expressible.

THEOREM 4. **Each basis of $\mathfrak{F}$ consists of exactly n elements.**

Proof. The set $(A_1, \ldots, A_n)$ is a particular basis. Suppose $(B_1, \ldots, B_m)$ is also a basis. Then (see Exercise 14 for an example)

$$(A.26) \qquad \begin{aligned} \text{(a)} \quad & B_i = \sum_{j=1}^{n} x_{ij} A_j \qquad (i = 1, \ldots, m), \\ \text{(b)} \quad & A_j = \sum_{k=1}^{m} y_{jk} B_k \qquad (j = 1, \ldots, n). \end{aligned}$$

Suppose $m > n$. The rank† of the matrix (x_{ij}) cannot exceed n (the number of its columns) and is therefore less than the number m of equations in the set (A.26a). Therefore the right side of at least one of these equations, say the one for which $i = r$, is linearly dependent, with rational coefficients, on the right sides of the other equations in the set. But this means that, for some integer $k \neq 0$, kB_r equals a linear expression in the other B's. The element $A = kB_r$ of $\mathfrak{F}$ is then expressible in two different ways in terms of the B's, namely as kB_r and as the linear expression just mentioned, contradicting the definition of $(B_1, \ldots, B_m)$ as a basis. Hence $m \leq n$. By symmetry, $n \leq m$, and hence $m = n$.

COROLLARY. **Two finitely generated free abelian groups are isomorphic if and only if they have the same number of generators** (Exercise 15).

The reader unfamiliar with matrix theory should study, in some standard text, the definition of the **product** XY of two matrices,

---

* That is, vectors whose components are integers.

† We assume a basic familiarity with linear equations, with the use of determinants in solving them, and also with some of the fundamental properties of matrices.

where the number of columns equals the number of rows. He should note that matrix multiplication is not commutative (Exercise 16) and that it is associative; that is, $X(YZ) = (XY)Z$.

A one-row matrix is a **row vector** and a one-column matrix is a **column vector**. The elements are the **components** of the vector. If X is a row vector $(x_1 \ldots x_n)$ and Y is a column vector* $(y_1 \ldots y_n)'$, then $XY = \Sigma_{i=1}^n x_i y_i$, while YX is the $n \times n$ matrix $(y_i x_j)$ $(i = 1, \ldots, n; j = 1, \ldots, n)$.

If $(A_1, \ldots, A_n)$ and $(B_1, \ldots, B_n)$ are two bases for the free additive (abelian) group with n generators, then, by (A.26) with $m = n$,

$$\text{(A.27)} \qquad B_i = \sum_{k=1}^n \sum_{j=1}^n x_{ij} y_{jk} B_k \qquad (i = 1, \ldots, n).$$

By definition of **basis**, the right side reduces to B_i, so that, using the **Kronecker delta** δ_{ik},

$$\text{(A.28)} \quad \sum_{j=1}^n x_{ij} y_{jk} = \delta_{ik} = \begin{cases} 1 \text{ if } i = k \\ 0 \text{ if } i \neq k \end{cases} \qquad (i = 1, \ldots, n; k = 1, \ldots, n).$$

But this implies that the product of the determinants $|x_{ij}| \cdot |y_{jk}|$ is $|\delta_{ij}| = 1$; so that $|x_{ij}| = |y_{jk}| = +1$ or -1, since the x's, the y's, and hence the determinants are integers.

A square matrix is **unimodular** if its determinant is $+1$ or -1.

LEMMA 1. **The matrix of a change of basis in a free additive abelian group $\mathfrak{F}$ with n generators is a unimodular matrix of order n. Conversely, any unimodular matrix of order n is the matrix of a change of basis in $\mathfrak{F}$.**

The first part of this lemma has just been proved. The second part presents no difficulty.

Let $\mathfrak{N}$ be a subgroup of $\mathfrak{F}$. Let $N_1, \ldots, N_m$ be a set of generators of $\mathfrak{N}$, not necessarily independent, and consider their expressions

$$\text{(A.29)} \qquad N_i = \sum_{j=1}^n e_{ij} A_j \qquad (i = 1, \ldots, m)$$

in terms of the A's.

(D) The matrix (e_{ij}) of m rows and n columns uniquely determines the N_i, hence $\mathfrak{N}$, and hence the group

$$\text{(A.30)} \qquad \overline{\mathfrak{F}} = \mathfrak{F}/\mathfrak{N}.$$

The same $\overline{\mathfrak{F}}$ would be determined by any coefficient matrix corresponding to different choices of generators for $\mathfrak{F}$ and $\mathfrak{N}$.

* The symbol for a matrix, modified by a prime, will denote its transpose.

This suggests the concept of an **equivalence class** of matrices, two $m \times n$ matrices being **equivalent** if and only if each of them is the matrix of a set of relations of the form (A.29) expressing some set of m generators of $\mathfrak{N}$ in terms of some basis of $\mathfrak{F}$.

LEMMA 2. **Two matrices (e_{ij}) and (e'_{ij}) belong to the same equivalence class, as just defined, if**

$$(A.31) \qquad\qquad (e'_{ih}) = (y_{ik})(e_{kj})(x_{jh})$$

where (y_{ik}) and (x_{jh}) are unimodular matrices of orders m and n respectively.

Proof of Lemma. Lemma 2 is a consequence of Lemma 1 applied (1) to a change of basis

$$(A.32) \qquad\qquad A_j = \sum_{h=1}^{n} x_{jh} B_h \qquad (j = 1, \ldots, n)$$

in $\mathfrak{F}$ and (2) to a change of generators

$$(A.33) \qquad\qquad M_i = \sum_{k=1}^{m} y_{ik} N_k \qquad (i = 1, \ldots, n)$$

in $\mathfrak{N}$. The matrix (e'_{ih}) is then the matrix of the expression of the generators M_i of $\mathfrak{N}$ in terms of the generators B_h of $\mathfrak{F}$.

(*E*) By multiplying (e_{ij}) on the right by a unimodular matrix of order n, any of the following effects can be achieved: (a) the multiplication of a column by -1, (b) the interchange of columns j and k, (c) the replacement of column k by column k plus an integral multiple of column j $(j \neq k)$ (Exercise 17). None of these operations affects the rank of the matrix. Since we can also suppose (e_{ij}) multiplied on the left by the identity matrix (δ_{ij}) of order m without affecting the result, we see that the operations mentioned are of the form (A.31), and hence transform (e_{ij}) into an equivalent matrix.

(*F*) Statement (*E*) holds for (e_{ij}) multiplied on the left by a unimodular matrix of order m and "columns" replaced by "rows" throughout.

THEOREM 5. **Let γ be the rank of the matrix (e_{ij}) of equations (A.29). Then (e_{ij}) is equivalent to an $m \times n$ matrix whose elements are all zeros except for the first γ elements on the main diagonal, which are positive integers $(\tau_1, \tau_2, \ldots, \tau_\gamma)$ such that τ_{i+1} divides τ_i $(i = 1, \ldots, \gamma - 1)$.**

Proof. If each of the e_{ij} equals zero, then $\mathfrak{N}$ contains only the null element of $\mathfrak{F}$. Hence $\overline{\mathfrak{F}} = \mathfrak{F}$ and (e_{ij}) is already in the specified form. We turn to the case where at least one e_{ij} is not zero.

(G) In proving Theorem 5, we lose no generality by assuming for (e_{ij}) any set of properties possessed by an equivalent matrix. We will use this principle to justify some convenient assumptions.

Assumption I. $e_{11} > 0$ and e_{11} is a minimum among the absolute values of the non-zero terms of (e_{ij}).

Justification. Let e_{gh} be a term of minimum absolute value among the non-zero terms of (e_{ij}). If $e_{gh} < 0$, change signs throughout row g. Next interchange rows 1 and g, then columns 1 and h. This leads to a matrix equivalent to (e_{ij}) and satisfying Assumption I.

The **greatest common divisor** of a set of integers is the largest integer which divides all of them.

LEMMA 3. **Either e_{11} divides each element e_{ij} or there exists an equivalent matrix (e'_{ij}) containing an element e'_{st} such that $0 < e'_{st} < e_{11}$.**

Case 1. The first row of (e_{ij}) contains an element e_{1h} not divisible by e_{11}. Let je_{11} be the largest integral multiple, positive or negative, of e_{11} such that $e_{1h} - je_{11} > 0$. Then,

(A.34) $e_{1h} = je_{11} + e'_{1h}$ where $e'_{1h} \in (1, 2, \ldots, e_{11} - 1)$

Hence, in this case, the replacement (see *(E)*) of column h by (col h) $-$ j(col 1) leads to an equivalent matrix containing a positive element $e'_{1h} < e_{11}$.

Case 2. The first column contains an element e_{h1} not divisible by e_{11}. This case is treated like Case 1, with rows replacing columns.

Case 3. The first row and column are both made up of multiples of e_{11}, but there exists an element e_{st} not divisible by e_{11}. By adding a suitable positive or negative multiple of row 1 to row s, we obtain an equivalent matrix in which the element in column 1 and row s is 0. Let the new row s be added to row 1 to obtain a new row 1, in which e_{11} is unchanged and a term of the form $(e_{st} + ke_{11})$, with k an integer, appears in row 1. This reduces Case 3 to Case 2.

Assumption II. e_{11} divides every element e_{ij}.

Justification. If e_{11} does not divide all the e_{ij}, let Lemma 3 be applied to obtain an equivalent matrix (e'_{ij}) with some positive element less than e_{11}. By Assumption I, this element can be assumed to be e'_{11}. If (e'_{ij}) does not satisfy Assumption II, there similarly exists an equivalent matrix (e''_{ij}) with $e_{11} > e'_{11} > e''_{11} > 0$. This process can be repeated only a finite number of times, since the number of integers between e_{11} and 0 is finite. Hence there exists a matrix (e^*_{ij}) equivalent to (e_{ij}), where $e^*_{11} > 0$ and e^*_{11} divides every e^*_{ij}, and the greatest common divisor of the elements of (e^*_{ij}) is the same as that of (e_{ij}).

We are now ready to complete the proof of Theorem 5. By subtracting suitable multiples of the first column from the other columns, then multiples of the first row from the other rows, let (e_{ij}) be reduced to the form

(A.35)

$$\begin{pmatrix} e_{11} & 0 & 0 & \cdots & 0 \\ 0 & e_{22} & e_{23} & \cdots & e_{2n} \\ 0 & e_{32} & e_{33} & \cdots & e_{3n} \\ \cdot & \cdot & \cdot & & \cdot \\ \cdot & \cdot & \cdot & & \cdot \\ \cdot & \cdot & \cdot & & \cdot \\ 0 & e_{m2} & e_{m3} & \cdots & e_{mn} \end{pmatrix}$$

where e_{11} divides all the other elements.

By operations involving only columns 2 to n and rows 2 to m, following the procedure just used to reduce (e_{ij}) to (A.35), let (e_{ij}) be next reduced to the form

(A.36)

$$\begin{pmatrix} e_{11} & 0 & 0 & \cdots & 0 \\ 0 & e_{22} & 0 & \cdots & 0 \\ 0 & 0 & e_{33} & \cdots & e_{3n} \\ \cdot & \cdot & \cdot & & \cdot \\ \cdot & \cdot & \cdot & & \cdot \\ \cdot & \cdot & \cdot & & \cdot \\ 0 & 0 & e_{m3} & \cdots & e_{mn} \end{pmatrix}$$

where e_{22} is the greatest common divisor of the terms other than e_{11} in (A.35). Hence e_{22} is divisible by e_{11}.

Continuing recurrently the process whereby (e_{ij}) was reduced first to (A.35) and then to (A.36), we reduce (e_{ij}) to a matrix in which all elements are zero, save the first γ elements on the main diagonal, which are positive integers $e_{11}, \ldots, e_{\gamma\gamma}$ where e_{ii} divides $e_{i+1, i+1}$ ($i = 1, \ldots, \gamma - 1$). The non-zero elements must be γ in number, since the operations we have used (see (E) and (F)) preserve rank. By suitable interchanges of rows and of columns, we can reverse the order of the e's, then let $e_{ii} = \tau_{\gamma-i+1}$, to obtain the form specified in Theorem 5, which we will call the **normal form** of (e_{ij}). It will be shown (see proof of Theorem 8 below) that the numbers $(\tau_1, \ldots, \tau_\gamma)$, called the **invariant factors** of (e_{ij}), are independent of the particular way in which (e_{ij}) was reduced to normal form.

(H) By Lemma 2, (e_{ij}) can be transformed into normal form by multiplying on the right by a unimodular matrix $X = (x_{jh})$ of order n and on the left by a unimodular matrix $Y = (y_{ki})$ of order m, where X and Y are the matrices of appropriate changes of generators in the groups $\mathfrak{F}$ and $\mathfrak{N}$ respectively. Let $(B_1, \ldots, B_n)$ be the new basis of $\mathfrak{F}$.

Then, since the transformed matrix is the matrix of the expression for the new generators of $\mathfrak{N}$ in terms of the B's, and any generator equal to zero can obviously be dropped, the new generators of $\mathfrak{N}$ are $(\tau_1 B_1, \ldots, \tau_\gamma B_\gamma)$.

Two elements

$$(A.37) \qquad A = \sum_{i=1}^{n} \alpha_i B_i, \qquad B = \sum_{i=1}^{n} \beta_i B_i$$

of $\mathfrak{F}$ belong to the same coset of $\mathfrak{F}$ mod $\mathfrak{N}$ if and only if their **difference**, defined as the first plus the negative of the second, belongs to $\mathfrak{N}$; that is, if and only if, for some integers $(\lambda_1, \ldots, \lambda_\gamma)$,

$$(A.38) \qquad \sum_{i=1}^{n} (\beta_i - \alpha_i) B_i = \sum_{i=1}^{\gamma} \lambda_i \tau_i B_i.$$

Since the B's are a basis, (A.38) holds if and only if

$$(A.39) \qquad \begin{aligned} \beta_i - \alpha_i &= \lambda_i \tau_i \qquad (i = 1, \ldots, \gamma), \\ \beta_j - \alpha_j &= 0 \qquad (j = \gamma + 1, \ldots, n). \end{aligned}$$

Since the only essential property of the λ's is that they are integers, their precise values being irrelevant, we arrive at the following statement.

Two elements B and A of $\mathfrak{F}$ belong to the same coset of $\mathfrak{F}$ mod $\mathfrak{N}$ if and only if, in the notation of (A.37),

$$(A.40) \qquad \begin{aligned} &\text{(a)} \ \ \alpha_i \equiv \beta_i \bmod \tau_i \qquad (i = 1, \ldots, \gamma), \\ &\text{(b)} \ \ \alpha_j = \beta_j \qquad\qquad\ (j = \gamma + 1, \ldots, n). \end{aligned}$$

The τ's are a sequence of positive integers each divisible by the next. Hence $\tau_j = 1$ implies $\tau_{j+1} = \cdots = \tau_\gamma = 1$. This means that there exists a number ρ ($0 \le \rho \le \gamma$) such that

$$(A.41) \qquad \begin{aligned} \tau_i &> 1 \qquad (i = 1, \ldots, \rho), \\ \tau_j &= 1 \qquad (j = \rho + 1, \ldots, \gamma). \end{aligned}$$

Every pair of integers α, β satisfies $\alpha \equiv \beta \bmod 1$. Since the last $\gamma - \rho$ conditions in (A.40a) accordingly impose no restriction on the α's and β's, (A.40) is equivalent to

$$(A.42) \qquad \begin{aligned} \alpha_i &\equiv \beta_i \bmod \tau_i \qquad (i = 1, \ldots, \rho \le \gamma), \\ \alpha_j &= \beta_j \qquad\qquad\ (j = \gamma + 1, \ldots, n). \end{aligned}$$

This proves the following result.

LEMMA 4. **Let the symbol for an element C of $\mathfrak{F}$, modified by a bar, denote the coset $\bar{C}$ of C in $\mathfrak{F}$ mod $\mathfrak{N}$, so that $\bar{C}$ is a typical element of $\mathfrak{F}/\mathfrak{N}$. Then each $\bar{C}$ can be expressed in exactly one way in the form**

$$(A.43) \qquad \bar{C} = \sum_{i=1}^{\rho} u_i \bar{B}_i + \sum_{j=\gamma+1}^{n} v_j \bar{B}_j \qquad (\text{see } (H) \text{ for the } B\text{'s})$$

where

$$u_i \in \mathbf{Z}_{\tau_i} \qquad \text{(integers mod } \tau_i\text{)} \qquad (i = 1, \ldots, \rho),$$

(A.44)

$$v_j \in \mathbf{Z} \qquad \text{(integers)}.$$

THEOREM 6. **If $\overline{\mathfrak{F}}$ is an abelian group with a finite number of generators $\bar{A}_1, \ldots, \bar{A}_m$, then $\overline{\mathfrak{F}}$ is isomorphic to some factor group $\mathfrak{F}/\mathfrak{N}$, where $\mathfrak{F}$ is a free abelian group.**

Outline of Proof. In particular, let $\mathfrak{F}$ be the free abelian group with m generators $A_1, \ldots, A_m$. Let each element $\Sigma_{i=1}^m a_i A_i$ of $\mathfrak{F}$ be mapped onto the element $\Sigma_{i=1}^m a_i \bar{A}_i$. The resulting map is a homomorphism of $\mathfrak{F}$ onto $\overline{\mathfrak{F}}$. The elements of $\mathfrak{F}$ which map onto the null element of $\overline{\mathfrak{F}}$ constitute a subgroup $\mathfrak{N}$ of $\mathfrak{F}$. The elements of $\overline{\mathfrak{F}}$ are images of the cosets of $\mathfrak{F}$ mod $\mathfrak{N}$, and $\overline{\mathfrak{F}}$ is isomorphic to $\mathfrak{F}/\mathfrak{N}$ (Exercise 18).

An element A of an additive group, abelian or not, is **of order** τ, if τ is the smallest positive integer such that $\tau A = \emptyset$, the null element of A. If no such integer exists, A is **of infinite order**. A similar definition of **order** applies to multiplicative groups, with $A^\tau = 1$ replacing $\tau A = \emptyset$.

THEOREM 7. **A finitely generated abelian group $\overline{\mathfrak{F}}$ is the product of (1) a number $\beta \geq 0$ of free cyclic groups and (2) a number $\rho \geq 0$ of finite cyclic groups of orders $\tau_1, \ldots, \tau_\rho$ where τ_{i+1} divides τ_i ($i = 1, \ldots, \rho - 1$) and all the τ's exceed 1.**

This theorem is a consequence of Theorem 6 and Lemma 4, with $\beta = n - \gamma$.

(*I*) The number β is the difference, $\beta = n - \gamma$, between the number, n, of columns of (e_{ij}) and the rank, γ, of (e_{ij}). It is called the **Betti number** of $\overline{\mathfrak{F}}$. The numbers τ_i are, as mentioned above, the invariant factors of (e_{ij}) exceeding 1. They are called the **torsion coefficients** of $\overline{\mathfrak{F}}$. The terminology is motivated by the geometric significance of these numbers in topological applications.

THEOREM 8. **Two finitely generated abelian groups are isomorphic if and only if they have the same Betti numbers and torsion coefficients.**

Proof. From Theorem 7 it follows that the Betti number and the torsion coefficients determine the structure of a finitely generated abelian group $\overline{\mathfrak{F}}$. It remains to prove the following.

(*J*) The numbers β and $(\tau_1, \ldots, \tau_\rho)$ of Theorem 7 are uniquely determined by $\overline{\mathfrak{F}}$; in other words, if $\overline{\mathfrak{F}}$ is expressed in a different way as the product of β' free cyclic groups and ρ' finite cyclic groups of orders $\tau_1', \ldots, \tau_{\rho'}'$ where τ_{i+1}' divides τ_i' ($i = 1, \ldots, \rho' - 1$) and $\tau_{\rho'}' > 1$, then

(A.45)   (a) $\beta' = \beta$ (b) $\rho' = \rho$ (c) $\tau_i' = \tau_i$ ($i = 1, \ldots, \rho$).

For simplicity, we replace $\bar{B}_{\gamma+j}$ by $\bar{C}_j$ ($j = 1, \ldots, \beta$) in the notation of Lemma 4, and denote (1) with $(\bar{C}_1, \ldots, \bar{C}_\beta)$ a set of generators of the free cyclic groups of Theorem 7 and (2) with $(\bar{B}_1, \ldots, \bar{B}_\rho)$ a set of generators of the cyclic groups of orders $(\tau_1, \ldots, \tau_\rho)$. We similarly denote with $(\bar{C}'_1, \ldots, \bar{C}'_{\beta'}, \bar{B}'_1, \ldots, \bar{B}'_{\rho'})$ the generators of a second expression for $\overline{\mathfrak{F}}$, as suggested in (J).

We now adapt an argument from Veblen's book ([V, pp. 129–130]).

(K) Condition (A.45) is equivalent to the following: For each integer r, the number of generators in $\{\bar{C}, \bar{B}\} = (\bar{C}_1, \ldots, \bar{C}_\beta, \bar{B}_1, \ldots, \bar{B}_\rho)$ each of order $>r$ equals the number of generators in $\{\bar{C}', \bar{B}'\} = (\bar{C}'_1, \ldots, \bar{C}'_{\beta'}, \bar{B}'_1, \ldots, \bar{B}'_{\rho'})$ each of order $>r$.

To verify (K), note first that β and β' are the numbers of generators in $\{\bar{C}, \bar{B}\}$ and $\{\bar{C}', \bar{B}'\}$ respectively of orders $> \max(\tau_1, \tau'_1)$. The rest of the argument is relegated to Exercise 19.

Assume the theorem false. Then $\{\bar{C}', \bar{B}'\}$ exists, as described above, such that for some r, the number of generators in $\{\bar{C}', \bar{B}'\}$ of orders $>r$ is unequal to (and we assume it greater than) the number of generators in $\{\bar{C}, \bar{B}\}$ of orders greater than r. The respective generators of orders exceeding r are as follows, for some k and k':

(A.46)

(a) $\bar{C}_1, \ldots, \bar{C}_\beta, \bar{B}_1, \ldots, \bar{B}_k$ $\qquad (\tau_k > r, \tau_{k+1} \leq r)$

(b) $\bar{C}'_1, \ldots, \bar{C}'_{\beta'}, \bar{B}'_1, \ldots, \bar{B}'_{k'}$ $\qquad (\tau'_{k'} > r, \tau'_{k'+1} \leq r)$

where $\beta' + k' > \beta + k$.

Because $\{B, C\}$ are generators, we have

(A.47)
$$\bar{C}'_h = \sum_{i=1}^{\beta} v_{hi}\bar{C}_i + \sum_{j=1}^{\rho} u_{hj}\bar{B}_j \qquad (h = 1, \ldots, \beta') \qquad u_{hj} \in \mathbf{Z}_{\tau_j}, v_{hi} \in \mathbf{Z},$$

$$\bar{B}'_t = \sum_{j=1}^{\rho} w_{tj}\bar{B}_j \qquad\qquad (t = 1, \ldots, k') \qquad w_{tj} \in \mathbf{Z}_{\tau_j}.$$

There are $\beta' + k' > \beta + k$ equations in the set (A.47). Hence there exists a set of $\beta' + k'$ integers $(r_1, \ldots, r_{\beta'}, s_1, \ldots, s_{k'})$, not all zero, such that, if we multiply the equations (A.47) by these respective integers and add the results, the coefficients of $(\bar{C}_1, \ldots, \bar{C}_\beta, \bar{B}_1, \ldots, \bar{B}_k)$ all reduce to zero; that is,

(A.48) $\qquad \displaystyle\sum_{h=1}^{\beta'} r_h\bar{C}'_h + \sum_{t=1}^{k'} s_t\bar{B}'_t = \sum_{j=k+1}^{\rho} \left(\sum_{h=1}^{\beta'} r_h u_{hj} + \sum_{t=1}^{k'} s_t w_{tj} \right) \bar{B}_j.$

We can so select the numbers $(r_1, \ldots, r_{\beta'}, s_1, \ldots, s_{k'})$ that 1 is the largest integer dividing all of them. Since the order of $\bar{B}_j$ divides $\bar{\tau}_{k+1}$ $(j = k+1, \ldots, \rho)$,

(A.49) $\qquad \displaystyle\sum_{h=1}^{\beta'} \bar{\tau}_{k+1}r_h\bar{C}'_h + \sum_{t=1}^{k'} \bar{\tau}_{k+1}s_t\bar{B}'_t = \emptyset.$

Since $\overline{\mathfrak{F}}$ is the direct product of the groups generated by the $\bar{C}'_h$, of infinite order, and the $\bar{B}'_t$, it follows that, in (A.49), $\bar{\tau}_{k+1}r_h = 0$, hence $r_h = 0$ $(h = 1, \ldots, \beta')$; and $\bar{\tau}_{k+1}s_t \equiv 0 \bmod \bar{\tau}'_t$ since $\bar{\tau}'_t$ is the order of $\bar{B}'_t (t = 1, \ldots, k')$. But this implies $\bar{\tau}_{k+1} s_t \equiv 0 \bmod \bar{\tau}'_{k'} > r$, since $\bar{\tau}'_{k'}$ divides $\bar{\tau}'_t$ $(t = 1, \ldots, k')$. Since all the r_h's are zero, the s_t's are not all zero and they have 1 as highest common factor. Therefore $(\bar{\tau}_{k+1} s_1, \ldots, \bar{\tau}_{k+1} s_{k'})$ has $\bar{\tau}_{k+1} \leq r$ as highest common factor, contradicting the set of relations $\bar{\tau}_{k+1} s_t \equiv 0 \bmod \bar{\tau}'_{k'} > r$ $(t = 1, \ldots, k')$. Hence the theorem is true.

EXERCISES

12. Prove (B). *Suggestion:* First discuss the cosets mod $\mathfrak{F}_i$ of an element of $\mathfrak{F}_j$.

13. Show that a free abelian group with n generators is the product of n free cyclic groups.

14. Show that $B_1 = 4A_1 - 5A_2$, $B_2 = 3A_1 - 4A_2$ is a basis for the free abelian additive group generated by A_1 and A_2.

15. Prove the corollary to Theorem 4.

16. Find the product matrix XY and, if defined, YX if

(a) $X = \begin{pmatrix} 2 & 1 & -2 & 1 \\ 0 & 5 & 4 & 1 \\ -3 & 7 & 0 & 1 \end{pmatrix}$, $Y = \begin{pmatrix} 1 & 2 & 0 & -1 \\ 2 & 1 & 0 & 1 \\ 3 & 2 & 1 & -2 \\ 4 & 1 & 1 & 1 \end{pmatrix}$;

(b) $X = \begin{pmatrix} 1 & 1 & 0 & 0 & 0 & 0 \\ 0 & 0 & 1 & 1 & 1 & 0 \\ 0 & 0 & 0 & 0 & 0 & 1 \end{pmatrix}$, $Y = \begin{pmatrix} 1 & 0 & 0 & 0 & 0 \\ 1 & 0 & 0 & 0 & 0 \\ 0 & 1 & 1 & 0 & 0 \\ 0 & 1 & 0 & 1 & 0 \\ 0 & 0 & 1 & 1 & 0 \\ 0 & 0 & 0 & 0 & 1 \end{pmatrix}$ (using mod 2 operations);

(c) $X = \begin{pmatrix} 2 & 1 & -2 \\ 5 & 1 & 4 \\ -3 & 7 & 1 \end{pmatrix}$, $Y = \begin{pmatrix} 2 & 1 & 1 \\ 3 & 2 & -1 \\ 4 & 1 & 1 \end{pmatrix}$.

17. Prove all parts of (E) and of (F).

18. Write out the outlined proof of Theorem 6.

19. Complete the proof of (K). *Suggestion:* Consider the implications as r decreases from max (τ_1, τ'_1) to 1.

A–4. Integral Modules, Contravariant and Covariant Components

The homology theory of a finite complex K is concerned with certain factor groups of abelian groups. All these factor groups are defined (Chapter 5) in terms of the so-called **chain** groups $\mathfrak{C}_k$ of K ($k = 0, 1, 2, \ldots$), where $\mathfrak{C}_k$ is the free abelian group generated by the oriented k-simplexes of K. The development of homology theory involves changes of basis in $\mathfrak{C}_k$. As background material, we discuss some of the properties of a free abelian group with a specified initial basis.

By the **integral module** $[s] = [s_1, \ldots, s_\alpha]$ we mean the free abelian group with basis $\{s\} = (s_1, \ldots, s_\alpha)$ and with integral coefficients. The particular basis $\{s\}$ is called the **initial basis** of $[s]$. The situation is much the same as when we work with a euclidean space R having a specified rectangular cartesian coordinate system and introduce other coordinate systems, skew or rectangular, by transformations of coordinates. Indeed, we can interpret $[s]$ as the additive group of integral vectors in R^α.

The scalar product $(C \cdot D)$ of two elements

$$\text{(A.50)} \quad \text{(a) } C = \sum_{i=1}^{\alpha} a^i s_i, \quad \text{(b) } D = \sum_{i=1}^{\alpha} b^i s_i \quad (a^i, b^i \text{ integers}),$$

of the integral module $[s]$ is the integer

$$\text{(A.51)} \quad (C \cdot D) = \sum_{i=1}^{\alpha} a^i b^i.$$

If the initial basis is interpreted as an orthogonal set of unit vectors in R^α, then $(C \cdot D)$ equals the product of the lengths of C and D by the cosine of the angle between them. Thus $(C \cdot D) = 0$ if and only if the vectors C and D are perpendicular or if one of them is zero.

For our purposes, however, it is more relevant to note that the scalar product $(C \cdot D)$ has important interpretations when C and D are appropriate elements of certain chain groups (see Art. 5–9, for example).

(A) The scalar product is clearly commutative, $(C \cdot D) = (D \cdot C)$, and linear, $(C \cdot (D_1 + D_2)) = (C \cdot D_1) + (C \cdot D_2)$, $(C_1 + C_2) \cdot D = (C_1 \cdot D) + (C_2 \cdot D)$.

According to Theorem 4, any basis for $[s]$ has just α elements. Let $\{t\} = (t_1, \ldots, t_\alpha)$ be an arbitrary basis for $[s]$, and consider the expression

$$\text{(A.52)} \quad C = \sum_{i=1}^{\alpha} c^i t_i$$

for an arbitrary element $C \in [s]$ in terms of $\{t\}$. The coefficients $(c^1, \ldots, c^\alpha)$ are called the **contravariant components** of C relative to $\{t\}$. They are merely the coordinates of the terminal point of C relative to the basis $\{t\}$, when C is interpreted as a vector with initial point at the origin. They are referred to as **contravariant** because of the way they **are** transformed corresponding to a change of basis, in comparison with the transformation of the **covariant components** of C **relative to** $\{t\}$, the latter being defined as the numbers

(A.53) $c_j = (C \cdot t_j) = (t_j \cdot C)$.

Note the use of superscripts and subscripts to distinguish between covariant and contravariant components.

Relative to the initial basis $\{s\}$, the contravariant and covariant components of a vector

(A.54) $C = b^1 s_1 + \cdots + b^\alpha s_\alpha$

are the same, since $(C \cdot s_i) = b^i$. In order to study their behavior under changes of basis, consider a typical such change $t_j = \Sigma\, a_{ji} s_i$, which is expressible also in the following matrix form:

(A.55)
$$\begin{pmatrix} t_1 \\ \cdot \\ \cdot \\ \cdot \\ t_\alpha \end{pmatrix} = A \begin{pmatrix} s_1 \\ \cdot \\ \cdot \\ \cdot \\ s_\alpha \end{pmatrix} \quad \text{with inverse} \quad \begin{pmatrix} s_1 \\ \cdot \\ \cdot \\ \cdot \\ s_\alpha \end{pmatrix} = A^{-1} \begin{pmatrix} t_1 \\ \cdot \\ \cdot \\ \cdot \\ t_\alpha \end{pmatrix}.$$

According to Lemma 1, A is unimodular.

The vector C can accordingly be formulated as follows:

(A.56) $C = (b^1 \dots b^\alpha) \begin{pmatrix} s_1 \\ \cdot \\ \cdot \\ s_\alpha \end{pmatrix} = (b^1 \dots b^\alpha) A^{-1} \begin{pmatrix} t_1 \\ \cdot \\ \cdot \\ t_\alpha \end{pmatrix}.$

Comparing (A.52), we find $(c^1 \dots c^\alpha) = (b^1 \dots b^\alpha) A^{-1}$ or, using a prime to indicate the transpose of a matrix, and using the fact that $(AB)' = B'A'$,

(A.57)
$$\begin{pmatrix} c^1 \\ \cdot \\ \cdot \\ \cdot \\ c^\alpha \end{pmatrix} = (A^{-1})' \begin{pmatrix} b^1 \\ \cdot \\ \cdot \\ b^\alpha \end{pmatrix}.$$

On the other hand, from (A.53), (A.55), and (A.54) we obtain $c_j = \Sigma\, a_{ji} b^i$ or

(A.58)
$$\begin{pmatrix} c_1 \\ \cdot \\ \cdot \\ \cdot \\ c_\alpha \end{pmatrix} = A \begin{pmatrix} b^1 \\ \cdot \\ \cdot \\ b^\alpha \end{pmatrix} = A \begin{pmatrix} b_1 \\ \cdot \\ \cdot \\ b_\alpha \end{pmatrix}.$$

Thus the transformation carrying the covariant vectors relative to $\{s\}$ into those relative to $\{t\}$ has exactly the same form as the transformation $\{s\} \to \{t\}$, which justifies the term **covariant**. The contravariant vectors transform in accordance with the quite different formula (A.57).

It now follows that if $\{t\}$ is carried into another basis as follows:

(A.59)
$$\begin{pmatrix} u_1 \\ \cdot \\ \cdot \\ \cdot \\ u_\alpha \end{pmatrix} = B \begin{pmatrix} t_1 \\ \cdot \\ \cdot \\ \cdot \\ t_\alpha \end{pmatrix} = BA \begin{pmatrix} s^1 \\ \cdot \\ \cdot \\ \cdot \\ s_\alpha \end{pmatrix},$$

then the covariant and contravariant components $(d_1, \ldots, d_\alpha)$ and $(d^1, \ldots, d^\alpha)$ of the vector C appearing in (A.54) are given by

(A.60)
$$\begin{pmatrix} d_1 \\ \cdot \\ \cdot \\ \cdot \\ d_\alpha \end{pmatrix} = B \begin{pmatrix} c_1 \\ \cdot \\ \cdot \\ \cdot \\ c_\alpha \end{pmatrix} = BA \begin{pmatrix} b^1 \\ \cdot \\ \cdot \\ \cdot \\ b^\alpha \end{pmatrix},$$

$$\begin{pmatrix} d^1 \\ \cdot \\ \cdot \\ \cdot \\ d^\alpha \end{pmatrix} = (B^{-1})' \begin{pmatrix} c^1 \\ \cdot \\ \cdot \\ \cdot \\ c^\alpha \end{pmatrix} = (B^{-1})' (A^{-1})' \begin{pmatrix} b^1 \\ \cdot \\ \cdot \\ \cdot \\ b^\alpha \end{pmatrix}.$$

From (A.58) and (A.57) we infer that

(A.61)
$$\begin{pmatrix} c_1 \\ \cdot \\ \cdot \\ \cdot \\ c_\alpha \end{pmatrix} = AA' \begin{pmatrix} c^1 \\ \cdot \\ \cdot \\ \cdot \\ c^\alpha \end{pmatrix}.$$

(B) *It is obvious that a vector is determined by its covariant, as well as by its contravariant, components relative to a given basis.*

A–5.   Dual Bases in a Module

A pair of bases $\{u\} = (u_1, \ldots, u_\alpha)$ and $\{v\} = (v_1, \ldots, v_\alpha)$ for the module $[s]$ are **dual** to one another if their scalar products satisfy the conditions

(A.62)
$$(u_i \cdot v_j) = \delta_{ij}.$$

The elements u_i and v_i are called **corresponding elements** of $\{u\}$ and $\{v\}$.

THEOREM 9. **There exists a unique basis $\{v\}$ dual to any given basis $\{u\}$ of $[s]$.**

Proof. Let the transformation $\{u\} \to \{s\}$ be expressed by

$$(A.63) \qquad s_j = \sum_{h=1}^{\alpha} b_{jh} u_h \qquad (j = 1, \ldots, \alpha).$$

Then

$$(A.64) \qquad (v_i \cdot s_j) = \left(v_i \cdot \sum_{h=1}^{\alpha} b_{jh} u_h \right) = \sum_{h=1}^{\alpha} b_{jh}(v_i \cdot u_h).$$

Hence, if $\{u\}$ and $\{v\}$ are dual, $(v_i \cdot s_j) = \Sigma_{h=1}^{\alpha} b_{jh} \delta_{ih} = b_{ji}$.

(*A*) Conversely, the duality of $\{u\}$ and $\{v\}$ is implied by the equations $(v_i \cdot s_j) = b_{ji}$ (Exercise 20). But this is equivalent to the set of equations

$$(A.65) \qquad v_i = \sum_{j=1}^{\alpha} b_{ji} s_j \qquad (i = 1, \ldots, \alpha),$$

which establishes the theorem and yields the following result.

COROLLARY. **The basis $\{v\}$ dual to $\{u\}$ is obtained from the initial basis $\{s\}$ by the transformation $\{s\} \to \{v\}$ whose matrix is the transpose of the inverse of the matrix of the transformation $\{s\} \to \{u\}$.** (Compare (A.63).)

A geometric interpretation of dual bases is illuminating. Let the initial basis $\{s\}$ be regarded as a set of mutually orthogonal unit vectors in R^{α}.

(*B*) Condition (A.62) means that (1) the vector v_j is normal to the $(\alpha - 1)$-plane $R_j^{\alpha-1}$ determined by the vectors u_i $(i \neq j)$, (2) the length of the vector v_j is the reciprocal of the length of the projection of u_j on v_j, and (3) the angle between u_j and v_j is acute.

It is easy to verify, either geometrically or algebraically, that the only self-dual bases of $[s]$ are (1) those of the form $\{\varepsilon_1 s_1, \ldots, \varepsilon_{\alpha} s_{\alpha}\}$ where $\varepsilon_i = +1$ or -1 and (2) transformations of them with orthogonal matrices.

Consider an element

$$(A.66) \qquad S = a_1 s_1 + \cdots + a_{\alpha} s_{\alpha}$$

of the module $[s]$. Expressed in terms of $\{u\}$, it is

$$(A.67) \qquad S = \sum_{h=1}^{\alpha} \sum_{j=1}^{\alpha} a_j b_{jh} u_h,$$

so that its contravariant components relative to $\{u\}$ are

$$(A.68) \qquad c^h = \sum_{j=1}^{\alpha} a_j b_{jh} \qquad (h = 1, \ldots, \alpha).$$

Its covariant components relative to $\{v\}$ are, by definition,

$$(A.69) \qquad d_h = (S \cdot v_h) = \left(\sum_{j=1}^{\alpha} a_j s_j \cdot \sum_{k=1}^{\alpha} b_{kh} s_k \right) = \sum_{j=1}^{\alpha} a_j b_{jh} = c^h.$$

This proves the following result.

THEOREM 10. **If $\{u\}$ and $\{v\}$ are dual bases of $[s]$, then the contravariant components of $s \in [s]$ relative to $\{u\}$ equal its covariant components relative to $\{v\}$.**

Next consider a pair of modules $[s] = [s_1, \ldots, s_\alpha]$ and $[w] = [w_1, \ldots, w_\zeta]$ and a pair of homomorphisms

$$(A.70) \qquad \begin{array}{ll} (a) & f : [s] \to [w], \\ (b) & g : [w] \to [s]. \end{array}$$

Then f and g are called **dual** to each other if, for each pair of elements $S \in [s]$ and $W \in [w]$, the following relationship holds between scalar products:

$$(A.71) \qquad (f(S) \cdot W) = (S \cdot g(W)).$$

THEOREM 11. **Let $\{t\}$, $\{u\}$ be dual bases of $[s]$ and let $\{x\}$, $\{y\}$ be dual bases of $[w]$. Let f and g be dual homomorphisms of $[s]$ into $[w]$ and of $[w]$ into $[s]$. Then if**

$$(A.72) \qquad f(t_i) = \sum_{j=1}^{\zeta} e_{ij} x_j \qquad (i = 1, \ldots, \alpha),$$

it follows that

$$(A.73) \qquad g(y_j) = \sum_{i=1}^{\alpha} e_{ij} u_i \qquad (j = 1, \ldots, \zeta).$$

Proof. The covariant components of $g(y_j)$ relative to $\{t\}$ are $(e_{1j}, \ldots, e_{\alpha j})$, since

$$
\begin{aligned}
(A.74) \qquad (g(y_j) \cdot t_h) &= (t_h \cdot g(y_j)) \\
&= (f(t_h) \cdot y_j) \qquad \text{by (A.71)} \\
&= \sum_{k=1}^{\zeta} e_{hk}(x_k \cdot y_j) = \sum_{k=1}^{\zeta} e_{hk} \delta_{kj} = e_{hj}
\end{aligned}
$$

because $\{x\}$ and $\{y\}$ are dual bases. The covariant components of $\Sigma_{i=1}^{\alpha} e_{ij} u_i$ relative to $\{t\}$ are also $(e_{1j}, \ldots, e_{\alpha j})$, since

$$(A.75) \qquad \left(\sum_{i=1}^{\alpha} e_{ij} u_i \cdot t_h \right) = \sum_{i=1}^{\alpha} e_{ij}(u_i \cdot t_h) = \sum_{i=1}^{\alpha} e_{ij} \delta_{ih} = e_{hj}.$$

Equations (A.74), (A.75), and Art. A–4(B) imply Eqs. (A.73) and also imply the following result.

COROLLARY. **The ith covariant component of $g(y_j)$ relative to $\{t\}$ equals the jth contravariant component of $f(t_i)$ relative to $\{x\}$.**

(C) The material in this article and the preceding article can be modified to the case where the integral coefficients are replaced by integers mod 2.

EXERCISE

20. Prove Statement (A). See Art. A–4(A).

Index of Symbols

General Index

239